H-1992

$5.⁹⁵

METHUEN'S MONOGRAPHS

ON PHYSICAL SUBJECTS

General Editor: B. L. WORSNOP, B.SC., PH.D.

FLUID DYNAMICS

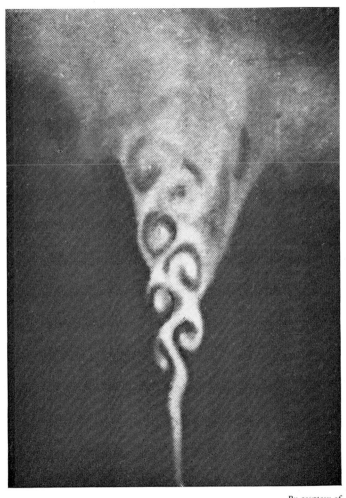

By courtesy of
Dr G. Burniston-Brown

Fluid Dynamics

An Introductory Account of Certain
Theoretical Aspects Involving
Low Velocities and Small Amplitudes

by G. H. A. Cole, B.Sc., Ph.D.

Clarke, Chapman & Co Ltd, Gateshead

LONDON: METHUEN & CO LTD

NEW YORK: JOHN WILEY & SONS INC

Contents

Introduction

Fluid dynamics is concerned with the motion, or tendency to motion, of liquids and gases (collectively called fluids) under the action of forces of various kinds. In the chapters to follow we will be concerned with some aspects of fluid dynamics where the fluid velocity neither approaches nor exceeds the sound velocity in the stationary fluid, and where the amplitude of any disturbance is small in comparison with the characteristic length scale of the flow. Thus our concern is with conditions of low velocity and small amplitude.

It will be supposed always that we are dealing only with matter in bulk (macroscopic matter), so that every portion of the fluid may be regarded as continuous, however small the portion may be. In addition, every portion of the fluid, however small, is to have properties in every way identical with those of the bulk fluid. This concept of a continuous fluid element of very small dimensions will be found in the pages to follow to be necessary in the development of the equations of fluid motion. This is because the Newtonian laws of particle mechanics will be invoked, and it is necessary in the application to fluids to consider the action of various forces (including those due to the fluid itself) on a representative fluid particle. Suppose an initially small continuous fluid element is decreased in size until it becomes indefinitely small on a macroscopic scale. The element, although macroscopically negligible, can still be sufficiently large on a molecular scale to contain an astronomically large number of molecules, i.e. to have a continuous structure in the limit of vanishing macroscopic size: such an element will be called a fluid particle. It is natural then to regard the elementary volume occupied by the (abstract) fluid particle as being virtually a point on the macroscopic scale, and so to call it a fluid point.

Although the discrete molecular (microscopic) properties of the fluid are not explicitly accounted for they will need implicit consideration because they determine the macroscopic properties. For equilibrium this is done within the continuum framework by the introduction of the usual thermodynamic functions; otherwise phenomenological transport coefficients are introduced for this purpose, such as viscosity and thermal conductivity.

Perhaps the most fundamental distinguishing property of a normal fluid is its complete lack of rigidity when subjected to some applied shearing stress (force per unit surface area), however small, applied over a time interval which is microscopically large even though it may be macroscopically small. On this basis alone, however, the distinction between fluids and solids is not sharp: for instance pitch is brittle when stuck impulsively but shows fluid type flow when subjected to even a small stress over many days. The requirement of macroscopic continuity to the limit of vanishing size does, however, allow a firm distinction to be made between a fluid and a fine powder of crystallites. Because the arguments to follow are of restricted scope it is insufficient to define a fluid as a continuous aggregate of matter whose motion under the action of stresses is adequately described by the equations of the theory contained in this monograph. A more general (though negative) statement of fluidity may be that of a bulk fluid as being a continuous macroscopic structure for which the conventional theory of elasticity, involving coefficients such as Young's modulus and Poisson's ratio, does not properly apply during the time interval of study.

Liquids and gases have several fairly distinct properties except in the critical region. Thus a liquid has a definite volume over a range of pressure and forms a free surface as it rests in gravitational equilibrium in a large container. In contrast, a gas always fills fully any container into which it is introduced and has no free surface. As a consequence a liquid has a definite density for a given temperature which is virtually independent of the size of the container, whereas this is not the case for a gas. In addition liquid densities are always larger than corresponding gaseous densities. These effects have their origins in the microscopic structure. In a liquid the molecules are held close together by the mutual intermolecular forces whereas in a gas the molecules are free of interaction almost all the time. It is not surprising, then, that a liquid is only slightly compressible whereas a gas is highly compressible. This, in fact, allows an immediate and important division in the study of fluids in bulk to be introduced, viz. incompressible and compressible fluids. For almost all studies, liquids can be regarded as being completely incompressible, there being no need to account for the complication of a pressure dependent volume. Although gases are in fact highly compressible, the effects of gaseous compressibility are usually negligible for gaseous flow if the velocity is less than about one-quarter the local sound velocity. Consequently a theory developed for strictly incompressible fluid flow has a rather wider range of validity than might be expected at first sight. The arguments to follow are very largely concerned with incompressible flow.

The study of fluid flow can be subdivided further. It is known that for a fluid at rest the mutual interaction between any two contiguous fluid elements is normal to the common surface. This will not usually be so for an actual fluid in motion; indeed it is the case only when the fluid moves as a rigid body. Otherwise, when adjoining fluid elements move relative to each other, tangential shear stresses generally appear whose size and importance depends upon the conditions of the flow. The appearance of tangential stresses is associated with the action of dissipative forces (such as viscosity) which oppose the motion to which they are due. If the fluid motion is very small the effect of the dissipative forces is small because the tangential stresses themselves are small. Because the theoretical discussion of bulk fluids is considerably complicated by the need to account for the tangential stresses, the fact that they may be small suggests that a discussion having some (at least qualitative) significance for special examples of the flow of real fluids can possibly result from their neglect altogether. Fluids for which there are no tangential stresses between adjoining portions in relative motion are said to be ideal; otherwise the fluid is said to be real. It must be said now that no exactly ideal fluid exists in practice.

The major developments in the rigorous theory of fluid motion up to about the beginning of the present century were centred very largely around ideal fluids, although the equations for real fluids were beginning to be discussed during the latter half of the last century. Comparison between theoretical predictions of the properties of the (hypothetical) ideal fluid and data measured using real fluids was, in fact, fairly satisfactory in certain directions (e.g. theory of the sea tides), although in other directions (e.g. problems involving fluid resistance or frictional drag) it was quite hopeless. For this reason two distinct and separate disciplines emerged: the first, usually called theoretical hydrodynamics, was very mathematical, rigorous, and elegant, but was restricted to only special flows; while the second, called hydraulics, was accumulated semi-empirical data about real fluids in real practical situations, compiled primarily for the engineer.

This situation, if allowed to continue, would surely have culminated in the extinction of theoretical hydrodynamics as a significant study, but fortunately this was not allowed to happen. Prandtl, in 1904, showed how theoretical hydrodynamics and practical hydraulics can be reconciled through the concept of the boundary layer. In particular, the flow of not too viscous fluids (such as water or air) past obstacles, and involving moderate internal tangential shearing stresses, can by this means be analytically discussed in many situations of practical importance, and the treatment of real effects (such as drag on a body and pressure drop) put on a quantitative basis in agreement with experience. The introduction of the boundary layer concept (according to which fluid viscous effects need be considered in detail only in the immediate neighbourhood of a boundary providing the viscosity is not too great, the main bulk of the flowing fluid behaving as if it were in simple flow) is a cornerstone in the development of the modern theory of fluid motion.

One further step was necessary, however, before the theory could claim to cover fully practical cases. At a certain fluid velocity (which depends upon the exact details of the flow for any particular case) the well-ordered stable flow patterns appearing below this velocity become unstable, and as the velocity is increased beyond this critical value the flow pattern breaks down into a seemingly fortuitous jumble: turbulence is said to have set in. The treatment of turbulent flows is still under discussion and our understanding of turbulence as a whole is still incomplete.

More recently, the importance of the flow of a fluid which is able to conduct electricity and which is permeated by a magnetic field has been recognized. If the fluid can be treated as having a continuous structure (macroscopic bulk fluid) then the study of the interaction between the moving conducting fluid and the impressed magnetic field is called hydromagnetics. This study must nowadays be recognized as forming an integral part of fluid dynamics.

Like so many other branches of human endeavour, the study of fluid dynamics in all its many aspects has shown an explosive quality over recent years. No single treatment of the subject can now ever hope to aim at completeness, leave alone attain it, and within the compass of the present monograph it is not possible to do more than introduce some of the more basic topics. The selection of material for inclusion has been largely due to personal preference but it is hoped that its fairly wide scope will be of interest and use to a range of readers.

CHAPTER 1

Equations of an Ideal Fluid

In the present chapter we derive the several equations which allow for the treatment of the motion of an ideal fluid. Irreversible effects such as those associated with viscosity and thermal conductivity are for the present neglected entirely; these more general conditions will be included into the theory in later chapters.

1.1. The total derivative

The motion of a fluid must involve some change of the general properties of the fluid with time. The quantities which specify its condition (such as velocity, density, and pressure) at any point depend not only on the time but also in general on the position of the point in the fluid. Consequently the change in any such quantity during some time interval depends not only on the time interval itself but also in general upon the position within the fluid. It is convenient in the theory now to be developed to express this dependence of variable quantities upon both time and position in the fluid by introducing explicitly at the outset the simple concept of the total derivative. Let us do this through an example.

Consider the fluid density which is in general a function of both the position vector $\mathbf{r}$ (a vector with components x, y, z along the three Cartesian axes) and the time; to show explicitly this dependence we denote the density by the symbol $\rho(x, y, z, t)$, although it is often sufficient to write it simply as ρ. The total change of the density $\delta\rho$ during some time interval δt is given by:

$$\delta\rho = \delta\rho(x, y, z, t) = \frac{\partial\rho}{\partial t}\delta t + \frac{\partial\rho}{\partial x}\delta x + \frac{\partial\rho}{\partial y}\delta y + \frac{\partial\rho}{\partial z}\delta z, \qquad (1.1)$$

where $(\delta x, \delta y, \delta z)$ are the corresponding increments of position components during δt. Dividing equation (1.1) throughout by δt we obtain

$$\frac{\delta\rho}{\delta t} = \frac{\partial\rho}{\partial t} + \frac{\partial\rho}{\partial x}\frac{\delta x}{\delta t} + \frac{\partial\rho}{\partial y}\frac{\delta y}{\delta t} + \frac{\partial\rho}{\partial z}\frac{\delta z}{\delta t}.$$

Suppose now we consider the limiting form of this expression as the time interval δt approaches zero. In the limit of $\delta t \rightarrow 0$ we have in the usual notation of the calculus,

$$\frac{\delta x}{\delta t} \rightarrow \frac{dx}{dt}, \quad \frac{\delta y}{\delta t} \rightarrow \frac{dy}{dt}, \quad \frac{\delta z}{\delta t} \rightarrow \frac{dz}{dt};$$

and the trio $(dx/dt, dy/dt, dz/dt)$ are the components of the fluid velocity vector $\mathbf{v}$ at the point (x, y, z) and at the time t, written respectively (v_x, v_y, v_z). If further we replace $\delta \rho/\delta t$ by $d\rho/dt$, then equation (1.1) can be rewritten as:

$$\frac{d\rho}{dt} = \frac{\partial \rho}{\partial t} + \frac{\partial \rho}{\partial x} v_x + \frac{\partial \rho}{\partial y} v_y + \frac{\partial \rho}{\partial z} v_z.$$

The last three terms on the right-hand side of this equation can be written more simply in vector notation using the scalar product of the velocity vector $\mathbf{v}$ and the vector $(\text{grad}\, \rho)$. For

$$v_x \frac{\partial \rho}{\partial x} + v_y \frac{\partial \rho}{\partial y} + v_z \frac{\partial \rho}{\partial z} = (\mathbf{v}.\,\text{grad})\, \rho. \tag{1.2}$$

Therefore we have finally

$$\frac{d\rho}{dt} = \frac{\partial \rho}{\partial t} + (\mathbf{v}.\,\text{grad})\, \rho. \tag{1.3}$$

The first term on the right-hand side is the time change of ρ at a given position (x, y, z) so that dx, dy, dz are all zero; this refers to a fixed point in space. The second term on the right-hand side is the change in density with position in the fluid at a given time (i.e. $dt = 0, dx \neq 0$, $dy \neq 0, dz \neq 0$). The right-hand side of the equation (1.3) is *in toto* the total rate of change of the density of a fluid particle (which, remember, is an elementary fluid volume macroscopically very small but microscopically very large so as to contain a very great number of molecules) as it moves in space with the fluid. This, then, is the physical interpretation of the quantity $d\rho/dt$, which is called the total time derivative of the fluid density.

The same arguments can be applied to any function of the position and the time to yield total derivatives. The expression

$$\frac{d}{dt} = \frac{\partial}{\partial t} + (\mathbf{v}\,.\,\mathrm{grad}) \tag{1.4}$$

can be abstracted as an entity and called simply the total derivative.

1.2. Component notation

It will be found very useful later to express our arguments in terms of the components of vectors rather than in terms of the complete vectors themselves, and we explain this component notation, as it may be called, here.

Every vector quantity having direct physical significance has three independent components; for example, the velocity vector $\mathbf{v}$ has the Cartesian components v_x, v_y, v_z. These components can equally well be written v_1, v_2, v_3, provided that we agree that the suffix 1 is to stand for x, the suffix 2 is to stand for y, and 3 is to stand for z. This apparent complication is in fact a simplification since the three components of the velocity vector can now be expressed by the single symbol v_i if we agree that the Latin subscript i is to take the values 1, 2, and 3 corresponding respectively to the components along the x, y, or z Cartesian axes. The extension of the notation to those reference axes which are not mutually perpendicular in pairs (non-Cartesian axes) is obvious.

Let us use this notation in connection with the total derivative (1.4). The first term $\partial/\partial t$ is not involved but the second term is. For, using the expression (1.2) together with the component notation we can make the following replacements:

$$\begin{aligned}
(\mathbf{v}\,.\,\mathrm{grad}) &= v_x \frac{\partial}{\partial x} + v_y \frac{\partial}{\partial y} + v_z \frac{\partial}{\partial z} \\
&= v_1 \frac{\partial}{\partial x_1} + v_2 \frac{\partial}{\partial x_2} + v_3 \frac{\partial}{\partial x_3} \quad (x_1 \equiv x; x_2 \equiv y; x_3 \equiv z) \tag{1.5} \\
&= \sum_{k=1}^{3} v_k \frac{\partial}{\partial x_k}.
\end{aligned}$$

2

The need to continually write in summation signs can be avoided if one more convention is introduced, viz. the summation convention. For this purpose we make the rule that repeated Latin suffixes are always summed while suffixes which are not repeated are never summed. Using the summation convention the scheme (1.5) can be expressed finally by the equivalence

$$(\mathbf{v} . \operatorname{grad}) \equiv v_k \frac{\partial}{\partial x_k},$$

so that the total derivative in component notation becomes

$$\frac{d}{dt} = \frac{\partial}{\partial t} + v_k \frac{\partial}{\partial x_k}. \tag{1.6}$$

The total derivative of the density is accordingly

$$\frac{d\rho}{dt} = \frac{\partial \rho}{\partial t} + v_k \frac{\partial \rho}{\partial x_k}.$$

The density is a scalar quantity, i.e. it has magnitude but has no directional properties. The total derivative for a vector quantity, such as the velocity of a fluid particle, is, however, readily included in the scheme. For the velocity, the total derivative is found by arguments exactly analogous to those which led to equation (1.3) to be

$$\frac{d\mathbf{v}}{dt} = \frac{\partial \mathbf{v}}{\partial t} + (\mathbf{v} . \operatorname{grad}) \mathbf{v}.$$

In component notation this is:

$$\frac{dv_i}{dt} = \frac{\partial v_i}{\partial t} + v_k \frac{\partial v_i}{\partial x_k}. \tag{1.7}$$

According to the summation convention the appearance of the repeated suffix k indicates a summation over k [see equations (1.5) and (1.6)] whereas the single appearance of the suffix i shows that the suffix i is not to be summed. However, the suffix i is to be given each of the values 1, 2, 3 (component notation) so that the single equation (1.7) represents in fact three constituent component equations, each one associated with components parallel to one of the three component axes. The suffix k, being summed, is not explicitly characteristic of any single component; it is usually called a 'dummy' suffix.

1.3. Mass conservation

Matter cannot be either created or destroyed in any classical system, and in particular fluid mass is conserved. This fact leads easily to a relation between the fluid density and the fluid velocity at any point, conventionally called the equation of continuity. This equation applies in fact whether the fluid is ideal or not.

To obtain the equation of continuity consider the mass of fluid associated with any elementary fluid volume during some time interval, both that contained in the volume element and that flowing into, or out from, it through the boundary walls. Let ΔV represent the magnitude of the small volume element centred about the point $\mathbf{r}$ having Cartesian components (x, y, z). If $\rho(x, y, z, t)$ is the density at point $\mathbf{r}$ at time t, then the mass of fluid in ΔV at time t is $\int_{\Delta V} \rho dV$, where dV is an element of ΔV. The increase in the fluid mass contained in the volume during some small time interval Δt is, therefore,

$$+\Delta t \frac{\partial}{\partial t} \int_{\Delta V} \rho dV. \tag{1.8}$$

Alternatively, the increase in the fluid mass inside a volume must be equal to the net inflow of fluid through the surface enclosing the volume, because fluid mass is conserved. Suppose we define the elementary vector $d\mathbf{s}$ at any point on the enclosing surface such that its magnitude be equal to an element of the enclosing surface area about the point, and such that its direction is (by convention) along the outward normal to the surface at the point. The mass of fluid moving with velocity $\mathbf{v}$ into the volume across the element $d\mathbf{s}$ in time Δt is easily seen to be equal to $-\rho(\mathbf{v}.d\mathbf{s})\Delta t$. Here the scalar product of $\mathbf{v}$ with $d\mathbf{s}$ is included to account for the fact that the fluid velocity is not necessary perpendicular to the surface element. The total mass of fluid entering the complete volume during Δt is then:

$$-\Delta t \oint \rho(\mathbf{v}.d\mathbf{s}), \tag{1.9}$$

where the integration is taken over the whole surface enclosing ΔV.

Equating the two expressions (1.8) and (1.9) gives the equation:

$$\frac{\partial}{\partial t} \int_{\Delta V} \rho \, dV = - \oint \rho(\mathbf{v}.d\mathbf{s}).$$

The surface integral appearing on the right-hand side can be transformed into a volume integral by using the Green's formula:

$$\oint \rho(\mathbf{v}.d\mathbf{s}) = \int_{\Delta V} \operatorname{div}(\rho \mathbf{v}) \, dV,$$

which means that

$$\int_{\Delta V} \left[\frac{\partial \rho}{\partial t} + \operatorname{div}(\rho \mathbf{v}) \right] dV = 0.$$

Because ΔV can be chosen quite arbitrarily, the integrand must be zero, and this leads immediately to the equation of continuity,

$$\boxed{\frac{\partial \rho}{\partial t} + \operatorname{div}(\rho \mathbf{v}) = 0.} \qquad (1.10)$$

Further rearrangement of this expression is often desirable. Thus, invoking the vector relation

$$\operatorname{div}(\rho \mathbf{v}) = \rho \operatorname{div} \mathbf{v} + (\mathbf{v}.\operatorname{grad})\rho,$$

the equation (1.10) can be rewritten to include the total derivative given by (1.3):

$$\boxed{\frac{d\rho}{dt} + \rho \operatorname{div} \mathbf{v} = 0.} \qquad (1.11)$$

In component form the equations (1.10) and (1.11) are:

$$\frac{\partial \rho}{\partial t} + \frac{\partial}{\partial x_k}(\rho v_k) = 0; \quad \frac{\partial \rho}{\partial t} + v_k \frac{\partial \rho}{\partial x_k} + \rho \frac{\partial v_k}{\partial x_k} = 0. \qquad (1.12)$$

The equivalence between the two vector equations (1.10) and (1.11) is immediately obvious in the component form (1.12).

The vector $\rho\mathbf{v} \equiv \mathbf{j}$ appearing in (1.10) is called the mass flux vector; it has a magnitude equal to the mass of fluid flowing across unit area perpendicular to the velocity direction in unit time, and a direction which is parallel to that of the fluid velocity at the point.

If the fluid is incompressible then $d\rho/dt = 0$ and the equation (1.11) for this case reduces to the simple form

$$\operatorname{div}\mathbf{v} = 0. \tag{1.13}$$

1.4. The momentum equation

The motion of each volume element of the fluid can be described by using Newton's laws of motion; in particular, the acceleration of the element due to the action of a force is proportional to the magnitude of the force. Because the force must act through neighbouring fluid elements we are again concerned with effects across the surface enclosing the volume element ΔV under consideration. Explicitly, the inwardly acting force over the surface is the sum of the pressures acting over the surface elements; if p is the pressure (force per unit area) at the point $\mathbf{r}$ and at time t then the total force over the surface enclosing ΔV is

$$-\oint p\,d\mathbf{s} = -\int_{\Delta V} \operatorname{grad} p\,dV.$$

The second expression follows from the usual vector transformation of a surface integral into a volume integral. It follows that the force exerted on any fluid element by the remaining fluid is $-\operatorname{grad} p$ per unit volume.

According to Newtonian mechanics the force causing the motion of the fluid volume element is to be equated to the inertial force of the element. The acceleration of the element moving with the fluid is $d\mathbf{v}/dt$ so that the inertial fluid force is $\rho(d\mathbf{v}/dt)$. Equating this to the force causing the fluid movement

$$\rho\frac{d\mathbf{v}}{dt} = -\operatorname{grad} p. \tag{1.14}$$

If in addition a force $\rho\mathbf{F}$ acts per unit fluid volume of each fluid element resulting from some source external to the fluid (e.g. gravitation, where $\mathbf{F} = \mathbf{g}$ the vector acceleration of gravity) this must be added to the right-hand side of (1.14). Using the expression (1.4) for the total derivative and dividing throughout by ρ:

$$\frac{\partial \mathbf{v}}{\partial t} + (\mathbf{v}\,.\,\mathrm{grad})\,\mathbf{v} = -\frac{1}{\rho}\,\mathrm{grad}\,p + \mathbf{F}. \qquad (1.15)$$

This equation, which applies only to ideal fluids since dissipative effects have not been considered, was first given by Euler in the latter part of the eighteenth century. It forms the core of many calculations of fluid flow. Unfortunately it is not always free of mathematical difficulty since it is non-linear in the velocity in the second term on the left-hand side.

In component notation, the equation (1.15) is:

$$\frac{\partial v_i}{\partial t} + v_k \frac{\partial v_i}{\partial x_k} = -\frac{1}{\rho}\frac{\partial p}{\partial x_i} + F_i. \qquad (1.16)$$

Because the equation (1.15) is equivalent to the statement that the total fluid momentum is conserved, this equation is often referred to as the momentum equation.

1.5. The momentum flux

It is often necessary to have a knowledge of the flux of momentum across a surface in the fluid; that is, to know the rate at which momentum is crossing a surface drawn in the fluid. This information can be derived from equation (1.15) using also the expression for fluid momentum.

The momentum of unit fluid volume is $\rho\mathbf{v}$ and the time rate of momentum change at a fixed point in space is (in component notation):

$$\frac{\partial}{\partial t}(\rho v_i) = \rho \frac{\partial v_i}{\partial t} + v_i \frac{\partial \rho}{\partial t}. \qquad (1.17)$$

The first term on the right-hand side can be replaced using the momentum equation (1.16), while the second term can be replaced using the continuity equation (1.12). Doing this, and after slight rearrangement, it is found that:

$$\frac{\partial}{\partial t}(\rho v_i) = -\frac{\partial p}{\partial x_i} - \frac{\partial}{\partial x_k}(\rho v_i v_k) + \rho F_i. \tag{1.18}$$

This equation can be rewritten into a more compact form by introducing the so-called Kronecker delta, written δ_{ik} in component form. This function is defined in a very simple way: each component of the sum δ_{ii} is unity and all other components vanish. Expressed mathematically:

$$\delta_{ik} = 1 \quad \text{if } i = k; \qquad \delta_{ik} = 0 \quad \text{if } i \neq k. \tag{1.19}$$

The great utility of δ_{ik} is that it allows the suffixes to be rearranged within a given term of an equation and this can be used as a means of simplifying the form of the equation. The equation (1.18) can be used to illustrate this procedure, for an incompressible fluid.

The pressure term in (1.18) can be written alternatively:

$$\frac{\partial p}{\partial x_i} = \delta_{ik}\frac{\partial p}{\partial x_k}, \tag{1.20}$$

as is obvious from the scheme (1.19). If further the force F_i is conservative, and so is derivable from a potential function Φ (say), a function of the position but not of the time, then

$$F_i = -\frac{\partial \Phi}{\partial x_i} = -\delta_{ik}\frac{\partial \Phi}{\partial x_k}. \tag{1.21}$$

Using (1.20) and (1.21), the equation (1.18) can be written in the simple compact form:

$$\boxed{\frac{\partial}{\partial t}(\rho v_i) = -\frac{\partial \pi_{ik}}{\partial x_k},} \tag{1.22}$$

where the quantity π_{ik} is defined by the expression:

$$\boxed{\pi_{ik} = (p + \rho\Phi)\,\delta_{ik} + \rho v_i v_k.} \tag{1.23}$$

π_{ik} is called the momentum flux density. Because $\delta_{ik} = \delta_{ki}$ it is immediately clear that π_{ik} is unaffected if the suffixes are interchanged. Any function which possesses this property is said to be symmetric, so that the momentum flux density is a symmetric function.

The exact physical meaning of π_{ik} follows from an integration of the equation (1.22) over an arbitrary volume in the fluid. Then,

$$\frac{\partial}{\partial t} \int \rho v_i dV = -\int \frac{\partial \pi_{ik}}{\partial x_k} dV. \tag{1.24}$$

The integral on the right-hand side can be replaced by a surface integral. If $\hat{n}$ is a unit vector along the outward normal to the surface element ds somewhere on the surface enclosing the volume, then we may write $ds_k = n_k ds$, where ds is the size of the surface element. Equation (1.24) then takes the modified form:

$$\frac{\partial}{\partial t} \int \rho v_i dV = -\oint \pi_{ik} n_k ds = -\oint [(p + \rho \Phi) n_i + \rho v_i v_k n_k] ds. \tag{1.25}$$

The left-hand side here is the time rate of change of the i-th component of the momentum of the fluid element, while the right-hand side in each alternative form is the i-th component of momentum flowing across the containing surface in unit time. In particular the quantity $\pi_{ik} n_k$ is the flux of the i-th component of momentum through unit surface area, and π_{ik} itself is the i-th component of momentum flowing through unit area perpendicular to the x_k-axis in unit time.

From the second form of the right-hand side of (1.25) it is evident that the flux density transported along the direction of the fluid velocity is $(p + \rho \Phi + \rho v^2)$, whereas that perpendicular to this direction is $(p + \rho \Phi)$ and is independent of the velocity. In vector notation the flux density is to be written

$$(p + \rho \Phi) \hat{n} + \rho \mathbf{v} (\mathbf{v} . \hat{n}). \tag{1.26}$$

In this notation the right-hand side of the equation (1.22) is minus the vectorial divergence of the i-th component of the momentum flux density.

If the fluid cannot be assumed incompressible a momentum flux density can still be defined if there are no external forces (i.e. $F_i = 0$

in (1.18)). In this case the momentum flux density is readily found to be

$$\pi_{ik} = p\delta_{ik} + \rho v_i v_k \qquad (1.23a)$$

in place of (1.23); (1.22) applies as before. In vector notation the flux density is

$$p\hat{n} + \rho \mathbf{v}(\mathbf{v}.\hat{n}) \qquad (1.26a)$$

in place of the expression (1.26).

1.6. Thermodynamics of the fluid

Irreversible processes do not occur in an ideal fluid (for this is its defining characteristic) and in particular the temperature must be everywhere the same. No heat therefore flows and the fluid motion does not involve any entropy change: in technical parlance the flow is isentropic. If S is the fluid entropy per unit mass, the adiabatic condition for the flow is

$$\frac{dS}{dt} = 0, \qquad (1.27)$$

since the entropy of a fluid particle moving with the fluid is constant. By using the expansion (1.4) for the total derivative together with the continuity equation in the form (1.11) it follows from (1.27) that:

$$\rho \frac{\partial S}{\partial t} + \rho \operatorname{div}(S\mathbf{v}) + S\frac{\partial \rho}{\partial t} + S(\mathbf{v}.\operatorname{grad})\rho = 0,$$

i.e.

$$\boxed{\frac{\partial}{\partial t}(\rho S) + \operatorname{div}(\rho S\mathbf{v}) = 0.} \qquad (1.28)$$

This entropy equation can be written in the same form as the continuity equation by introducing the entropy per unit volume, i.e. the entropy density ϕ, in place of the entropy per unit mass, S. Obviously $\phi = \rho S$, and (1.28) becomes alternatively

$$\boxed{\frac{\partial \phi}{\partial t} + \operatorname{div}(\mathbf{v}\phi) = 0.} \qquad (1.29)$$

The vector $\mathbf{v}\phi = \mathbf{v}\rho S$ is often called the entropy flux density and is the present analogue of the previous mass flux vector $\mathbf{j}$ appearing in the continuity equation (1.10). In fact by comparing equations (1.10) and (1.29) it is evident that the fluid entropy per unit volume and the fluid mass per unit volume both satisfy equations of the same form.

Further thermodynamic relations are of interest, and particularly those involving the enthalpy, h. Let U be the fluid internal energy per unit mass: the enthalpy per unit mass of the fluid is defined as

$$h = U + pV, \tag{1.30}$$

where V is now the volume of unit mass. Thus

$$\frac{dh}{dp} = \frac{dU}{dp} + V + p\frac{dV}{dp}. \tag{1.30a}$$

However, the Second Law of Thermodynamics can be written mathematically:

$$T\,dS = dU + p\,dV, \tag{1.30b}$$

where T is the absolute temperature. Combining the two expressions (1.30a) and (1.30b) it follows that:

$$dh = T\,dS + V\,dp. \tag{1.30c}$$

If the entropy remains unchanged, so that $dS = 0$, then

$$dh = V\,dp.$$

But V, referring to unit mass, is the inverse of the density (mass per unit volume), so that we have finally

$$dh = \frac{1}{\rho}dp, \tag{1.30d}$$

which is the relation between the enthalpy and pressure increments under conditions of constant entropy. Consequently for these conditions we may write

$$\boxed{\frac{1}{\rho}\operatorname{grad} p = \operatorname{grad} h.} \tag{1.31}$$

1.7. The energy equation and energy flux

With the thermodynamic relations now set down an equation for the fluid energy, being a companion to the momentum and continuity equations, can be constructed. For this purpose we consider the energy per unit volume of a volume fixed in space, and through which the fluid is passing.

There are two contributions to the energy of the fluid: one is purely macroscopic and arises from the actual fluid motion; the other is the internal energy which arises ultimately from the microscopic molecular movement. Whereas the first contribution involves the velocity, the second involves the temperature.

The fluid energy per unit volume is explicitly

$$\mathscr{E} = \tfrac{1}{2}\rho v^2 + \rho U, \tag{1.32a}$$

and its time rate of change is (in vectorial form)

$$\frac{\partial \mathscr{E}}{\partial t} = \tfrac{1}{2}v^2\frac{\partial \rho}{\partial t} + \rho\left(\mathbf{v}\cdot\frac{\partial \mathbf{v}}{\partial t}\right) + \frac{\partial}{\partial t}(\rho U). \tag{1.32b}$$

The first term on the right-hand side will be rewritten using the continuity equation (1.10):

$$\tfrac{1}{2}v^2\frac{\partial \rho}{\partial t} = -\tfrac{1}{2}v^2\operatorname{div}(\rho\mathbf{v}). \tag{1.33a}$$

The second term will be rewritten using the momentum equation (1.15):

$$\rho\left(\mathbf{v}\cdot\frac{\partial \mathbf{v}}{\partial t}\right) = -(\mathbf{v}\cdot\operatorname{grad}p) - \frac{\rho}{2}(\mathbf{v}\cdot\operatorname{grad}v^2). \tag{1.33b}$$

The term involving the pressure will be replaced by appealing to the thermodynamic relation (1.30c):

$$(\mathbf{v}\cdot\operatorname{grad}p) = \rho(\mathbf{v}\cdot\operatorname{grad}h) - \rho T(\mathbf{v}\cdot\operatorname{grad}S). \tag{1.33c}$$

The remaining term on the right-hand side of (1.32b) will be transformed by invoking the Second Law of Thermodynamics written out explicitly in (1.30b), together with the definition of the enthalpy (1.30). We get then successively the following relations:

$$\frac{\partial}{\partial t}(\rho U) = \rho \frac{\partial U}{\partial t} - h \operatorname{div}(\rho \mathbf{v}) + \frac{p}{\rho} \operatorname{div}(\rho \mathbf{v}) \qquad (1.34a)$$

where the continuity equation (1.10) has been used together with the identity $V = 1/\rho$ which applies because we are dealing with unit fluid mass; and

$$T\frac{\partial S}{\partial t} = \frac{\partial U}{\partial t} - \frac{p}{\rho^2}\frac{\partial \rho}{\partial t}, \qquad (1.34b)$$

which follows from (1.30b). The time change in the entropy appearing here can be replaced by the space dependence $-(\mathbf{v} \cdot \operatorname{grad})S$ according to (1.27). Inserting the expressions (1.33a), (1.33b), (1.34a), and (1.34b) into the initial expression (1.32b) it is found, after some simple rearrangements, that

$$\frac{\partial}{\partial t}(\tfrac{1}{2}\rho v^2 + \rho U) = -\operatorname{div}\left[\rho \mathbf{v}(\tfrac{1}{2}v^2 + h)\right]. \qquad (1.35)$$

This is the energy equation and it is an expression for the conservation of energy; it relates the total energy per unit fluid volume to the fluid velocity and the enthalpy. It should be noticed that the *entropy* itself does not explicitly appear.

A physically interesting variant of this expression is obtained when the enthalpy is replaced using (1.30), i.e. $h = U + p/\rho$. With this substitution the expression $\rho \mathbf{v}(\tfrac{1}{2}v^2 + h)$ becomes $\rho \mathbf{v}(\tfrac{1}{2}v^2 + U + p/\rho)$ which equals $(\mathbf{v}\mathscr{E} + p\mathbf{v})$. Therefore

$$\operatorname{div}\left[\rho \mathbf{v}(\tfrac{1}{2}v^2 + h)\right] = \operatorname{div}(\mathbf{v}\mathscr{E}) + \operatorname{div}(p\mathbf{v}),$$

and the energy equation (1.35) is:

$$\boxed{\frac{\partial \mathscr{E}}{\partial t} + \operatorname{div}(\mathbf{v}\mathscr{E}) = -\operatorname{div}(p\mathbf{v}).} \qquad (1.36)$$

The fluid pressure now explicitly appears in the equation. Because of the vector relation

$$\operatorname{div}(\mathbf{v}\mathscr{E}) = \mathscr{E} \operatorname{div}\mathbf{v} + (\mathbf{v} \cdot \operatorname{grad}) \mathscr{E},$$

the equation (1.36) can be rearranged further to include the total derivative of the fluid energy per unit volume: thus,

$$\frac{d\mathscr{E}}{dt} = -\mathscr{E}\operatorname{div}\mathbf{v} - \operatorname{div}(p\mathbf{v}). \tag{1.37}$$

The physical significance of the separate terms in (1.37) can be extracted by performing a volume integration, and transforming in the usual way the right-hand side of the resulting expression into two surface integrals over the surface enclosing the volume. Carrying through this procedure there results the relation.

$$\int_{\Delta V} \frac{d\mathscr{E}}{dt}\,dV = -\oint \mathscr{E}(\mathbf{v}.d\mathbf{s}) - \oint p(\mathbf{v}.d\mathbf{s}).$$

The left-hand side is simply the total change in energy of the fluid in the volume ΔV as it moves with the fluid. The first term on the right-hand side represents the direct transfer of energy by the fluid, and is the energy flowing perpendicularly through unit area of the surface surrounding the volume ΔV per unit time. The second term involves the product of force and velocity and is the work done on the fluid within the volume by the pressure forces acting normally on the enclosing surface in unit time.

The equation (1.35) can be used to define the energy flux density vector. As before we integrate the expression over some volume ΔV and transform the resulting right-hand side into an integral over the containing surface. The result is:

$$\frac{\partial}{\partial t}\int_{\Delta V} \mathscr{E}\,dV = -\oint \rho(\tfrac{1}{2}v^2 + h)(\mathbf{v}.d\mathbf{s}).$$

The left-hand side here represents the time rate of change of fluid energy in the volume ΔV; the right-hand side describes the necessary flow of energy through the surface enclosing the volume in unit time. The vector quantity $\rho\mathbf{v}(\tfrac{1}{2}v^2 + h)$ is therefore the energy flux density, denoted by $\mathbf{Q}_1$:

$$\mathbf{Q}_1 = \rho\mathbf{v}(\tfrac{1}{2}v^2 + h). \tag{1.38}$$

In magnitude it is the amount of energy passing through a unit area located within the fluid about some point, perpendicular to the direction of the fluid velocity at that point, and again in unit time.

1.8. The Bernoulli equation

An important equation which applies for steady fluid motion was derived by Bernoulli in the eighteenth century. We start with the momentum equation (1.15) which, for steady conditions where $\partial \mathbf{v}/\partial t = 0$, is:

$$(\mathbf{v}.\mathrm{grad})\,\mathbf{v} = -\frac{1}{\rho}\mathrm{grad}\,p + \mathbf{F}. \qquad (1.39)$$

But by applying the standard vector relation:

$$(\mathbf{v}.\mathrm{grad})\,\mathbf{v} = -[\mathrm{curl}\,\mathbf{v} \times \mathbf{v}] + \mathrm{grad}\left(\frac{v^2}{2}\right) \qquad (1.39a)$$

the equation (1.39) becomes alternatively

$$[\mathrm{curl}\,\mathbf{v} \times \mathbf{v}] = \mathrm{grad}\left(\frac{v^2}{2} + h + \Phi\right), \qquad (1.39b)$$

where we have used (1.31) which applies for isentropic conditions and we have assumed the external force to be conservative so that $\mathbf{F} = -\mathrm{grad}\,\Phi$.

To consider equation (1.39b) further we introduce the concept of a streamline. A streamline is defined as a line such that the tangent to the line at any point is the direction of the fluid velocity at that point. From this definition it follows that the mathematical equations of a streamline† are

$$\frac{dx}{v_x} = \frac{dy}{v_y} = \frac{dz}{v_z}. \qquad (1.40)$$

Let us consider these equations in relation to any arbitrarily chosen streamline in the fluid.

The vector $[\mathrm{curl}\,\mathbf{v} \times \mathbf{v}]$ is perpendicular to the vector $\mathbf{v}$: since the streamline by definition coincides with $\mathbf{v}$ at any point this means that

† For steady motion the streamlines coincide with the paths of the fluid particles; this is not so for non-steady motion.

[curl $\mathbf{v} \times \mathbf{v}$] is perpendicular to the streamline. Consequently it has no component along the streamline itself, and equation (1.39b) shows that along a streamline:

$$\text{grad}\left(h + \Phi + \frac{v^2}{2}\right) = 0.$$

This relation implies that along a streamline

$$h + \frac{v^2}{2} + \Phi = C \qquad (1.41)$$

where C is a constant characteristic of the particular streamline in question and varies from streamline to streamline. The equation (1.41) is called the Bernoulli equation. In applications of this equation it is often convenient to introduce the fluid pressure by replacing the enthalpy according to (1.30d): in this case the Bernoulli equation takes on its more usual form

$$\int \frac{dp}{\rho} + \frac{v^2}{2} + \Phi = C. \qquad (1.41a)$$

The integration here is to be made along the streamline corresponding to the constant C.

If the external force is due to gravitation then, if the gravitational force acts along the z-axis increasing as z decreases and $\mathbf{g}$ is the vector acceleration of gravity,

$$\mathbf{F} = -\mathbf{g} \quad \text{and} \quad \Phi = +gz.$$

This gives

$$h + \frac{v^2}{2} + gz = \text{constant along a streamline.}$$

1.9. Vorticity equation

The quantity curl $\mathbf{v}$ is called the vorticity, denoted by the symbol $\boldsymbol{\omega}$. The vorticity is twice the angular velocity of an infinitesimally small fluid element: if a spherical fluid element were instantaneously solidified and completely isolated from the remaining fluid then it would rotate with an angular velocity which is one-half the vorticity value.

An equation for the vorticity follows by taking the curl of each term of the momentum equation (1.15). We assume the force **F** to be conservative and also use the equation (1.39a). Then if follows that

$$\frac{\partial \boldsymbol{\omega}}{\partial t} + \operatorname{curl}[\boldsymbol{\omega} \times \mathbf{v}] = 0. \tag{1.42}$$

This expression can be rearranged by using the vector relation:

$$\operatorname{curl}[\boldsymbol{\omega} \times \mathbf{v}] = (\mathbf{v}.\operatorname{grad})\boldsymbol{\omega} - (\boldsymbol{\omega}.\operatorname{grad})\mathbf{v} + \boldsymbol{\omega} \operatorname{div} \mathbf{v}. \tag{1.43}$$

Inserting (1.43) into (1.42) and remembering the expression for the total derivative (1.4), there results the equation:

$$\frac{d\boldsymbol{\omega}}{dt} = (\boldsymbol{\omega}.\operatorname{grad})\mathbf{v} - \boldsymbol{\omega} \operatorname{div} \mathbf{v}. \tag{1.44}$$

If the fluid is incompressible then $\operatorname{div} \mathbf{v} = 0$ so that (1.44) reduces to the expression

$$\frac{d\boldsymbol{\omega}}{dt} = (\boldsymbol{\omega}.\operatorname{grad})\mathbf{v}. \tag{1.45}$$

Any situation for which the right-hand side of the equation (1.44) vanishes identically is of especial interest since then the total derivative of the vorticity is zero. This means that for such fluid flow any initial condition of vorticity is maintained throughout the motion. In this connection an important result for incompressible fluid flow follows immediately from (1.45). If $\boldsymbol{\omega}$ is zero at any point on a streamline at any given time it is zero everywhere along the streamline, for from (1.45) it follows that if $\boldsymbol{\omega} = 0$ at any point on a streamline then

$$\frac{d\boldsymbol{\omega}}{dt} = 0 \tag{1.46}$$

at all points along the streamline. As a corollary to this result it follows also that the regions where the vorticity is zero and those where it is not are sharply and permanently separated for ideal incompressible fluid flow by a set of streamlines. It will be found later that these results can be modified by the effects of dissipative forces (such as viscosity) and that for dissipative systems an initially vortex region of fluid can move with time to the condition of no vorticity. But for an ideal fluid this is not so, the appearance or not of vorticity depending upon the ultimate source of the fluid motion.

There is one special situation for which the right-hand side of equation (1.45) for incompressible flow is always zero so that (1.46) applies over a wide range of conditions. This is the situation of flow for which the space variation of the velocity is at right angles to the plane of the motion, i.e. to the vorticity. This is the situation if all the lines of fluid motion are parallel to a fixed plane and further if the velocity vectors at corresponding points of all planes parallel to the reference plane are identical. Such motion is called two dimensional and will be considered further in a later chapter. For two dimensional incompressible motion, then, $(\boldsymbol{\omega} . \mathrm{grad}) \mathbf{v} = 0$ and the expression (1.45) reduces simply to the equation (1.46). In this case the vorticity, whatever its value may be, is conserved in each fluid element as it moves in the fluid. The result does not hold, however, if the fluid is compressible, for then although the first term on the right-hand side of (1.44) still vanishes for two-dimensional flow, the second term does not:

$$\frac{d\boldsymbol{\omega}}{dt} = -\boldsymbol{\omega} \, \mathrm{div} \, \mathbf{v} \tag{1.46a}$$

1.10. The circulation

Suppose some closed contour is isolated in the fluid at some time instant. Then if $\mathbf{v}$ is the velocity at some point of the contour located in the contour length element $d\mathbf{l}$, the integral Γ defined by:

$$\Gamma = \oint (\mathbf{v} . d\mathbf{l}) \tag{1.47}$$

taken around the closed contour is called the circulation of the velocity, or more often just the circulation.

Consider the total time derivative of Γ. Then:

$$\frac{d}{dt}\oint (\mathbf{v}.d\mathbf{l}) = \oint \left(\frac{d\mathbf{v}}{dt}.d\mathbf{l}\right) + \oint \left(\mathbf{v}.\frac{d(d\mathbf{l})}{dt}\right). \qquad (1.48)$$

The second term on the right-hand side can be rewritten:

$$\oint \left(\mathbf{v}.\frac{d(d\mathbf{l})}{dt}\right) = \oint (\mathbf{v}.d\mathbf{v}) = \oint d(\tfrac{1}{2}v^2) = 0,$$

the vanishing of the third form resulting from an integration around a closed contour.

The first term on the right-hand side of (1.48) also vanishes; this follows from an appeal to the momentum equation (1.15) and the thermodynamic relation (1.31). For,

$$\oint \left(\frac{d\mathbf{v}}{dt}.d\mathbf{l}\right) = -\oint (\operatorname{grad} h.d\mathbf{l}).$$

By using Stoke's theorem a line integral can be replaced by an integral over any surface bounded by the line:

$$\oint_{\text{line}} (\operatorname{grad} h.d\mathbf{l}) = \oint_{\text{surface}} (\operatorname{curl}\operatorname{grad} h.d\mathbf{s}).$$

But the second integral vanishes because $\operatorname{curl}\operatorname{grad} h = 0$. Consequently (1.48) reduces to

$$\boxed{\frac{d\Gamma}{dt} = 0,} \qquad (1.49)$$

which expresses the fact that the circulation round a closed contour moving with the fluid is constant in time: this result was first obtained by Lord Kelvin and (1.49) is often quoted as being a statement of Kelvin's theorem. It should be remembered that no dissipative effects have been included in our discussion so far.

1.11. Condition for incompressible flow

Flow in an incompressible fluid must, by definition, proceed under the condition $\rho = \text{constant}$. This can never be exactly true in any real fluid, but it may lead to negligible error to believe that it is under circumstances which we now investigate.

The flow is strictly incompressible if any density variation $\delta\rho$ cannot occur; it can, however, be regarded as virtually incompressible if $\delta\rho$ is essentially zero, i.e., if $\delta\rho \ll \rho$. If δp is the pressure variation corresponding to the density variation $\delta\rho$, then $\delta\rho = (\partial\rho/\partial p)\,\delta p$ since pressure and density are related through the fluid equation of state. It will be found later (in Chapter 4) that the velocity of sound in the fluid, c_s, is related to the change in pressure consequent upon density change; explicitly that $c_s^2 = \partial p/\partial\rho$. Consequently, $\delta p = c_s^2\,\delta\rho$. If the flow is also steady, then the Bernoulli equation (1.41a) can be used to relate δp to the fluid velocity, viz. $\delta p = \frac{1}{2}\rho v^2 \sim \rho v^2$. Using these various relations it follows that, as regards to orders of magnitude, $\delta p \sim \rho v^2/c_s^2$. Thus for steady fluid flow the condition for virtually incompressible flow becomes finally:

$$\boxed{\dfrac{\delta\rho}{\rho} \sim \dfrac{v^2}{c_s^2} \ll 1.}\qquad(1.50)$$

That is, the fluid velocity in any region must be very small in comparison with the velocity of sound in the medium occupying this region.

For non-steady flow the Bernoulli equation cannot be invoked to relate δp to $\mathbf{v}$ but the momentum equation (1.15) can be used to do this instead. If τ and L denote respectively the time and distance required for the (non-steady) fluid velocity to undergo any significant change, then (1.15) leads to the relation $v/\tau \sim (\delta p/L\rho)$, i.e.

$$\delta p \sim \frac{Lv\rho}{\tau}.$$

Introducing the local sound velocity c_s:

$$\delta\rho \sim \frac{L\rho}{\tau}\cdot\frac{v}{c_s}.\qquad(1.51)$$

Using the continuity equation (1.11) it is clear that the previous incompressibility condition (1.13) is true only if $(1/\rho)(d\rho/dt) \ll \operatorname{div}\mathbf{v}$, i.e., in terms of τ and L, if

$$\frac{\delta\rho}{\tau} \ll \frac{\rho v}{L}.\qquad(1.52)$$

The insertion of (1.51) into (1.52) leads at once to the condition:

$$\tau \gg \frac{L}{c_s}. \tag{1.53}$$

Expressed in words, the time taken for a sound wave to travel the distance over which the fluid velocity changes appreciably is very small in comparison with the time taken for the fluid to travel this distance. In other words, any interactional disturbance in the fluid such as changing conditions at a boundary travels with effectively infinite velocity when the fluid sound velocity is taken as standard. If this is the case then the flow can be regarded as incompressible to very good approximation.

1.12. Boundary conditions

For an ideal fluid the motion is to be described by five equations, viz. the momentum equation (1.15) (a vector equation with three components and so being in fact three equations), the continuity equation (1.10) or (1.11) and the energy equation (1.37) which in fact is closely linked to the entropy equation (1.28). In this way the conservation laws of momentum, mass, and energy are invoked.

Solutions of physical interest are obtained by the requirement that they satisfy certain boundary conditions inferred independently from physical criteria. For the present case of an ideal fluid, in which irreversible dissipative effects are absent, the condition at a solid boundary is that fluid shall not penetrate the boundary, and for the boundary between two immiscible fluids it is that the fluids shall not mix. Explicitly, at a solid boundary the *normal* component of the fluid velocity must be zero with respect to the boundary, whether the boundary be at rest or be moving. There is no restriction to be placed on the velocity components tangential to the boundary. At the boundary between two immiscible fluids both the normal pressure and velocity components must be the same on each side of, and also through, the boundary.

Irrotational Motion: General Arguments

Fluid motion in a given region is said to be irrotational if the vorticity vector vanishes in that region. Such motion, sometimes also called potential flow, has important properties, some of which we now investigate.

2.1. The velocity potential

It is a well-known result of vector analysis that if ϕ is a scalar function then

$$\operatorname{curl} \operatorname{grad} \phi = 0. \qquad (2.1)$$

Now grad ϕ is a vector; the condition that the fluid flow be irrotation in any region is that the vorticity vector $\boldsymbol{\omega}$ should have zero curl throughout the region. Consequently the condition $\operatorname{curl} \mathbf{v} = 0$ can be combined with (2.1) to give the result that the fluid velocity for irrotational flow can be written as the gradient of some scalar quantity ϕ:

$$\mathbf{v} = -\operatorname{grad} \phi. \qquad (2.2)$$

The negative sign is chosen here as a convention; many other authors use instead a positive sign, but this is completely immaterial provided whichever choice is made is applied consistently throughout the arguments. The scalar ϕ is called the velocity potential, and is in general a function of the position and the time.

The existence of a velocity potential is associated with a vanishing circulation, as can be seen by invoking Stokes' theorem in the rearrangement of equation (1.47) defining the circulation. For:

$$\Gamma = \oint (\mathbf{v} . d\mathbf{l}) = \oint (\operatorname{curl} \mathbf{v} . d\mathbf{s}),$$

where $d\mathbf{s}$ is an element of the surface enclosed by the line contour of the circulation. Using equations (2.1) and (2.2) it follows that $\oint (\operatorname{curl} \mathbf{v} . d\mathbf{s}) = 0$, i.e. that $\Gamma = 0$. This means that $d\phi = (\mathbf{v} . d\mathbf{l})$ is a perfect differential, and closed streamlines cannot occur in irrotational flow. A fluid in irrotational flow, such that the fluid velocity on each plane perpendicular to the direction of motion is constant, will often be referred to as being in plane flow.

2.2. Integration of the momentum equation

A very important property of irrotational flow is that the momentum equation (1.15) can be readily integrated in this case. Using the vector relation (1.39a), which now becomes

$$(\mathbf{v}.\mathrm{grad})\mathbf{v} = \mathrm{grad}\,(v^2/2),$$

and assuming $\mathbf{F}$ to be a conservative force, the insertion of (2.2) into (1.15) gives, after a little rearrangement

$$\mathrm{grad}\left(-\frac{\partial\phi}{\partial t}+\frac{v^2}{2}+h+\Phi\right) = 0.$$

This equation can be integrated at once to give as solution:

$$\frac{\partial\phi}{\partial t} = \frac{v^2}{2}+h+\Phi+f(t), \tag{2.3}$$

where $f(t)$ is some arbitrary function of the time alone. This is a generalization of the previous Bernoulli equation (1.41) for steady motion. It is easily seen that the Bernoulli equation for irrotational motion (2.3) reduces to (1.41) if the motion is also steady, since then $\partial\phi/\partial t = 0$ and $f(t)$ is simply a constant throughout the fluid. There is, therefore, this one very significant difference between the Bernoulli equations appropriate to irrotational flow, and that appropriate to other (rotational) flows. In the former case, i.e. when equation (2.3) is valid, the function $f(t)$, whether it be a constant (steady flow) or a function of the time (non-steady flow), has the same value throughout the fluid region where the flow is irrotational; but alternatively for rotational flow, where equation (1.41) applies for steady conditions, the function f differs from streamline to streamline. This is one facet of the simplicity of irrotational flow in comparison with rotational flow.

There is no loss of generality in our arguments if in equation (2.3) we set $f(t) = 0$; for the velocity is unaffected according to (2.2) if ϕ

is replaced by $\phi + \int f(t)\,dt$. Consequently we can regard $f(t)$ as having been absorbed into $\partial\phi/\partial t$ and write (2.3) more simply as

$$\frac{\partial\phi}{\partial t} = \frac{v^2}{2} + h + \Phi. \tag{2.3a}$$

If the irrotational flow is steady this reduces to

$$\frac{v^2}{2} + h + \Phi = 0. \tag{2.3b}$$

2.3. Incompressible flow

When the fluid is incompressible the velocity satisfies the condition (1.13); if the motion is also irrotational we may use the equation (2.2) to obtain:

$$\boxed{\operatorname{div}\operatorname{grad}\phi = \nabla^2\phi = 0} \tag{2.4}$$

in this case. This means that the velocity potential satisfies the Laplace equation, and this is an extremely important result. The Laplace equation is to be solved subject to the general boundary condition that the normal component of the velocity must vanish at a rigid boundary. If $\hat{n}$ is the unit vector normal to the surface then the general boundary condition to be applied to solutions of equation (2.4) is:

$$\frac{\partial\phi}{\partial n} = 0. \tag{2.5}$$

Of course, additional conditions will also be available if non-rigid boundaries are also involved.

The solutions of the Laplace equation have been extensively investigated because the equation arises in many branches of physics and engineering; we do not need to rehearse this work here since it is very readily available elsewhere.

2.4. Stagnation points

In a region of general fluid flow any points at which the velocity is always zero are clearly special points; they are called stagnation points and are associated with the presence of obstacles to the flow.

A simple physical picture of the way stagnation points arise follows from an example; we consider here the fluid flow past a rigid sphere. At large distances (i.e. compared to the radius of the sphere) the flow is essentially uninfluenced by the presence of the sphere, but at small distances this is not so. In particular, any fluid encountering the sphere must move aside from its original path since the sphere is rigid. If the initial fluid flow is uniform the streamlines must show complete symmetry when passing the sphere (see Fig. 1), and the symmetry is with respect to that diameter of the sphere which lies in the direction of the flow (marked XY in Fig. 1). The central streamline is checked by the sphere, the velocity at point X being zero; this point

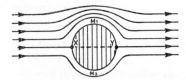

Fig. 1. *Showing the irrotational flow pattern of an ideal fluid past a circular cross-section of a cylinder (no dissipation).*

is thus a stagnation point. The energy of the fluid is split at point X, the single initial streamline resulting in two streamlines which pass round the section but keeping always in contact with the surface. They reunite again at point Y, which is also a stagnation point. The flow pattern is unchanged in profile if the fluid velocity is exactly reversed. What we have said here refers to an ideal fluid and the situation is modified in a real fluid; it will be seen later that the stagnation point Y then will be displaced downstream (i.e. to the right of the diagram) and may even be indefinitely far from the sphere (i.e. at infinity).

2.5. Stream function: two-dimensional flow

If the irrotational flow of an incompressible fluid is two-dimensional, in the sense of Art. 1.9, great advantage results from defining a new function, the stream function ψ, which is closely related to the velocity potential and which supplements it. We give first a mathematical definition for ψ [i.e. relations (2.7)] and follow this with a physical interpretation [summarized in equation (2.14)].

The continuity equation in the form (1.13) for an incompressible fluid is, in Cartesian co-ordinates for two-dimensional flow in the $(x-y)$ plane:

$$\frac{\partial v_x}{\partial x} + \frac{\partial v_y}{\partial y} = 0. \tag{2.6}$$

Now, the continuity equation (2.6) is satisfied identically if the velocity components are written as derivatives of some stream function $\psi(x, y)$, defined so that the following relations hold true:

$$v_x = -\frac{\partial \psi}{\partial y}; \quad v_y = +\frac{\partial \psi}{\partial x}. \tag{2.7}$$

This is immediately demonstrated by inserting (2.7) into (2.6). But the flow is irrotational so that curl $\mathbf{v} = 0$: if $(\hat{\imath}, \hat{\jmath}, \hat{k})$ are the unit vectors along respectively the x, y, z Cartesian axes, the condition for irrotational flow means

$$\hat{\imath}\left(\frac{\partial v_z}{\partial y} - \frac{\partial v_y}{\partial z}\right) + \hat{\jmath}\left(\frac{\partial v_x}{\partial z} - \frac{\partial v_z}{\partial x}\right) + \hat{k}\left(\frac{\partial v_y}{\partial x} - \frac{\partial v_x}{\partial y}\right) = 0. \tag{2.8}$$

However, $v_z = 0$ and v_x and v_y are both independent of z (two-dimensional flow in a three-dimensional fluid); consequently the insertion of (2.7) into (2.8) gives

$$\boxed{\frac{\partial^2 \psi}{\partial x^2} + \frac{\partial^2 \psi}{\partial y^2} = 0.} \tag{2.9}$$

Thus the stream function is a solution of the Laplace equation in its two-dimensional form.

Using the equations for a streamline (1.40) for the present two-dimensional flow, i.e.

$$v_y \, dx - v_x \, dy = 0, \tag{2.10}$$

then it follows from the substitution of the expressions (2.7) that

$$\frac{\partial \psi}{\partial x} dx + \frac{\partial \psi}{\partial y} dy = d\psi = 0. \qquad (2.11)$$

Consequently $\psi =$ constant, i.e. the stream function is constant along a streamline.

The physical significance of ψ can be deduced by considering the flow of mass in unit time (i.e. the mass flux) Q across some line in the $(x-y)$ plane joining any two fixed points, labelled 1 and 2, say. If v_n is the fluid velocity component normal to the line at each point, the definition of Q gives:

$$Q = \rho \int_1^2 v_n dl \qquad (2.12)$$

where dl is any line element. Because the line is not a streamline:

$$v_n dl = v_x dy - v_y dx = d\psi \neq 0. \qquad (2.13)$$

Therefore

$$Q = \rho \int_1^2 d\psi = \rho(\psi_2 - \psi_1), \qquad (2.14)$$

where ψ_1 and ψ_2 are respectively the stream functions at points 1 and 2. Thus the mass flux density (Q/ρ), which is the mass flux per unit mass, across the line joining two points is the simple difference of the stream functions appropriate to these points. This is fully consistent with the previous result that $\psi =$ constant along a streamline since the fluid mass flux across a streamline is zero.

2.6. Complex potential

Any two lines are at right angles at a point if their slopes (i.e. gradients) are perpendicular at that point. Let us apply this statement to the two functions ϕ and ψ. We are concerned with the expression

$$(\text{grad } \phi . \text{grad } \psi),$$

which for two-dimensional flow becomes, in terms of components:

$$\frac{\partial \phi}{\partial x_i} \frac{\partial \psi}{\partial x_i} = \frac{\partial \phi}{\partial x} \frac{\partial \psi}{\partial x} + \frac{\partial \phi}{\partial y} \frac{\partial \psi}{\partial y}. \tag{2.15}$$

But the velocity components v_x and v_y are given in two alternative forms in equations (2.2) and (2.7):

$$v_x = -\frac{\partial \phi}{\partial x} = -\frac{\partial \psi}{\partial y}; \quad v_y = -\frac{\partial \phi}{\partial y} = +\frac{\partial \psi}{\partial x}. \tag{2.16}$$

It is now very apparent that the fluid velocity is defined if either the stream function or the velocity potential is known. The insertion of the relations (2.16) into (2.15) leads at once to the result

$$\boxed{\frac{\partial \phi}{\partial x_i} \frac{\partial \psi}{\partial x_i} = 0} \tag{2.17}$$

for two-dimensional flow. But this is the statement that the functions ϕ and ψ are mutually perpendicular at any point, which is a very important result.

The fact that the velocity potential and the stream function are always mutually perpendicular can be expressed very concisely in the notation of complex numbers. Remembering that the imaginary unit $i = \sqrt{-1}$ denotes the rotation through a right angle we define the so-called complex potential according to:

$$\boxed{\omega = \phi + i\psi.} \tag{2.18}$$

Since the position co-ordinate components x and y are mutually perpendicular we can introduce the complex number z as the independent variable in place of r, and so use the full apparatus of the theory of complex numbers. The complex number z is

$$z = x + iy, \tag{2.19}$$

and for the complex potential we have $\omega = \omega(z)$.

To demonstrate that the complex potential completely specifies the flow it is necessary to deduce the relations (2.16) from it. Let us first differentiate (2.18) with respect to x, and then with respect to y, and then use (2.19): the result is the following expressions

$$\frac{\partial}{\partial x}(\phi + i\psi) = \frac{\partial}{\partial z}(\phi + i\psi)\frac{\partial z}{\partial x} = \frac{\partial}{\partial z}(\phi + i\psi)$$

$$\frac{\partial}{\partial y}(\phi + i\psi) = \frac{\partial}{\partial z}(\phi + i\psi)\frac{\partial z}{\partial y} = i\frac{\partial}{\partial z}(\phi + i\psi).$$

Consequently

$$\frac{\partial}{\partial y}(\phi + i\psi) = i\frac{\partial}{\partial x}(\phi + i\psi).$$

Equating the real and imaginary parts of this expression we obtain the two relations

$$\boxed{\frac{\partial \phi}{\partial y} = -\frac{\partial \psi}{\partial x}; \quad \frac{\partial \phi}{\partial x} = \frac{\partial \psi}{\partial y}.} \tag{2.20}$$

These relations (incidentally associated with the names of Riemann and Cauchy in a wider connection) are in fact the expressions (2.16).

From (2.18) it follows that

$$\frac{\partial \phi}{\partial x} + i\frac{\partial \psi}{\partial x} = \frac{\partial \omega}{\partial x} = \frac{d\omega}{dz}\frac{\partial z}{\partial x} = \frac{d\omega}{dz}.$$

Using the relations (2.16) this becomes:

$$\boxed{v_x - iv_y = -\frac{d\omega}{dz}.} \tag{2.21}$$

The expression $(v_x - iv_y)$ is called the complex velocity, being the negative complex gradient of the complex potential. According to the theory of complex numbers we may write

$$-\frac{d\omega}{dz} = v\exp\{-i\vartheta\}, \tag{2.21a}$$

where

$$v = \sqrt{(v_x^2 + v_y^2)}; \quad \vartheta = \tan^{-1}(v_y/v_x). \tag{2.21b}$$

Consequently, the complex velocity gives the magnitude of the velocity through the modulus of the complex number (2.21), and the angle ϑ between the direction of the velocity and the x-axis through the argument of (2.21). The negative sign in (2.21a) must be remembered carefully in calculations, as must be the fact that (2.21) involves the complex conjugate of the quantity $v_x + iv_y$ and not this quantity itself. Clearly, the speed of the fluid at any point is given by

$$\left(\frac{d\omega}{dz} \cdot \frac{d\omega^*}{dz^*}\right),$$

where the superscript * denotes the complex conjugate of the complex quantity.

For two-dimensional flow a stagnation point is, then, by definition characterized by the relations

$$\mathbf{v} = 0; \quad \frac{d\omega}{dz} = 0; \quad \frac{d\psi}{\partial x} = \frac{\partial \psi}{\partial y} = 0. \qquad (2.22)$$

There is no loss of generality if we set $\psi = 0$ at the stagnation point and let this be at the origin of co-ordinates. Then we can apply the Maclaurin expansion formula for the immediate vicinity of the origin:

$$\psi = \frac{1}{2}\left[x^2\left(\frac{\partial^2 \psi}{\partial x^2}\right)_0 + 2xy\left(\frac{\partial^2 \psi}{\partial x\, \partial y}\right)_0 + y^2\left(\frac{\partial^2 \psi}{\partial y^2}\right)_0\right] + \ldots \qquad (2.23)$$

But in the neighbourhood of the origin this is the equation of two straight lines; this can be seen by making the substitution:

$$a = \left(\frac{\partial^2 \psi}{\partial x^2}\right)_0; \quad b = \left(\frac{\partial^2 \psi}{\partial y^2}\right)_0; \quad h = \left(\frac{\partial^2 \psi}{\partial x\, \partial y}\right)_0.$$

We then have in the origin region:

$$ax^2 + 2hxy + by^2 = 0.$$

These two straight lines are known to be at an angle

$$\tan^{-1}\left\{\frac{2\sqrt{(h^2 - ab)}}{a+b}\right\},$$

and this is a right angle if $a + b = 0$. If the flow is irrotational this is certainly the case [remember equation (2.9) which applies now]; for *irrotational* flow, therefore, a single streamline breaks into two at a stagnation point, and the two resulting component streamlines are mutually perpendicular.

2.7. Some examples of complex potential flow

We give now one or two examples of two-dimensional flow to illustrate the use of the complex potentials introduced so far; this is very cursory and reference must be made to more extensive studies for a proper detailed account. Broadly speaking it is not possible to construct deliberately a complex potential function for any specific flow pattern. Instead it is necessary to determine the flow pattern which is associated with a chosen potential function; the function appropriate to any specific flow is then to be guessed by a trial-and-error procedure based largely on past experience.

(a) Flow in a corner

Let us assume

$$\omega = Az^n, \tag{2.24}$$

where A is a real constant and n is a real number. In polar co-ordinates (r, ϑ) we may use the well-known relation of complex numbers:

$$z^n = r^n (\cos n\vartheta + i \sin n\vartheta)$$

to get from equation (2.18):

$$\phi = Ar^n \cos n\vartheta, \quad \psi = Ar^n \sin n\vartheta \tag{2.25}$$

by equating real and imaginary parts. These are respectively the velocity potential and the stream function for the fluid flow described by (2.24). We next deduce what flow is thus represented; there are many cases depending on the value of n, and we consider some of them now. (i) $n = 1$: in this case $\phi = Ar \cos \vartheta$; $\psi = Ar \sin \vartheta$. The streamlines are a system of parallel straight lines along the x-axis, while the corresponding stream functions are straight lines parallel to the y-axis. Since $d\omega/dz = A$, and $A \neq 0$, then there are no stagnation points. If it is known that stagnation points are present in any given flow pattern, then (2.24) cannot apply. (ii) $n = 2$: in this case $\phi = Ar^2 \cos 2\vartheta$; $\psi = Ar^2 \sin 2\vartheta$. The curves for which $\phi = $ constant, or $\psi = $ constant, are both a system of rectangular hyperbolae with the axis of the co-ordinates as principal axis or asymptotes respectively. By using the relations (2.20) it follows that the streamline $\psi = 0$ contains the regions $\vartheta = 0$ and $\vartheta = \pi/2$: consequently we may take the positive parts of the (x, y) axis as rigid boundaries. The flow is now that in the apex between two walls at right angles. (iii) For the general case, by

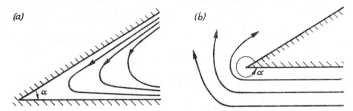

FIG. 2. *Showing the irrotational two-dimensions flow pattern for an ideal fluid at a corner of angle α in the fluid: (a) $\alpha < \pi/2$; (b) $\alpha > \pi/2$.*

suitably choosing n the flow can be determined between two rigid walls enclosed at a general angle α. For then the streamlines have the equation

$$r^n \sin n\vartheta = \text{constant},$$

and the lines $\vartheta = 0$ and $\vartheta = \pi/n$ are parts of the same streamline. Writing $n\alpha = \pi$ it is easy to find that

$$\phi = Ar^{\pi/\alpha} \cos \frac{\pi\vartheta}{\alpha}, \psi = Ar^{\pi/\alpha} \sin \frac{\pi\vartheta}{\alpha}. \qquad (2.26)$$

The velocity component perpendicular to r is

$$v_\perp = -\frac{A\pi}{\alpha} r^{(\pi/\alpha - 1)} \cos \frac{\pi\vartheta}{\alpha}, \qquad (2.27a)$$

while the parallel component is

$$v_\parallel = \frac{A\pi}{\alpha} r^{(\pi/\alpha - 1)} \sin \frac{\pi\vartheta}{\alpha}. \qquad (2.27b)$$

The flow pattern is sketched in Fig. 2.

(b) Flow through an aperture in a partition, or around a flat plate

Instead of expressing ω as a function of z it is often convenient to choose z as some function of ω. Consider the relation

$$z = C \cosh \omega, \tag{2.28}$$

where C is a real constant.

Then:

$$x = C \cosh \phi \cos \psi; \quad y = C \sinh \phi \sin \psi. \tag{2.28a}$$

The curves $\phi = $ constant and $\psi = $ constant satisfy respectively the equations

$$\frac{x^2}{C^2 \cosh^2 \phi} + \frac{y^2}{C^2 \sinh^2 \phi} = 1, \tag{2.28b}$$

$$\frac{x^2}{C^2 \cos^2 \psi} + \frac{y^2}{C^2 \sin^2 \psi} = 1.$$

These are conics (the first an ellipse and the second a hyperbola) having the common foci ($\pm C, 0$). These two sets of curves are shown in Fig. 3. At the foci, $\phi = 0$ and $\psi = n\pi$ (n is some integer) and the

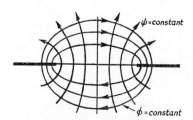

Fig. 3. *The Ellipse-Hyperbola system for flow through an aperture (ψ-lines as streamlines) or around a plate (ϕ-lines as streamlines).*

velocity is therefore infinite there. Suppose we take the hyperbolae as streamlines: then the x-axis which lies outside the foci (heavily marked in Fig. 3) can be regarded as a rigid boundary. The associated fluid flow is that through an aperture in a thin plate.

Alternatively, the system of ellipses may be taken as fluid stream-lines. Then the flow is that around an elliptical cylinder, or in the limit of vanishing thickness, around a thin plate joining the foci $(\pm C, 0)$. At indefinitely large distances the fluid velocity is zero in each case.

(c) Flow into a canal from a large reservoir

Let us assume

$$z = \omega + \exp \omega, \qquad (2.29)$$

so that

$$x = \phi + (\exp \phi) \cos \psi, \quad y = \psi + (\exp \phi) \sin \psi. \qquad (2.29a)$$

Taking the streamline as $\psi = $ constant, $\psi = 0$ is along the x-axis; the streamline $\psi = \pi$ bends back on itself in the region $x = -\infty$ to

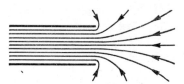

FIG. 4. *Streamlines for flow into a canal from a large reservoir.*

$x = -1$. The flow is therefore that of fluid into a parallel channel from a large volume (i.e. a reservoir) and is sketched in Fig. 4. The velocity is infinite at the ends of the walls. If the walls are not parallel but each make an angle θ with the symmetry line $\psi = 0$ then (2.29) is to be replaced by:

$$z = \frac{1-n}{n}[1 - \exp(-n\omega)] + \exp[(1-n)\omega] \qquad (2.29b)$$

where $\theta = n\pi$. As $\theta \to 0$, the expression (2.29b) reduces to the original form (2.29), since $\exp(-n\omega) \to 1 - n\omega$, when n is sufficiently small.

This brief section gives some small indication of the power of the theory associated with the complex potential representation of two-dimensional irrotational flow. Unfortunately the theory cannot be generalized to include three-dimensional flow due to the two-dimensional properties of complex numbers.

2.8. Sources and sinks

Although in the real world fluid cannot be created or destroyed at any point† there is often great theoretical advantage in introducing certain abstract points in the fluid field at which such creation or annihilation of fluid is supposed hypothetically to occur. Any point where fluid is assumed to be created is called a source, while annihilation occurs at a sink; if the created fluid is supposed to flow out radially and uniformly in all directions the corresponding point is called a simple source, while if the fluid moves in uniformly from all directions to disappear at a single point we have, there, a simple sink. If the rate of emission or reception of fluid at such a simple singular point is steady the point is said to be a steady simple source, or alternatively a steady simple sink.

The strength of a source (or sink) is defined in terms of the fluid mass flow out from (or into) the point; more specifically the source has a strength m if m is the fluid *volume* emitted in unit time. Alternatively, the sink is defined as being of strength m if the fluid *volume* m is absorbed by the sink in unit time. Because the fluid is continuous away from the source (or sink) the volume of fluid emitted by a simple source (or absorbed by a simple sink) must equal that crossing the surface of a small surrounding sphere having the source (or sink) as centre. If the fluid has velocity v_n normal to this spherical surface, which itself has a radius r, then the fluid volume crossing this surface in unit time (which by definition is the flux crossing the surface) is $\iint v_n\, ds = \iint v\, ds$. Clearly $v_n = v$ for the radial flow of a simple source (or sink). From the definition of the strength of the source

$$m = \int\int v\, ds. \qquad (2.30a)$$

For a sink, the same expression holds though with opposite sign because fluid is flowing into the sphere and not out from it.

† We are not concerned here with recent conjectures in cosmology.

For irrotational motion the velocity potential is defined by (2.2), and then (2.30a) is written in terms of this potential as:

$$m = - \int \int \frac{\partial \phi}{\partial r} ds. \qquad (2.30b)$$

Integrating this expression, the velocity potential at any point distance r from a simple source is

$$\phi = \frac{m}{4\pi r}. \qquad (2.31a)$$

The same expression, although with a minus sign, applies for a simple sink.

A source and a sink of equal strengths can be combined to form a double source of strength μ. The sources are supposed of strength $\pm m$ and are distant dl apart; dl is now made vanishingly small and $\pm m$ indefinitely great but in such a way that $\mu = m \, dl$ remains finite. The joining line dl defines the axis of the double source, and the direction of this axis is (by convention) from sink to source. The velocity potential at any point distance r from a double source is readily found to be given by

$$\phi = \frac{\mu}{4\pi} \cdot \frac{\cos \vartheta}{r^2} \qquad (2.31b)$$

where ϑ is the angle between the line of length r (joining the source to the point) and the axis of the source. There is an obvious analogy between this expression and that for the magnetic potential due to a magnetic dipole. Double and single sources can be combined to provide more complex sources but we will not pursue this further. In addition, hypothetical simple or double sources can be distributed continuously over lines, surfaces, or volumes to reproduce complex flow patterns actually occurring. We state here without proof that no representation of given flow by a surface distribution of simple *and* double sources is unique, but a distribution of simple sources *alone*, or of double sources *alone* over the boundary surface enclosing the fluid flow is a unique distribution for a given fluid flow pattern.

For two-dimensional flow the stream function for a simple source of strength m can be derived from considerations of fluid flux; for a source at the origin, the flux at the point $r = (x, y)$ is

$$2\pi\psi = -m\tan^{-1}(y/x). \qquad (2.32)$$

We give now several expressions relevant to two-dimensional flow, although unfortunately without proof, through lack of space. The

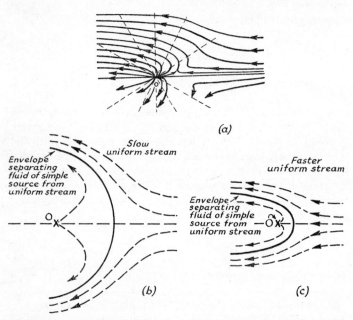

FIG. 5. *Flow pattern for simple source in a uniform fluid stream. The reversal of the flow arrows would give the flow pattern for a simple sink in a uniform fluid stream. The flow pattern for a source-sink system in a uniform stream can then be constructed by superposition of the appropriate flow patterns. General flow pattern for the source in the stream is shown in (a): in (b) is schematically a source O of given strength in a slow uniform stream: in (c) is schematically the same source in a faster stream.*

complex potential for a simple source at the origin and of strength $2\pi m$ is:

$$\omega = -m\log z. \qquad (2.33a)$$

For a simple source located at the point z_1 the complex potential is modified to become

$$\omega = -m\log(z - z_1). \tag{2.33b}$$

A series of N sources, a typical one located at the point z_i and having strength $2\pi m_i$ has the complex potential

$$\omega = -\sum_{i=1}^{N} m_i \log(z - z_i). \tag{2.34a}$$

By appropriately changing the sign of m_i, sinks can also be included into this series. If in addition the fluid has independently a flow velocity U parallel to the x-axis, then (2.34a) is replaced by

$$\omega = -Uz + \sum_i (-m_i)\log(z - z_i). \tag{2.34b}$$

A special case of (2.34b) is that referring to an equal source and sink combination in a free stream. Let the source and sink each lie on the x-axis at points $(a, 0)$ and $(-a, 0)$ respectively; then

$$\omega = Uz - m\log(z - a) + m\log(z + a), \tag{2.34c}$$

where the free stream direction is in the negative x-direction from source to sink. Such a situation is shown in Fig. 5

In each of the above cases the corresponding velocity potential and stream function is found by using (2.18) and so equating real and imaginary parts in the expression for the complex potential.

CHAPTER 3

Irrotational Motion: Surface Waves in Liquids

The theory of wave motions in a liquid in the presence of gravity is one of the most successful and fully studied sections of irrotational fluid dynamics. This is especially true when the liquid is water since then it has been found possible to explain fully such problems as the motion of the tides, waves on an open sea, the wave resistance of ships, and many other practical problems, by a direct application of the theory. It is not surprising that a very extensive literature should exist on the subject and no account of the motion of fluids would be complete without some consideration of the theory of waves in liquids. This, therefore, forms the subject of the present chapter; because space is limited we must refer the reader elsewhere for a detailed account of applications to physical and geophysical situations.

Emphasis will be placed on surface waves, where the vertical acceleration of the fluid cannot be neglected. Such is the case when the wave-length is small in comparison with the depth of water. Tidal waves describe the alternative limit where the wave-length is large in comparison with the depth, and here the vertical accelerations can be assumed negligible.

3.1. Irrotational nature of the flow

The equilibrium configuration of a liquid in a container of general laboratory size is one of rest with a plane surface. Any disturbance of the surface due to either the direct or indirect action of some external perturbing force will cause motion in the liquid, possibly of an oscillatory type, which will propagate over the whole surface. An impulsive perturbation will produce some isolated disturbance (in certain circumstances a solitary wave), while a continuous periodic perturbation will produce an oscillatory wave train. The disturbance is most noticeable on the liquid surface, but we shall find that the whole body of the liquid is also affected to a greater or lesser extent. In general the effect decreases markedly with depth in the liquid. In what follows we shall be concerned with sinusoidal disturbances.

Wave motion is due to the action of gravity which acts in the direction of restoring the undisturbed state of rest, energy being transferred by the waves from regions of relative excess to those of relative deficiency. A liquid has no permanent rigidity. As a consequence it can transmit only oscillatory disturbances in which the oscillations take place along the direction of propagation – this is called a longitudinal wave motion. Transverse waves (where the oscillations are perpendicular to the propagation direction) cannot pass through a liquid without strong damping.† We will neglect the cause of the perturbation (this may, e.g., be some wave making machine).

The gravitational force is conservative with a potential function Φ where

$$\Phi = gz, \tag{3.1}$$

and g is the gravitational acceleration. We have here chosen the z-axis in the vertical direction, and positive *upwards*.

Because we are dealing with a liquid it is an adequate approximation to assume the flow to be incompressible. The continuity equation is now div $\mathbf{v} = 0$. For the present case, therefore, the momentum equation (1.15) has the form:

$$\frac{d\mathbf{v}}{dt} = -\frac{1}{\rho}\operatorname{grad} p + \mathbf{g}, \tag{3.2}$$

and the vorticity equation (1.45) is:

$$\frac{d\boldsymbol{\omega}}{dt} = (\boldsymbol{\omega}.\operatorname{grad})\mathbf{v}. \tag{3.3}$$

Because the wave motion is oscillatory, $\partial\mathbf{v}/\partial t$ is not zero; suppose the fluid velocity is sufficiently small for the condition

$$\frac{\partial\mathbf{v}}{\partial t} \gg (\mathbf{v}.\operatorname{grad})\mathbf{v}$$

---

† This statement requires some qualification since it will be seen later in Chapter 10 that a fluid is, in fact, able to support transverse waves under very special circumstances: viz. if the fluid is able to conduct electricity and if it is permeated by a magnetic field aligned in a special way.

to be valid. Under this approximation:

$$\frac{\partial \boldsymbol{\omega}}{\partial t} = 0$$

i.e. $\qquad\qquad \operatorname{curl} \mathbf{v} = \text{constant.}$

The mean velocity taken over one complete period of oscillation will be zero, so that as a first approximation we may set curl **v** equal to zero. This means that to this approximation the flow is irrotational. Thus a velocity potential ϕ can be defined throughout the body of the liquid (see equation (2.1)), which also satisfies a Laplace equation (because the fluid is incompressible). The momentum equation can be integrated directly to yield the time – dependent Bernoulli equation since Φ refers to a conservative force.

3.2. Conditions at the boundaries

With the positive z-axis taken vertically upwards, the $(x$–$y)$ plane will be taken to be in the plane surface of the undisturbed liquid. The height of any wave disturbance at any point, taken relative to the undisturbed surface, will be written ξ : ξ is simply the z-component specifying the liquid free surface, and is a function of (x, y, t) in general.

Conditions at the liquid surface can be specified by an appeal to the Bernoulli equation, including the time, i.e. to equation (2.3). For the present problem this is:

$$\frac{\partial \phi}{\partial t} = \frac{p}{\rho} + gz$$

where $(v^2/2)$ has been neglected in comparison with the remaining terms, and $f(t)$ has been adsorbed into $(\partial \phi / \partial t)$. At any point in the liquid the pressure is clearly given by

$$p = -g\rho z + \rho \frac{\partial \phi}{\partial t}. \qquad (3.4)$$

But the surface of the liquid is a surface of constant pressure, p_0 say, which will usually be the atmospheric pressure. Consequently, (3.4) becomes at the surface:

$$p_0 = -\rho g \xi + \rho \left(\frac{\partial \phi}{\partial t} \right)_{z=\xi}. \tag{3.4a}$$

By differentiating with respect to the time the wave height can be replaced by the velocity potential, for

$$\rho g \frac{\partial \xi}{\partial t} - \rho \left(\frac{\partial^2 \phi}{\partial t^2} \right)_{z=\xi} = 0. \tag{3.5}$$

Now, $(\partial \xi / \partial t)$ is nothing other than the z-component of the fluid velocity so that from (2.1):

$$\frac{\partial \xi}{\partial t} = -\frac{\partial \phi}{\partial z}. \tag{3.6}$$

The insertion of (3.6) into (3.5) gives at once the condition at the free surface

$$g \left(\frac{\partial \phi}{\partial z} + \frac{\partial^2 \phi}{\partial t^2} \right)_{z=\xi} = 0, \tag{3.7}$$

which involves the velocity potential alone, and not the wave disturbance amplitude.

A condition upon ϕ also applies at the bottom of the liquid. For an impenetrable bed the z-component of velocity must vanish, i.e. $-v_z = 0$. If the liquid is of depth h:

$$v_z = \frac{\partial \phi}{\partial z} \bigg|_{z=-h} = 0. \tag{3.8}$$

At any other impenetrable boundary the normal component of the fluid velocity relative to the boundary must vanish at all times.

3.3. Equation for progressive waves

Suppose the liquid is of unlimited extent in the $(x-y)$ plane, but is of uniform depth h. Suppose waves are propagated in the liquid in the x-direction; let the wavelength be λ, the wave frequency v, and the wave velocity be c. The motion is assumed uniform in the y-direction so that all quantities are two-dimensional depending on both x and z, and also on the time.

The Laplace equation is, for this case

$$\nabla^2 \phi = \frac{\partial^2 \phi}{\partial x^2} + \frac{\partial^2 \phi}{\partial z^2} = 0. \tag{3.9}$$

This equation is to be solved subject to the boundary conditions (3.7) and (3.8).

In applying the condition (3.7) we will make an approximation. Let us restrict our arguments to those cases in which the oscillations in the liquid are small in the sense that conditions at the free surface are virtually the same when $z = \xi$ as when $z = 0$. Under this approximation the equation (3.9) is to be solved subject to the conditions

$$\left(\frac{\partial \phi}{\partial z} + \frac{1}{g} \frac{\partial^2 \phi}{\partial t^2} \right)_{z=0} = 0, \tag{3.10a}$$

and

$$\left. \frac{\partial \phi}{\partial z} \right|_{z=-h} = 0. \tag{3.10b}$$

The Laplace equation (3.9) is separable in the variables z and x, and we can write:

$$\phi(x, z, t) = f(z) F(x, t). \tag{3.11}$$

Because we are dealing with a progressive wave motion we know at once that

$$F(x, t) = \cos(kx - \omega t) \tag{3.12}$$

where

$$k = \frac{2\pi}{\lambda} \quad \text{and} \quad \omega = 2\pi\nu = \frac{2\pi c}{\lambda} = kc. \tag{3.13}$$

Here k is called the wave number.

An equation satisfied by the function $f(z)$ follows from the insertion of (3.11) and (3.12) into (3.9); that is

$$\frac{d^2 f}{dz^2} - k^2 f = 0. \tag{3.14}$$

3.4. Velocity potential and surface displacement

As solution of (3.14) try:

$$f(z) = A \exp (\lambda_0 z), \tag{3.15}$$

where the quantities A and λ_0 are as yet undefined. The insertion of (3.15) into (3.14) shows that (3.15) is indeed a solution provided $\lambda_0 = \pm k$. Consequently the velocity potential for the wave motion is:

$$\phi = [A_1 \exp (kz) + A_2 \exp (-kz)] \cos (kx - \omega t). \tag{3.16}$$

The boundary condition (3.10b) gives at once a relation between the two constants A_1 and A_2, viz.

$$A_1 \exp (-kh) = A_2 \exp (kh) = D/2 \quad \text{(say)}.$$

Thus

$$A_1 \exp (kz) + A_2 \exp (-kz) = \frac{D}{2} [\exp (k(z+h)) + \exp (-k(z+h))].$$

The expression included between the brackets, however, is

$$2 \cosh k(z+h),$$

so that (3.16) transforms to:

$$\boxed{\phi = D \cosh k(z+h) \cos (kx - \omega t).} \tag{3.17}$$

D is a constant determined by the initial amplitude of the wave. The expression (3.17) is the velocity potential for the wave motion.

With the velocity potential known, the surface displacement is obtained directly from the Bernoulli equation applied to the surface, i.e. equation (3.4a). In this connection we notice that since p_0/ρ is constant, it can be absorbed in the term $\partial\phi/\partial t$. For the velocity is unaffected if we replace ϕ by $\phi + (p_0/\rho)t$. Consequently we have

$$\xi = -\frac{1}{g}\left(\frac{\partial\phi}{\partial t}\right)_{z=0}, \tag{3.18}$$

where we have used the approximation that $(\partial\phi/\partial t)$ is to be evaluated on the plane $z = 0$ instead of at $z = \xi$. Using (3.17):

$$\xi = E \sin (kx - \omega t), \tag{3.19}$$

where

$$E = \frac{Dck}{g}\cosh kh \tag{3.20a}$$

It is seen that both ϕ and ξ satisfy the standard wave equation in one dimension, which for ξ is:

$$\frac{\partial^2 \xi}{\partial x^2} = \frac{1}{c^2}\frac{\partial^2 \xi}{\partial t^2} \tag{3.20b}$$

since $\omega = ck$.

3.5. Wave and group velocities

The wave velocity is obtained in terms of the wave length by combining (3.17) and (3.10a). It easily follows that

$$\omega^2 = gk \tanh kh, \tag{3.21}$$

or, using the notation of (3.13):

$$\boxed{c^2 = \frac{\lambda g}{2\pi}\tanh\left(\frac{2\pi h}{\lambda}\right).} \tag{3.22}$$

It is seen that the wave velocity is different for different frequencies (except in the special case where $\lambda \gg h$: see later); that is, a liquid is a dispersive medium for wave propagation except in the limit of very long waves.

Any general profile, being the superposition of harmonic wave trains, moves with a velocity different from c; the group velocity V_g is known to be related to the wave frequency and number according to

$$V_g = \frac{d\omega}{dk}. \tag{3.23}$$

From (3.21) it follows readily that:

$$V_g = \frac{1}{2}\left(\frac{g}{k\tanh(kh)}\right)^{1/2}\left[\tanh(kh) + \frac{kh}{\cosh^2(kh)}\right]. \tag{3.24}$$

This can be rewritten in terms of the wave velocity by using (3.22). Thus

$$V_g = \tfrac{1}{2}c\left[1 + \frac{4\pi h}{\lambda}\,\text{cosech}\left(\frac{4\pi h}{\lambda}\right)\right]. \qquad (3.25)$$

The limiting cases of these expressions when $\lambda \gg h$ and $\lambda \ll h$ are important. When h is very large in comparison with λ, then $(2\pi h)/\lambda$ is very large. In this case:

$$\tanh\left(\frac{2\pi h}{\lambda}\right) \to 1 \quad \text{and} \quad \text{cosech}\left(\frac{4\pi h}{\lambda}\right) \to 0$$

so that for very deep water (for it is this situation that is now represented)

$$c^2 = \frac{\lambda g}{2\pi} \quad \text{and} \quad V_g = \frac{c}{2}. \qquad (3.26)$$

The wave velocity is seen to be proportional to the square root of the wavelength, and is independent of the water depth; also the group velocity is one half of the wave velocity in this limit. As the wave profile moves, individual waves appear at the back, overtake the group with relative velocity $(c/2)$ and then disappear at the front of the profile. From the tables of hyperbolic functions it is found that this situation, which depends upon $\tanh(kh)$ being exactly unity, is in fact obtained to high approximation if h is five or six times λ.

The other limit, when h is very small in comparison with λ, means that $(2\pi h)/\lambda$ is very small. Then:

$$\tanh\left(\frac{2\pi h}{\lambda}\right) \to \frac{2\pi h}{\lambda} \quad \text{and} \quad \text{cosech}\left(\frac{4\pi h}{\lambda}\right) \to 1,$$

so that

$$c_0^2 = gh \quad \text{and} \quad V_{g_0} = c_0. \qquad (3.27)$$

where the subscript 0 on c is used to denote very long wavelength. In this limit the wave velocity c_0 is proportional to the square root of the depth, but is independent of the wavelength; the group velocity V_{g_0} is equal to the wave velocity.

The dependence of wave velocity and group velocity on the ratio $2\pi h/\lambda$ is shown graphically in Figs. 6 and 7.

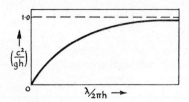

FIG. 6. *Wave velocity as function of the liquid depth.*

The limiting case (3.26) well represents waves on the ocean due to wind and storm disturbances, and such waves are usually referred to

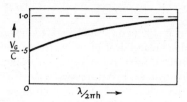

FIG. 7. *Group velocity as function of the liquid depth.*

as surface waves.† The alternative limit (3.27) is that appropriate to tidal conditions resulting from the gravitational effect of the Sun and

† The Gerstner trochoidal wave, with a particle position (x, z) which depends upon the time according to

$$x = a + \frac{1}{k} \exp(kb) \sin k(a + ct)$$

$$\text{and} \quad z = b - \frac{1}{k} \exp(kb) \cos k(a + ct),$$

where (a, b) are parameters, gives a wave profile in deep water which is a surface of constant pressure and involves no approximation. It is not, however, associated with irrotational motion and so will not be treated here.

Moon on the seas and oceans of the world; these waves are consequently usually called tidal waves, although they can be called more properly long gravity waves. It will be realized that the velocity of long gravity (tidal) waves is the maximum velocity that a gravity wave may have for any given depth of liquid.

3.6. Tidal wave equation

Consider a tank of essentially unlimited length containing a liquid and let a wave of length λ be propagated along the tank. If h is the undisturbed liquid depth, assume $\lambda \gg h$ (tidal wave). The cross-sectional area of the liquid at any point at any time will be written $A(x, t)$ where the x-direction is chosen as being along the axis of the tank; the breadth of liquid b will be assumed as being very small in comparison with λ.

If the flow conditions are such that v_z is small in comparison with v_x, the x- and z-components of the momentum equation (1.15) are:

$$\frac{\partial v_x}{\partial t} = -\frac{1}{\rho}\frac{\partial p}{\partial x}; \quad \frac{1}{\rho}\frac{\partial p}{\partial z} = -g. \tag{3.28}$$

Also, the Bernoulli equation for any point in the liquid is:

$$p = p_0 + g\rho(\xi - z),$$

so that from (3.28)

$$\frac{\partial v_x}{\partial t} = -g\frac{\partial \xi}{\partial x} \tag{3.29}$$

The wave height ξ will be assumed to be small.

A second, independent, relation between v_x and ξ is given by the continuity equation. Consider two planes in the liquid perpendicular to the wave propagation direction at the points x and $(x+dx)$ and labelled respectively the planes R and S. The fluid crossing plane R in unit time is $v_x(x) A(x)$; that crossing the neighbouring plane S in unit time is $v_x(x+dx) A(x+dx)$. Consequently, to the first order of small quantities the difference between these quantities is:

$$v_x(x+dx) A(x+dx) - v_x(x) A(x) = \frac{\partial}{\partial x}(Av_x)\, dx. \tag{3.30}$$

Now, the fluid is incompressible so that any excess of liquid volume between the two planes must be compensated for by a surface elevation. The change in liquid volume between the planes in unit time can be written as $(\partial A/\partial t)\,dx$. Consequently,

$$\frac{\partial A}{\partial t} + \frac{\partial(Av_x)}{\partial x} = 0. \tag{3.31}$$

Let A_0 be the equilibrium value of the liquid cross-section. Then we can write for the area when the wave is passing:

$$A = A_0 + b\xi. \tag{3.32}$$

The insertion of (3.32) into (3.31) gives to first order of small quantities

$$b\frac{\partial \xi}{\partial t} + \frac{\partial(A_0 v_x)}{\partial x} = 0,$$

and this is the form of the continuity equation appropriate to the present problem. Upon differentiation with respect to the time:

$$b\frac{\partial^2 \xi}{\partial t^2} + \frac{\partial}{\partial x}\left(A_0 \frac{\partial v_x}{\partial t}\right) = 0.$$

By using the previous relation (3.29), this equation can be arranged to involve ξ but not v_x:

$$\frac{\partial^2 \xi}{\partial t^2} - g\frac{\partial}{\partial x}\left(\frac{A_0}{b}\frac{\partial \xi}{\partial x}\right) = 0. \tag{3.33}$$

This is the equation for the wave propagation along the channel. If the ratio (A_0/b) is constant along the tank, i.e. if the wave depth is constant, equation (3.33) simplifies to become

$$\boxed{\frac{\partial^2 \xi}{\partial x^2} = \frac{1}{c_0^2}\frac{\partial^2 \xi}{\partial t^2},} \tag{3.34}$$

where $c_0^2 = gA/b = gh$, in agreement with (3.27) and (3.20). The arguments can be readily repeated to include also motion in the

y-direction: in this case the wave equation (3.34) is generalized to become

$$\frac{\partial^2 \xi}{\partial x^2} + \frac{\partial^2 \xi}{\partial y^2} = \frac{1}{c_0^2}\frac{\partial^2 \xi}{\partial t^2}, \tag{3.34a}$$

where the velocity c_0 is again the same as that occurring in (3.34).

3.7. Energy of progressive waves

We find now the energy to be associated with a progressive wave travelling in a liquid of uniform depth $h \gg \lambda$; we will consider the mean energy in one wave-length and of unit thickness (i.e. liquid one unit thick in the y-direction if wave propagation is along the x-direction as usual).

The potential energy is due entirely to the surface elevation and depression. With wave height ξ, the mass of liquid standing in the length dx and of unit thickness is $\rho\xi\,dx$. Its centre of mass is at height $\xi/2$ above the undisturbed level so that:

$$\text{Potential Energy} = \int\limits_0^\lambda \tfrac{1}{2}g\rho\xi^2\,dx. \tag{3.35}$$

Inserting equation (3.19) into this expression we get:

$$\text{Potential Energy} = \tfrac{1}{4}g\rho E^2 \int\limits_0^\lambda 2\sin^2(kx-\omega t)\,dx = \tfrac{1}{4}\rho g E^2 \lambda.$$

Here E is given by (3.20a) and involves the quantities c, λ, g and h.

The kinetic energy of the liquid in the volume encompassed by one wavelength is:

$$\text{Kinetic Energy} = \int\limits_{\text{volume}} \tfrac{1}{2}\rho v^2\,dV,$$

where the volume is that of the liquid depth h, unit width, and of length λ. According to equation (2.2):

$$v^2 = \left[\left(\frac{\partial \phi}{\partial x}\right)^2 + \left(\frac{\partial \phi}{\partial y}\right)^2 + \left(\frac{\partial \phi}{\partial z}\right)^2\right].$$

5

Thus

$$\text{Kinetic Energy} = \tfrac{1}{2}\rho \int\limits_{\text{volume}} \left(\frac{\partial \phi}{\partial x_i}\frac{\partial \phi}{\partial x_i}\right) dV = \tfrac{1}{2}\rho \int\limits_{\text{surface}} \phi\frac{\partial \phi}{\partial n} ds.$$

The last form follows from an application of Green's theorem well-known in vector analysis; the surface integration is to be taken over the total area enclosing the volume V. If the wave amplitude is sufficiently small we may write $\partial \phi/\partial n = \partial \phi/\partial z$ at the liquid surface, i.e. at $z = 0$. Further, $\partial \phi/\partial y = 0$. Using the expression (3.17) for ϕ it follows after a little calculation that:

$$\text{Kinetic Energy} = \tfrac{1}{4}\rho g E^2 \lambda. \tag{3.36}$$

Comparing (3.35) and (3.36) we see that the potential and kinetic energies are equal in a progressive wave. Adding these expressions together we find that the total energy content of one wavelength of the progressive wave is $\tfrac{1}{2}g\rho E^2\lambda$: in unit length of the wave there is energy $\tfrac{1}{2}\rho g E^2$.

Apparently a progressive wave transfers energy from a region of excess away to regions of deficit. The mean rate at which this energy is being transmitted will now be calculated: this will lead to an important result. Consider an elementary area in the liquid perpendicular to the flow direction (i.e. the x-axis) at depth z and extent dz (with, or course, unit width), located at point x. The pressure acting across this area at depth z is $p(z)$: from the Bernoulli equation

$$p = p_0 + \rho \frac{\partial \phi}{\partial t} - g\rho z,$$

where $(v^2/2)$ has been neglected, as we agreed earlier that it can be. The total rate at which work is being done on the fluid located on the upstream side of the elementary area is:

$$\int\limits_{-h}^{0} p v_x dz = \int\limits_{-h}^{0} \left(p_0 + \rho \frac{\partial \phi}{\partial t} - g\rho z\right)\left(-\frac{\partial \phi}{\partial x}\right) dz.$$

The mean rate of energy transfer is this quantity averaged over the time period of one wave. By using the expression (3.17) for ϕ and carrying through the two integrations, first over z and then over the time, it follows – after a certain amount of calculation – that the mean rate at which work is being done is:

$$\tfrac{1}{4}\rho g E^2 c\left[1+\frac{4\pi h}{\lambda}\operatorname{cosech}\left(\frac{4\pi h}{\lambda}\right)\right].$$

Remembering (3.25), this is alternatively

$$\tfrac{1}{2}\rho g E^2 V_g. \tag{3.37}$$

This is the energy per unit length of wave multiplied by the group velocity of the waves. It follows that the group velocity has the important physical property of being that velocity with which energy is transmitted: this result was first deduced by Reynolds for the special case $h \gg \lambda$, but was later shown to apply quite generally by Lord Rayleigh.

3.8. Fluid particle trajectories

For a particle with undistorted position (x_0, z_0) in the liquid, the displacements (X, Z) due to the wave follow from the expressions:

$$\frac{\partial X}{\partial t} = -\frac{\partial \phi}{\partial x} = \frac{gE}{c}\frac{\cosh k(z+h)}{\cosh kh}\sin(kx-\omega t)$$

$$\frac{\partial Z}{\partial t} = -\frac{\partial \phi}{\partial z} = -\frac{gE}{c}\frac{\sinh k(z+h)}{\cosh kh}\cos(kx-\omega t).$$

On carrying through the necessary integration with respect to the time:

$$X = \frac{gE}{kc^2}\cdot\frac{\cosh k(z+h)}{\cosh kh}\cos(kx-\omega t)$$

$$Z = \frac{gE}{kc^2}\cdot\frac{\sinh k(z+h)}{\cosh kh}\sin(kx-\omega t).$$

Eliminating t from these two expressions it is seen that the particle is displaced so as to move in a path described by the equation:

$$\frac{X^2}{\alpha^2}+\frac{Z^2}{\beta^2} = 1 \tag{3.38}$$

where

$$\alpha = \frac{gE}{kc^2} \cdot \frac{\cosh k(z+h)}{\cosh kh} \tag{3.39a}$$

$$\beta = \frac{gE}{kc^2} \cdot \frac{\sinh k(z+h)}{\cosh kh}. \tag{3.39b}$$

Clearly the path of the particle is an ellipse with semi-axes α and β, respectively horizontal and vertical. All the ellipses, each centre of which is at an undisturbed position, have the same distance between the foci, viz. $(2gE)/(kc^2)\operatorname{sech} kh$.

At the bottom of the liquid (where $z = -h$) the ellipse degenerates into a straight line since $\sinh(0) = 0$: consequently the particles on the bottom move to and fro only, and do not rise and fall. Any undisturbed vertical liquid plane, therefore, is bent by the passage of a wave, most at the surface and progressively less within until the bottom is reached. The movement can be likened to the bending in the wind of a stiff blade of grass which at the same time suffers oscillatory translation: the analogy is improved, however, if the blade has elastic properties which enable it to differentially expand when at its maximum amplitude but to be contracted at the undisturbed plane, the effect decreasing with depth and vanishing at the bottom.

The ratio (β/α) is, according to the equation (3.39):

$$\beta/\alpha = \frac{\sinh \dfrac{2\pi}{\lambda}(h+z)}{\cosh \dfrac{2\pi}{\lambda}(h+z)}.$$

When $\lambda \gg h$ (tidal waves), $\beta/\alpha \to 0$ for all depths so that for this case the motion is entirely in the horizontal direction. Thus tidal waves may be characterized by the feature that there is no *vertical* acceleration within the liquid, any $(y$–$z)$ plane remaining a vertical plane throughout the motion. On the other hand, when $\lambda \ll h$ (surface waves) the particle motion is circular, the radius of the circle decreasing with depth until it ultimately vanishes. In this connection the term deep water means that $\tanh(2\pi h)/\lambda = 1$, to the appropriate degree of accuracy. From the standard tables it is found that $\tanh(2\cdot65) = 0\cdot99$: consequently deep water conditions very nearly apply when

$$\frac{2\pi h}{\lambda} > 2\cdot65,$$

i.e. when $h > \lambda/2$. The disturbance in the liquid therefore becomes negligibly small at the depth of about one-half a wavelength for surface waves. It is for this reason that a submarine will submerge to avoid the worst effect of a storm at sea.

3.9. Pressure due to progressive waves

The pressure at any point in the liquid can be calculated from the Bernoulli equation with the velocity potential given by (3.17). For tidal waves ($\lambda \gg h$) this equation gives:

$$p - g\rho z - \rho \frac{\partial \phi}{\partial t} = p_0 + g\rho\xi - \rho \frac{\partial \phi}{\partial t},$$

i.e.
$$p = p_0 + g\rho(z + \xi). \tag{3.40}$$

Thus the pressure at any point is that due to the hydrostatic pressure head at the point; this, in fact, follows immediately from the condition that the vertical acceleration is negligible in this case.

For a surface wave ($\lambda \ll h$) the Bernoulli equation gives the alternative pressure equation:

$$p - \rho g(z + z_0) - \rho \frac{\partial \phi}{\partial t} = \text{constant}.$$

But because now $-\rho g z_0 = \rho \partial \phi / \partial t (c^2 = g\lambda/2\pi)$ this reduces to:

$$p - \rho g z = \text{constant}.$$

Consequently the pressure at any fluid particle position is equal to that at the undisturbed particle position.

3.10. Finite amplitude

Two distinct and independent restrictions have been placed on our arguments up to this point: one is that the velocity is small so that the motion is irrotational to a very high degree of approximation;

while the other is that the wave disturbance is always sufficiently small for the boundary condition (3.10a) to be used in place of the correct form (3.7). The second restriction may be removed without violating the first thus allowing the irrotational waves to have a finite amplitude. An interesting feature of such waves can be appreciated from the following approximate argument.

The expression (3.17) for ϕ still holds but the dispersion relation (3.21) is changed to become

$$\omega^2 = gk \tanh{[k(h+\xi)]} = gk \tanh{(kh)}\left[\frac{1+\coth{(kh)}\tanh{(k\xi)}}{1+\tanh{(kh)}\tanh{(k\xi)}}\right].$$

$$(3.41)$$

If, in addition to $\xi \ll h$, we have also $\lambda \ll h$ this expression reduced further:

$$\omega^2 = gk \tanh{kh}\left(1+\frac{\xi}{h}\right).$$

$$(3.42)$$

But, according to (3.13), $\omega = kc$ so that (3.42) becomes, to the first order in the ratio (ξ/h):

$$\omega^2 = k^2 c^2 g \tanh{[kh(1+\xi/h)]}.$$

$$(3.42a)$$

The velocity now differs from that considered in the previous Article (where ξ is zero), viz. that given by equation (3.27). In particular it is seen that c depends upon the ratio (ξ/h): it is greater when $\xi > 0$ than when $\xi < 0$. This means that a wave crest will travel faster than a trough, and any wave profile will gradually steepen until it ultimately falls over forwards, as is witnessed by the breaking of waves on the sea shore.

3.11. Circular sheet of liquid

Suppose there is a source of energy, confined to a small volume of space, from which a progressive wave system diverges. It is now not sufficient to consider motion only in the x-direction; the three-dimensional Laplace equation for the velocity potential ϕ is:

$$\frac{\partial^2 \phi}{\partial x^2}+\frac{\partial^2 \phi}{\partial y^2}+\frac{\partial^2 \phi}{\partial z^2} = 0.$$

$$(3.43)$$

Let us introduce the new variable $r = \sqrt{(x^2 + y^2)}$ which refers to positions in any horizontal plane ($z =$ constant). Then the Laplace equation (3.43) becomes

$$\frac{\partial^2 \phi}{\partial r^2} + \frac{1}{r}\frac{\partial \phi}{\partial r} + \frac{\partial^2 \phi}{\partial z^2} = 0. \tag{3.44}$$

The general boundary conditions (3.10) again apply and we seek a separated solution in the form:

$$\phi(r, z, t) = f(z)\, F(r, t). \tag{3.45a}$$

Because we are dealing with progressive waves write:

$$F(r, t) = G(r) \cos \omega t. \tag{3.45b}$$

The insertion of the expressions (3.45) into equation (3.44) then leads to two equations for the two unknown functions $f(z)$ and $G(r)$, viz.

$$\frac{\partial^2 G}{\partial r^2} + \frac{1}{r}\frac{\partial G}{\partial r} + k^2 G = 0 \tag{3.46a}$$

$$\frac{\partial^2 f}{\partial z^2} - k^2 f = 0. \tag{3.46b}$$

Here $kc = \omega$. The equation (3.46a) is a Bessel equation of zero order and its solution is written $J_0(kr)$. The solution of the second equation is given by (3.15). The velocity potential for the present case is, therefore:

$$\phi = D J_0(kr) \cosh k(z+h) \cos \omega t. \tag{3.46c}$$

This solution is to satisfy the condition that the energy must nowhere become infinite so that the amplitude constants are to be adjusted so that (3.46c) leads to the correct energy input near to the origin. For tidal waves, the form of J_0 at large distances is such that $\phi \propto r^{-1/2}$ there. It follows that the energy per unit length of wave front decreases like r^{-1}.

3.12. Stationary wave

A constantly maintained wave system in a container of finite extent and fixed boundaries can have a profile which does not move. The characteristic feature of this profile is the superposition of progressive waves to form a stationary wave. The equations of the wave theory used so far are again applicable but must be supplemented by the boundary condition that the horizontal liquid velocity normal to a boundary wall must vanish. For a liquid in a rectangular tank with one corner taken as co-ordinate origin and sides given by the planes $(x = 0, a)$ and $(y = 0, b)$ this means that

$$v_x \text{ must vanish when } y = 0, b$$

$$v_y \text{ must vanish when } x = 0, a.$$

These conditions are satisfied by a solution of equation (3.43) of the form

$$\phi = Df(z)\cos\frac{p\pi x}{a}\cos\frac{q\pi y}{b}\cos\omega t, \qquad (3.47)$$

where $f(z)$ is a solution of (3.46b). In (3.47), p and q are allowed to have any of the values 1, 2, 3, 4, ... This means that

$$\phi = \frac{E_1 g}{kc} \cdot \frac{\cosh k(h+z)}{\cosh kh} \cdot \cos\frac{p\pi x}{a}\cos\frac{q\pi y}{b}\cos\omega t \qquad (3.47a)$$

is a stationary solution of (3.43) if k is given by:

$$k^2 = \left(\frac{\omega}{c}\right)^2 \pi^2\left(\frac{p^2}{a^2}+\frac{q^2}{b^2}\right), \qquad (3.47b)$$

and $k^2 c^2 = g\tanh(kh)$, as before.

For a circular tank of radius R the corresponding solution is:

$$\phi = E_2 J_m(kr)\cos m\vartheta\cosh k(z+h)\cos\omega t, \qquad (3.48)$$

where the origin of co-ordinates is now located on the central symmetry axis of the tank. The quantities m and k are related through the boundary condition at the rim, viz.

$$\frac{dJ_m(kr)}{dr} = 0 \quad \text{when } r = R. \qquad (3.48a)$$

In the equations (3.47a) and (3.48a), E_1 and E_2 are arbitrary amplitude constants. The corresponding wave heights then follow from the equation (3.18). It is seen that only certain frequencies of vibration are allowable to the liquid: for, whenever m is chosen to have some definite value then k, c ,and ω all immediately are determined.

3.13. Capillary waves

We now take account of the fact that a liquid surface is in practice always under a tension which tends towards reducing its area to a minimum. It is shown in books on surface tension that when a liquid surface (originally in the $(x–y)$ plane) is distorted from its equilibrium configuration by amount $\xi(r)$, there is a force of strength

$$\mathcal{T} . \left(\frac{\partial^2 \xi}{\partial x^2} + \frac{\partial^2 \xi}{\partial y^2} \right)$$

tending to restore the original conditions, where $\mathcal{T}$ is the surface tension for the surface interface. Consequently, the pressure just inside a liquid surface which is distorted is not simply the atmospheric pressure p_0 but is instead

$$p = p_0 - \mathcal{T} . \left(\frac{\partial^2 \xi}{\partial x^2} + \frac{\partial^2 \xi}{\partial y^2} \right). \tag{3.49}$$

Clearly $p = p_0$ in the absence of any disturbance ($\xi = 0$). It is this pressure including the contribution due to surface tension which is now to be inserted into equation (3.4a); this gives at the free surface

$$\left[\frac{\partial^2 \phi}{\partial t^2} + g \frac{\partial \phi}{\partial z} - \frac{\mathcal{T}}{\rho} . \left(\frac{\partial^2}{\partial x^2} + \frac{\partial^2}{\partial y^2} \right) \frac{\partial \phi}{\partial z} \right]_{z=\xi} = 0 \tag{3.50}$$

in place of the previous expression (3.7).

The flow is irrotational (because the criteria of Art. 3.1 still apply) so that ϕ satisfies the Laplace equation within the main body of the liquid, and the remaining previous boundary conditions also still apply.

Consider a progressive wave propagated in the x-direction in a liquid of uniform depth h. The velocity potential is given by:

$$\phi = D \cosh k(z+h) \cos (kx - \omega t). \tag{3.51}$$

This equation must satisfy the condition (3.50) in the form which obtains when $z = 0$ if we again use the approximation of neglecting the wave amplitude in the boundary condition. It follows immediately that we must have:

$$\omega^2 = \left(gk + \frac{\mathscr{T}}{\rho}k^3\right)\tanh(kh) \tag{3.52}$$

for the angular frequency of the wave disturbance.

Waves on sufficiently deep water present the simplest case. Then we can rewrite (3.52) in terms of the wave velocity as:

$$c^2 = \frac{g\lambda}{2\pi} + \frac{2\pi\mathscr{T}}{\lambda\rho}. \tag{3.52a}$$

The velocity is seen to depend upon λ in a more complicated way when account is made of the effects of surface tension than when the effect is neglected; however, the wave velocity still does not depend upon the wave depth. It is important to notice that the velocity given by (3.52a) has a minimum value at a specific value of λ, say λ_0: this is immediately clear from the fact that c becomes indefinitely large either when $\lambda \to 0$ or when $\lambda \to \infty$. It is readily found from (3.52a) that

$$\lambda_c = \sqrt{\left(\frac{4\pi^2\mathscr{T}}{\rho g}\right)}, \tag{3.53a}$$

which, using (3.52a), gives for the minimum velocity the expression

$$c_{\min} = \left(\frac{4g\mathscr{T}}{\rho}\right)^{1/4}. \tag{3.53b}$$

The expressions for λ_c and $c_{\min}$ are functions only of the ratio $(\mathscr{T}/\rho)$ for a given gravitational acceleration.

It is a matter of nomenclature that waves for which $\lambda < \lambda_c$ are called ripples, while only those for which $\lambda > \lambda_c$ are regarded as being true surface waves. For water, $c_{\min} \sim 23$ cm/sec. and $\lambda_c \sim 17$ cm. If $c > c_{\min}$ for any disturbance, two wave modes will be propagated, one a ripple and the other a surface wave. The same qualitative behaviour is found for wave motion including surface tension, for any liquid depth, when (3.52) is used in place of (3.52a).

CHAPTER 4

Irrotational Motion: Sound Waves

Wave motion in a gas differs from that in a liquid in two important respects, viz. that a gas is compressible whereas a liquid essentially is not; and that a gas does not have a definite cohesive surface whereas a liquid does. In the present chapter we treat small oscillations in a gas: such small oscillations are called sound waves. A sound wave passing through a gas causes alternatively a small compression and then a small rarefaction at each point in its path. The instantaneous movement of gas caused by the passage of the wave is in consequence along the direction of propagation, i.e. it is longitudinal. Because (like a liquid) a gas lacks rigidity, transverse waves cannot be propagated through it.†

Any adequate account of the propagation of sound in a gas would occupy a monograph by itself. However, we include some mention of the subject here primarily for completeness and will do no more than indicate some simple equations which are basic to the subject. It will be supposed in what follows that we are concerned with plane waves unless an alternative geometry is stated explicitly.

4.1. Equations involving compressibility

Because we assume the oscillations to be small, the arguments of Art. 3.1 apply also here and the gas motion is irrotational. Consequently a velocity potential can be defined according to equation (2.1). A gas is compressible; the equation of continuity must be used in its full form (1.10), the reduced form (1.13) being quite inadequate since it involves the now invalid condition $\operatorname{div} \mathbf{v} = 0$. An immediate consequence of this is that ϕ is not a solution of the Laplace equation, and in this respect the treatment of motion in a gas differs from that in a liquid.

The gas motion proceeds according to the description given by the

† But see, later, Chapter 10 for the conditions where the gas is also able to conduct electricity.

momentum equation (1.15) simplified in some respects. Since the gas velocity is always assumed small, the term $(\mathbf{v}.\mathrm{grad})\,\mathbf{v}$ will be neglected. In addition, it is not necessary for sound waves to include effects arising from external forces other than restraints due to the boundaries; i.e. $\rho\mathbf{F} = 0$.

The momentum equation now reduces to the Bernoulli equation which has the form:

$$\int \frac{dp}{\rho} - \frac{\partial\phi}{\partial t} = \text{constant.} \tag{4.1}$$

It is convenient for what follows to write this expression in an alternative form. The first term can be rearranged:

$$\int \frac{dp}{\rho} = \int \frac{dp}{d\rho}\frac{d\rho}{\rho}.$$

The disturbance is small, and in particular the change in pressure consequent upon density changes can be treated as constant to a first approximation. Writing this constant as c_s^2 so that

$$c_s^2 = \frac{dp}{d\rho}, \tag{4.2}$$

it follows on this assumption that

$$\int \frac{dp}{d\rho}\frac{d\rho}{\rho} = c_s^2 \int \frac{d\rho}{\rho} = c_s^2 \log\rho.$$

The Bernoulli equation (4.1) then becomes:

$$c_s^2 \log\rho = \frac{\partial\phi}{\partial t}. \tag{4.3}$$

At this point we introduce another quantity called the condensation, and denoted by s. If ρ is the density at any point of the fluid at any given time, and further if ρ_0 is the corresponding undisturbed density, we define s according to:

$$\rho = \rho_0(1+s) \quad \text{i.e. } s = \frac{\rho - \rho_0}{\rho_0}. \tag{4.4}$$

Thus the condensation is the relative density change due to the wave: it is a small quantity (because the wave disturbance is small), which is a function of both the position and the time. Clearly to first order in s:

$$\log \rho = \log \rho_0 + \log(1+s) = \log \rho_0 + s$$

so that (4.3) becomes

$$\frac{\partial \phi}{\partial t} = c_s^2 s + c_s^2 \log \rho_0, \tag{4.5}$$

i.e.

$$c_s^2 \frac{\partial s}{\partial t} = \frac{\partial^2 \phi}{\partial t^2}. \tag{4.5a}$$

An independent relation involving s follows from the insertion of (4.4) into the continuity equation (1.10). Remembering that s is a small quantity it is found that:

$$\rho_0 \frac{\partial s}{\partial t} = \rho \nabla^2 \phi = \rho_0(1+s) \nabla^2 \phi = \rho_0 \nabla^2 \phi, \tag{4.6}$$

since the term $(\rho_0 s \nabla^2 \phi)$ is negligibly small in comparison with the remainder. The insertion of (4.6) into (4.5a) leads finally to the wave equation for ϕ

$$\boxed{\nabla^2 \phi = \frac{1}{c_s^2} \frac{\partial^2 \phi}{\partial t^2}.} \tag{4.7}$$

If ξ is the amplitude of the wave disturbance, it follows from (4.4) and the momentum equation that, to the present approximation:

$$s = -\frac{\partial \xi}{\partial \nu}, \tag{4.8}$$

where ν is along the direction of sound propagation. Using (4.8), the wave equation for the velocity potential (4.7) is converted immediately into an equation for the wave amplitude:

$$\boxed{\nabla^2 \xi = \frac{1}{c_s^2} \frac{\partial^2 \xi}{\partial t^2}.} \tag{4.9}$$

Finally, a relation between the velocity potential and the wave disturbance amplitude follows from the expressions (4.5) and (4.8). If in the latter equation the constant term $c_s^2 \log \rho_0$ is absorbed in the term $(\partial \phi / \partial t)$, which can be formally achieved by replacing ϕ by $\phi - c_s^2 \log \rho_0$, then for the v-direction:

$$s = -\frac{\partial \xi}{\partial v} = \frac{1}{c_s^2} \frac{\partial \phi}{\partial t} \tag{4.10}$$

and this relates s to the time rate of change of ϕ.

The relation (4.10) is completely known if the velocity of sound, c_s, is known in terms of the properties of the gas. To obtain this information we notice that a sound wave disturbance travels in a gas too rapidly for temperature equilibrium to be set up at each point of the wave, so that the motion is adiabatic .The equilibrium equation of state for the gas under adiabatic conditions is:

$$p_0 = B \rho_0^\gamma \tag{4.11}$$

where γ is the ratio of the specific heats at constant pressure, C_p and at constant volume, C_V i.e. $\gamma = C_p / C_V$, and B is a constant characteristic of the particular gas. From equation (4.2) it follows that the velocity of sound is given by:

$$c_s = \sqrt{\left(\frac{\gamma p_0}{\rho_0}\right)} \tag{4.12}$$

in terms of the equilibrium properties pertaining in the absence of the disturbance. If conditions are isothermal then $\gamma = 1$. It is seen from (4.12) that the velocity of sound is independent of the sound disturbance wavelength, and in this repect sound waves bear some analogy to long gravity waves in a liquid: and in each case the non-dispersive property of the fluid is destroyed if the disturbance amplitude grows to the point where it can no longer be taken as very small. For unit mass of a perfect gas we know that $p = \rho \mathcal{R} T$, where $\mathcal{R}$ is the molar gas constant: this means that for this case the velocity of sound is $c_s = \sqrt{(\gamma \mathcal{R} T)}$.

Because γ is for most gases only weakly dependent upon the temperature it follows that the velocity of sound in a gas is very nearly directly proportional to the square root of the absolute temperature of the gas in the absence of the disturbance.

The general solution of equations (4.7) or (4.9) for a progressive wave has the form

$$\left.\begin{matrix} \phi \\ \xi \end{matrix}\right\} \sim f_1(r - c_s t) + f_2(r + c_s t)$$

where f_1 and f_2 are arbitrary functions. These are disturbances travelling in opposite directions with equal velocity, c_s.

4.2. Boundary conditions

The wave equation (4.7), or its equivalent (4.9) is to be solved subject to boundary conditions derived from physical criteria. At any fixed boundary the normal velocity component is zero; in addition the wave displacement must vanish. These requirements mean respectively

$$\frac{\partial \phi}{\partial \nu} = 0 \quad \text{and} \quad \xi_\nu = 0 \quad \text{(rigid boundary)} \qquad (4.13)$$

where ξ_ν denotes the wave amplitude in the ν-direction.

A very important type of problem in acoustics is that concerning a sound wave system in a tube ('organ pipe') which may be closed or open at the ends. For a closed end the conditions (4.13) hold true. If the end is open to the atmosphere then at the opening $p = p_0$, and so $\rho = \rho_0$, i.e. $s = 0$. From equation (4.3) this is equivalent to the requirement:

$$\frac{\partial \phi}{\partial t} = 0 \quad \text{and} \quad \frac{\partial \xi}{\partial \nu} = 0, \qquad (4.14)$$

where the second form follows from equation (4.8). In practice the conditions (4.14) do not apply at the open end itself but instead at a small distance outside the tube; this is the 'end effect'. Although corrections can be applied which account for the effect at least qualitatively, they are a refinement which will not be considered here.

4.3. Stationary waves

We apply now the equations derived so far in turn to wave motion in a cylindrical tube, and alternatively in a closed sphere.

(i) Cylindrical tube

The x-axis will be arranged to lie along the axis of the tube of length l which is also the direction of wave propagation. One end of the tube has $x = 0$ while the other has $x = l$.

If the tube has at least one end closed we take as the appropriate solution of the wave equation (4.7):

$$\phi = a \cos kx \cos(\omega t + \epsilon), \tag{4.15}$$

where a is an arbitrary amplitude constant and ϵ is some phase angle. At the closed end (say, $x = 0$) the condition (4.13) is satisfied automatically. If the other end, i.e., $x = l$, is also closed then we must have (with $\nu \equiv x$):

$$k = \frac{n\pi}{l} = \frac{\omega}{c_s} \quad (n = 1, 2, 3, 4, \ldots) \tag{4.15a}$$

so that in the case of a tube closed at both ends:

$$\phi = a_n \cos \frac{n\pi x}{l} \cos\left(\frac{n\pi c_s t}{l} + \epsilon_n\right). \tag{4.16a}$$

From the equation (4.10) the amplitude is also defined: then setting $\nu \equiv x$.

$$\xi = \frac{a_n}{c_s} \sin \frac{n\pi x}{l} \sin\left(\frac{n\pi c_s t}{l} + \epsilon_n\right) \tag{4.16b}$$

Alternatively, the end $x = l$ may be open; then equation (4.15) has to satisfy the condition (4.14) so that now:

$$k = \frac{(n + \frac{1}{2})\pi}{l} \quad (n = 0, 1, 2, 3, 4, \ldots).$$

The velocity potential is

$$\phi = a_n \cos\left(\frac{(n + \frac{1}{2})\pi x}{l}\right) \cos\left((n + \frac{1}{2})\frac{\pi c_s t}{l} + \epsilon_n\right). \tag{4.17a}$$

The corresponding amplitude is:

$$\xi = \frac{a_n}{c_s}\sin\left((n+\tfrac{1}{2})\frac{\pi x}{l}\right)\sin\left((n+\tfrac{1}{2})\frac{\pi c_s t}{l}+\epsilon_n\right). \quad (4.17b)$$

Finally both ends may be open. Then we must have for k:

$$kx = \frac{n\pi x}{l}+\frac{\pi}{2} \quad (n = 0, 1, 2, 3, 4, \ldots)$$

giving

$$\phi = a_n\sin\frac{n\pi x}{l}\cos\left(\frac{n\pi c_s t}{l}+\epsilon_n\right) \quad (4.18a)$$

and

$$\xi = \frac{a_n}{c_s}\cos\frac{n\pi x}{l}\cos\left(\frac{n\pi c_s t}{l}+\epsilon_n\right). \quad (4.18b)$$

In each case the complete solution of the wave equations is the sum of terms having different values of n. As a matter of nomenclature, that disturbance for which $n = 0$ is called the fundamental, while those for which $n \neq 0$ are called harmonics.

(ii) Sphere of radius R

Here there is spherical symmetry about the origin and the wave equation is:

$$\frac{\partial^2 \phi}{\partial r^2}+\frac{2}{r}\frac{\partial \phi}{\partial r} = \frac{1}{c_s^2}\frac{\partial^2 \phi}{\partial t^2}, \quad (4.19)$$

where $r^2 = x^2+y^2+z^2$. The general solution of this equation is of the progressive type

$$r\phi = f_1(r-c_s t)+f_2(r+c_s t), \quad (4.20)$$

where f_1 and f_2 are arbitrary functions. It is well known that this represents two waves travelling with velocity c_s in opposite directions, i.e. a diverging and converging disturbance. The superposition of two such waves leads to a stationary wave:

$$r\phi = a_n\cos kr\cos(c_s t+\epsilon_n). \quad (4.21)$$

The conditions to be imposed here are that ϕ must remain finite when $r = 0$, and that the disturbance is confined by a rigid wall at

6

distance $r = R$, i.e. $\partial\phi/\partial r = 0$ when $r = R$. The expression (4.21) satisfies these conditions if:

$$\tan(kR) = kR. \tag{4.22a}$$

When k is sufficiently large

$$kR \to (n+\tfrac{1}{2})\pi - \frac{1}{(n+\tfrac{1}{2})\pi}, \tag{4.22b}$$

to give roots of (4.22a). Thus when n is sufficiently great for

$$(n+\tfrac{1}{2})\pi \gg [(n+\tfrac{1}{2})\pi]^{-1},$$

the present solution becomes very similar to (4.17a) which describes a cylindrical tube closed at one end only, The higher harmonics of the present spherical problem, therefore, are very like those found in a cylindrical pipe open at one end only.

4.4. Energy in a wave

As the sound disturbance passes any point contained in a very small gaseous volume the associated compression and rarefaction causes energy to be stored in elements of the gas.

The work done *by* a unit mass of gas in expanding through a small volume element from volume V_1 to the equilibrium volume V_0, with corresponding pressures p_1 and p_0, the work done is, to a good first approximation

$$dW = \tfrac{1}{2}(p_0+p_1)(V_0-V_1). \tag{4.23}$$

Now

$$p_1 = p_0 + \frac{\partial p}{\partial\rho}(\rho_1-\rho_0) = p_0 + c_s^2\rho_0 s_1, \tag{4.24a}$$

and to the first order in s_1:

$$V_1 - V_0 = -V_0 s_1$$

where s_1 is the value of the condensation when $V = V_1$. Inserting the expressions (4.24) into (4.23) gives to first order of approximation:

$$dW = p_0(V_0-V_1) + \tfrac{1}{2}\rho_0 c_s^2 s_1^2 V_0. \tag{4.25}$$

The total potential energy follows from integration over the whole fluid mass: if the total volume of the fluid is unaffected by the passage of the disturbance through the fluid then the first term of (4.25) when referred to the total fluid makes no contribution. Thus we obtain:

$$\text{Potential Energy} = \int \tfrac{1}{2} c_s^2 \rho_0 s^2 \, dV. \tag{4.26}$$

For adiabatic conditions, which are assumed here, this energy can be identified with the fluid internal energy; for isothermal conditions it is instead to be treated as the thermodynamic free energy.

The kinetic energy of the total gas is easily seen to be:

$$\text{Kinetic Energy} = \int \tfrac{1}{2} \rho_0 v^2 \, dV, \tag{4.26a}$$

where v is the gas velocity at some point at time t. The total energy, therefore, is to our present approximation:

$$\text{Total Energy} = \tfrac{1}{2} \int [c_s^2 \rho_0 s^2 + \rho_0 v^2] \, dV. \tag{4.26b}$$

In a progressive wave, $c_s s = \pm v$, so that the kinetic and potential energies are equal. For a stationary wave this is not so, but the total energy remains constant.

The mean rate at which energy is transmitted across unit area of the wave front can be identified in terms of the intensity of the sound wave. Consider wave propagation in the x-direction. The rate of working of the pressure is $p v_x$; then if I is the wave intensity

$$I = A p v_x = A \left(p_0 + \rho_0 \frac{\partial \phi}{\partial t} \right) \left(-\frac{\partial \phi}{\partial x} \right)$$

where A is a constant factor of proportionality. Taking the mean value of this expression over one period of oscillation of a progressive wave:

$$I = \frac{2\pi^2 A a^2 c_s \rho_0}{\lambda^2}. \tag{4.27}$$

Here a is the wave amplitude. The wave intensity is proportional to the square of the amplitude and is inversely proportional to the square of the wavelength. Because the period of oscillation ($\equiv 1/\nu$) is proportional to the wavelength, the wave intensity is also inversely proportional to the period. It is for this reason that the fundamental note is also the most intense.

4.5. Finite amplitudes

If the displacement ξ is not indefinitely small the equation of wave motion is modified. For a progressive wave propagated in the x-direction the continuity equation is now:

$$\frac{\rho}{\rho_0} = \frac{1}{(1 + \partial \xi / \partial x)}$$

which leads to the condensation expression

$$s = -\frac{\partial \xi / \partial x}{(1 + \partial \xi / \partial x)}.$$

The resulting equation of motion of the gas can be shown to be:

$$\frac{\partial^2 \xi}{\partial x^2} = \frac{1}{c_1^2} \frac{\partial^2 \xi}{\partial t^2}$$

where the wave velocity is

$$c_1^2 = \frac{c_s^2}{(1 + \partial \xi / \partial x)^{\gamma + 1}}$$

for adiabatic conditions. Clearly the velocity of propagation depends upon the amplitude: this means that the group velocity is different from the wave velocity, i.e. the gas acts as a dispersive medium.

Just as for waves in a liquid so also for sound waves it follows that any initially sinusoidal wave steepens, and approaches the form of a vertical profile. The disturbance is now called a shock wave: the thermodynamic properties (such as density, pressure, and entropy) are discontinuous across the shock although the Bernoulli equation can be applied through it. The present arguments are restricted to small continuous motions so that shock conditions are outside its scope.

4.6. Air tides

The velocity of a small disturbance, written c and given by equation (4.12), bears a striking formal similarity to long (tidal) waves in water for the case of an iosthermal atmosphere. For then we set $\gamma = 1$, and p_0 (the pressure just above the solid surface upon which the atmosphere rests) is equal to $\rho g H$. H is the effective height of the atmosphere, sometimes called the height of the homogeneous atmosphere. Although introduced here for isothermal conditions, being independent of γ it has the same value for adiabatic conditions. It easily follows that

$$c_s^2 = gH.$$

For the earth and its atmosphere the measurements on the sound velocity at sea level provide a value for H of around 10 km.

The atmosphere as a whole undergoes tidal oscillations due to the action of the Sun and Moon which are very similar to those experienced by the oceans due to the same sources; one difference, however, is that for the atmosphere the self gravity between different constituent volumes may be neglected. The gravitational attraction of both the Sun and Moon provide tidal oscillations, all be it small ones, but the thermal expansion effects of the atmospheric gas due to the Sun's heating (which are, of course, periodic) play a predominant rôle in this connection. Although the heating has a period of about 24 hours it would seem that the modes of vibration of the atmosphere include contributions not only with a 24-hour period but also one with a period of about 12 hours. Lord Rayleigh suggested that this effect might result in an accelerating couple on the Earth through the atmosphere which could compensate in some measure for the decelerating effects of the ocean tidal friction. It has been suggested that some quasi-equilbirium between these two opposing effects may dictate the length of the terrestrial day but this has not yet been adequately substantiated.

CHAPTER 5

Viscous Effects

So far we have been concerned with ideal fluids where the interaction between contiguous fluid elements does not involve tangential components even though the fluid be in differential motion. Real fluids, however, are characterized by the appearance of such tangential stresses which are a macroscopic manifestation of miscroscopic fluid properties. Differential macroscopic fluid flow is incompatible with microscopic molecular equilibrium, and the forces between the molecules act in such a manner as to restore, and then maintain, equilibrium: tangential stresses in the continuum approximation represent this micro-molecular behaviour. The macroscopic effect, then, is for any fluid motion to be reduced to a state of uniformity throughout, and ultimately, due to boundaries, to be reduced to rest. Momentum is transferred irreversibly from regions of excess to regions of deficiency, and the directed fluid motion is converted ultimately into a random molecular movement, i.e. into heat. The process can be described macroscopically in terms of an effective internal friction called viscosity and in the present chapter we consider the modifications to our previous discussion which are necessary to include this effect. It will be found that the flow cannot be taken as irrotational everywhere even approximately, i.e. there must be some regions (e.g. connected with boundary surfaces) where $\operatorname{curl} \mathbf{v}$ cannot be assumed to vanish to any approximation.

A numerical measure of the viscous effects for shear fluid flow (where there is a velocity gradient in the fluid) is taken as being the shearing stress exerted across an area in the fluid per unit velocity gradient normal to the area, and this defines the coefficient of shear viscosity μ, sometimes called the shear viscosity, or even simply the viscosity. For all simple fluids (which are neither composed of complex molecules nor of gross molecular aggregates) in laminar flow (with the streamlines in parallel sheets so that $\operatorname{curl} \mathbf{v}$ is constant and thus associated with rotational flow: it must be made clear that the criterion for rotational flow is that curl $\mathbf{v}$ is not zero – the actual paths traced out by fluid particles are not of themselves a criterion) it is found in practice that μ is independent of the velocity gradient and so also independent of the time rate of shear, which is equal to the velocity gradient. For historical reasons such simple fluids are called Newtonian; examples are water and air. If μ is dependent on the rate of shear (as is the case for colloidal suspensions, emulsions, etc.) the fluid is non-Newtonian. Only simple Newtonian fluids with not too high viscosity (thus for example glasses are excluded) will be considered in this book, no reference whatever being made to non-Newtonian fluids. Further, a second viscosity coefficient ζ associated with dilatation will appear in the full discussion of a compressible fluid (in addition to the viscosity μ which applies also for incompressible fluids), and for completeness we will introduce both μ and ζ in our derivation of the general equations of motion of a viscous fluid. Because our main concern is with essentially incompressible fluid flow ζ will not be included in the subsequent application of the equations of motion to specific situations.

5.1. Momentum flux with dissipation

For an ideal fluid it was seen earlier that the momentum equation can be written in the form (1.22) where the quantity π_{ik}, the momentum flux, is the i-th component of the amount of fluid momentum flowing through unit area perpendicular to the x_k-axis in unit time. π_{ik} is written out explicitly in equation (1.23): it includes only the reversible transfer of momentum due to the transfer of fluid particles moving according to the laws of classical mechanics, augmented by that due to the fluid pressure and externally applied conservative forces. Any correct modification of the momentum flux expression for an ideal fluid to include the irreversible flow of momentum must involve the micro-molecular arguments of kinetic theory, but this is quite outside the scope of our present arguments. Instead we present plausible phenomenological arguments of macrophysics which lead to equations that are generally agreed to be adequate at the present time. The ultimate test of all arguments must, anyway, be the closeness with which they describe those phenomena of the real world which are claimed to fall within their scope.

We will include the viscous momentum transfer formally by adding to π_{ik} (which previously applied only to the ideal fluid) the quantity written $-\sigma_{ik}$ which is to include the irreversible effects. Physical meaning is put into our arguments by specifying the quantity σ_{ik} in detail. External forces will be neglected for the time being. Thus we write now:

$$\pi_{ik} = p\delta_{ik} + \rho v_i v_k - \sigma_{ik} \equiv -_0\sigma_{ik} + \rho v_i v_k, \tag{5.1}$$

where

$$_0\sigma_{ik} = -p\delta_{ik} + \sigma_{ik}. \tag{5.2}$$

In consequence, π_{ik} is now the momentum flux including irreversibility.

In order to isolate the dependence of the irreversible flux contribution σ_{ik} on the flow parameters, it is necessary to recall the way in which viscous dissipation varies with the fluid motion. Viscous effects arise only when neighbouring fluid elements move relative to each other; on physical grounds it is reasonable to assume that when this relative velocity is small the viscous effect itself will also be small. According to experimental data the viscous force on a moving fluid element at any point is proportional to the space gradient of the velocity at that point. Consequently we can assume that σ_{ik} depends upon the gradient of the velocity through some Taylor series expansion, and that if the flow is sufficiently slow (in a way to be made more precise later) only the first derivative of the velocity need be included. Because σ_{ik} is to vanish when the relative velocity is zero (fluid effectively at rest, no viscous effects) then the expression for σ_{ik} cannot involve a constant term. Finally, it is known that a fluid in *uniform* rotation does not exhibit internal viscous effects (those effects at the boundary with some container are irrelevant here). The most general expression for σ_{ik} which satisfies these conditions is known to be:

$$\sigma_{ik} = a\left(\frac{\partial v_i}{\partial x_k} + \frac{\partial v_k}{\partial x_i}\right) + b\frac{\partial v_l}{\partial x_l}\delta_{ik}, \tag{5.3}$$

where a and b are suitable coefficients. For an isotropic liquid (i.e. one whose properties in the region about any point depend upon the distance from the point but not on the direction from the point), then the coefficients a and b are independent of the velocity though they may depend upon the position in the fluid thermodynamic equation of state. These coefficients are closely analogous to the Lamé coefficients which appear in the theory of the elasticity of solids.

It is convenient and conventional to rewrite the expression (5.3) by introducing two new coefficients, μ and ζ, in place of the original pair a and b. The reason for this is to allow the effects due to any general distortion of a fluid element to be broken down into the two constituent contributions, viz. those arising from the change in the geometrical shape of the element, at constant volume (shear distortion), and those arising from changes of volume, the geometrical shape remaining unchanged (dilatation). Thus, define the two quantities μ and ζ according to

$$\mu = a; \quad \zeta = \tfrac{2}{3}a + b. \tag{5.4}$$

The utility of this substitution will be clear later in the present chapter. Inserting (5.4) into (5.3) gives at once:

$$\sigma_{ik} = \mu\left(\frac{\partial v_i}{\partial x_k} + \frac{\partial v_k}{\partial x_i} - \tfrac{2}{3}\delta_{ik}\frac{\partial v_l}{\partial x_l}\right) + \zeta\delta_{ik}\frac{\partial v_l}{\partial x_l}, \tag{5.5}$$

so that (5.2) becomes alternatively

$$_0\sigma_{ik} = -p\delta_{ik} + \mu\left(\frac{\partial v_i}{\partial x_k} + \frac{\partial v_k}{\partial x_i}\right) - (\tfrac{2}{3}\mu - \zeta)\frac{\partial v_l}{\partial x_l}\delta_{ik}. \tag{5.5a}$$

The coefficients μ and ζ are called the coefficients of viscosity. According to their usual phenomenological definition, the coefficient μ is defined as the viscous tangential force per unit are per unit velocity gradient. The coefficient ζ, on the other hand, is defined in terms of $\partial v_l/\partial x_l$, which is the component notation for the scalar quantity div$\mathbf{v}$; because div$\mathbf{v}$ expresses the net expansion (or contraction) of material in a given volume, the coefficient ζ is often called the viscosity coefficient for dilatation, or sometimes the second viscosity coefficient. It does not appear for incompressible flow, where div$\mathbf{v} = 0$.

The expression (5.1) for π_{ik} including the viscosity now becomes

$$\pi_{ik} = \left(p - \zeta \frac{\partial v_l}{\partial x_l}\right)\delta_{ik} + \rho v_i v_k - \mu\left(\frac{\partial v_i}{\partial x_k} + \frac{\partial v_k}{\partial x_i} - \tfrac{2}{3}\delta_{ik}\frac{\partial v_l}{\partial x_l}\right). \quad (5.6)$$

Written this way the momentum flux has the Cartesian components:

$$\pi_{xx} = (p - \zeta \operatorname{div}\mathbf{v}) + \rho v_x^2 - 2\mu\frac{\partial v_x}{\partial x} + \tfrac{2}{3}\mu \operatorname{div}\mathbf{v} \quad (5.6a)$$

$$\pi_{xy} = \rho v_x v_y - \mu\left(\frac{\partial v_x}{\partial y} + \frac{\partial v_y}{\partial x}\right) \quad (5.6b)$$

and similarly for the remaining coefficients. It will be seen later in our arguments that both μ and ζ are positive quantities in keeping with the dissipative nature of the viscous force.

Experimentally it is known that the shear viscosity coefficients depend markedly upon the temperature, but is only weakly dependent upon the pressure. For a dilute gas μ is proportional to the square root of the temperature, *increasing* with increasing temperature; alternatively, for a liquid μ decreases with temperature, very nearly exponentially for simple liquids over restricted temperature ranges.

5.2. The Navier-Stokes equation

The insertion of the momentum flux expression (5.6) into the momentum equation (1.22) gives at once the momentum equation including the viscosity. There results the equation which has for its i-th component

$$\frac{\partial}{\partial t}(\rho v_i) = -\frac{\partial}{\partial x_k}\left[\left(p + \zeta\frac{\partial v_l}{\partial x_l}\right)\delta_{ik}\right] - \frac{\partial}{\partial x_k}(\rho v_i v_k) + \\ + \frac{\partial}{\partial x_k}\left[\mu\left(\frac{\partial v_i}{\partial x_k} + \frac{\partial v_k}{\partial x_i} - \tfrac{2}{3}\delta_{ik}\frac{\partial v_l}{\partial x_l}\right)\right]. \quad (5.7)$$

It will be seen that the right-hand side of this expression contains terms proportional to $\partial\zeta/\partial x_k$ and $\partial\mu/\partial x_k$. But in many cases of practical importance both μ and ζ are virtually independent of both the position and the time so that derivatives of the viscosity coefficients with respect to position or time may be equated to zero to very good approximation. In such cases the right-hand side of (5.7) can be written:

$$-\frac{\partial}{\partial x_k}[p\delta_{ik}] - v_k\frac{\partial v_i}{\partial x_k} + \mu\frac{\partial^2 v_i}{\partial x_k\,\partial x_k} + (\zeta + \tfrac{1}{3}\mu)\frac{\partial}{\partial x_i}\left(\frac{\partial v_l}{\partial x_l}\right)\delta_{ik} -$$

$$-v_i\left(v_k\frac{\partial \rho}{\partial x_k} + \rho\frac{\partial v_k}{\partial x_k}\right). \qquad (5.7a)$$

No account has yet been taken of the action of external forces which may be acting on the fluid. If the fluid were incompressible and the external forces were conservative then the expression (1.23) could be employed directly with π_{ik} replaced by $\pi_{ik} + \sigma_{ik}$: as the direct result the term $[+\rho(\partial\Phi/\partial x_k)]$ would appear on the right-hand side of (5.7) and in (5.7a). In this case, of course, it would also be necessary to put $(\partial v_l/\partial x_l) = 0$ (i.e. div $\mathbf{v} = 0$). For compressible fluids, or for non-conservative forces, the general term ρF_i is to be added to the various terms in (5.7a). The full momentum equation for which μ and ζ are both constant is obtained by equating the left-hand side of (5.7) to (5.7a) including any external forces: in vector form this equation is

$$\boxed{\rho\frac{d\mathbf{v}}{dt} = -\operatorname{grad} p + \rho\mathbf{F} + \mu\nabla^2\mathbf{v} + (\zeta + \tfrac{1}{3}\mu)\operatorname{grad}\operatorname{div}\mathbf{v},} \qquad (5.8)$$

where the continuity equation has been used in connection with the last term of (5.7a). If the fluid is also incompressible, then div $\mathbf{v} = 0$ and this equation reduces (after division throughout by ρ) to

$$\boxed{\frac{d\mathbf{v}}{dt} = -\frac{1}{\rho}\operatorname{grad} p + \mathbf{F} + \nu\nabla^2\mathbf{v}.} \qquad (5.9)$$

Here ν is the kinematic viscosity and is defined by

$$\nu = \mu/\rho. \qquad (5.9a)$$

It will be found useful in later arguments to be familiar with the form of the equation of motion showing explicitly the viscous stress components; in this form (5.8) is alternatively

$$\rho\frac{dv_i}{dt} = -\frac{\partial p}{\partial x_i} + \rho F_i + \frac{\partial\sigma_{ik}}{\partial x_k} \qquad (5.8a)$$

where σ_{ik} is given by (5.5). For incompressible flow (5.5) reduces to

$$\sigma_{ik} = \mu\left(\frac{\partial v_i}{\partial x_k} + \frac{\partial v_k}{\partial x_i}\right). \tag{5.8b}$$

The equation (5.9) is called the Navier-Stokes equation; it will be required later in the component form:

$$\frac{\partial v_i}{\partial t} + v_k\frac{\partial v_i}{\partial x_k} = -\frac{1}{\rho}\frac{\partial p}{\partial x_k} + F_i + \nu\frac{\partial^2 v_i}{\partial x_k\,\partial x_k}. \tag{5.9b}$$

The equation (5.8) including the effects of compressibility is sometimes also simply referred to as the Navier-Stokes equation, but to avoid confusion we will refer to (5.8) as being the Navier-Stokes equation including the compressibility. Viscous effects in (5.9) are now fully described by the single viscosity coefficient μ relating to shear (distortion); remember that μ is in general a function of the temperature and possibly the pressure.

Some comment on these arguments is important. Any final assessment of an equation for any real situation must be made on the basis of a detailed experimental comparison with its many diverse predictions. The theoretical background is important in suggesting the equation in the first place, and in suggesting further related equations but appeal to experiment is vital. There is, of course, the basic task of making sure that theory and experiment are discussing precisely the same thing (which is not always as easy as it may sound), but here the onus is largely on the theory through its initial axioms. From the theory contained in the foregoing pages it would seem that the equation (1.15) is more likely to be accurate than the equation (5.9). The former equation is based solely on the conservation of the particle momentum (a very fully and carefully tested statement), whereas the latter equation involves in addition the effect of friction through the (somewhat phenomenological) expression (5.5). Unfortunately no exactly ideal fluid is known so that equation (1.15) can never, even in principle, apply exactly in practice although it may sometimes be sufficient, for instance in certain low velocity flow of a fluid of low viscosity like water. For low velocity viscous flow the fluid conditions are essentially those of incompressible flow (cf. Art. 1.11); the equation (5.9) is then to apply and it has received convincing experimental verification under these conditions. In particular the viscosity coefficient can be assumed known to good accuracy in this case. If the fluid is compressible the situation is difficult even if the compressibility is only small since the term $(\zeta + \frac{1}{3}\mu)$ grad div **v** is hardly known exactly here. If the compression is large, however, the situation is effectively out of hand if only because the behaviour of both μ and ζ under strong compression is not adequately known. Consequently it is almost inevitable in the theory at the present time to include the viscous effects only through the approximation involved in the equation (5.9). While the accurate theory involving the viscosity is to be restricted to incompressible fluids only, that for an ideal fluid (zero viscosity) can also apply to compressible fluids. It is also worth noting that even for the ideal equation (1.15) the mathematical difficulties are such as to be soluble in only very few cases of practical interest; there is a real need to appeal to experiment for help (in this connection see also Chapter 7).

5.3. Vorticity and viscosity

An equation for the vorticity follows by taking the curl of each term of the equation (5.9). Remembering the conservative nature of **F** it follows that (since curl grad $\Phi = 0$):

$$\frac{d\boldsymbol{\omega}}{dt} = (\boldsymbol{\omega} . \mathrm{grad})\,\mathbf{v} + \nu\nabla^2\boldsymbol{\omega}. \tag{5.10}$$

Thus even when $\boldsymbol{\omega} = 0$, $d\boldsymbol{\omega}/dt \neq 0$; a viscous fluid may ultimately contain vortex flow (which moves in from the boundaries with a finite velocity) even though it was initially in irrotational flow. For incompressible flow variations of the velocity due to boundary changes are transmitted instantaneously through the fluid, as distinct from the vorticity which still has a finite velocity.

For two-dimensional flow, $\boldsymbol{\omega}$ is perpendicular to the plane of fluid flow and equation (5.10) becomes always

$$\frac{d\boldsymbol{\omega}}{dt} = \nu\nabla^2\boldsymbol{\omega}. \tag{5.11}$$

Because of the presence of the viscous term, Bernoulli's equation does not apply. For rotating motion where the velocity is a function of the distance **r** from the rotation axis, (5.11) takes the form

$$\frac{d\boldsymbol{\omega}}{dt} = \nu\left(\frac{\partial^2 \omega}{\partial r^2} + \frac{1}{r}\frac{\partial \omega}{\partial r}\right). \tag{5.11a}$$

This equation has the solution

$$\omega = \frac{A}{\sqrt{(\pi\nu t)}}\exp\left\{-\frac{r^2}{4\nu t}\right\},$$

where A is a constant, and shows the dissipative effect of viscosity.

5.4. Kinetic energy equation

Viscous forces cause energy dissipation which ultimately appears as heat. The energy equation must account for this dissipation. For an incompressible fluid volume the total kinetic energy $\mathscr{E}_k$ is:

$$\mathscr{E}_k = \tfrac{1}{2}\rho \int v^2\, dV. \tag{5.12}$$

The energy equation is concerned with the time dependence of the energy. This is obtained by differentiating (5.12) with respect to the time and invoking the momentum equation in component form (5.8a) in the rearrangement of the resulting integral. The integrand of the right-hand side of the resulting equation (i.e. $\tfrac{1}{2}\rho[\partial(v^2)/\partial t]$) is readily found to be:

$$\frac{\partial}{\partial t}(\tfrac{1}{2}\rho v^2) = -\frac{\partial}{\partial x_k}\left[\rho v_k(\tfrac{1}{2}v^2 + p/\rho) - \mu v_k\left(\frac{\partial v_i}{\partial x_k} + \frac{\partial v_k}{\partial x_i}\right)\right]$$
$$-\mu\left(\frac{\partial v_i}{\partial x_k} + \frac{\partial v_k}{\partial x_i}\right)\frac{\partial v_i}{\partial x_k}. \tag{5.13}$$

The divergence term contained in the bracket is the energy flux density for the fluid; as the viscosity vanishes the term reduces to the right-hand side of equation (1.33) applying to the ideal case. The second vector term in this bracket on the right-hand side is entirely new and describes the energy transfer associated with the viscous momentum transfer in the fluid. This term will be written formally as

$\partial \mathbf{Q}_2 / \partial x_k$: it will not be necessary to isolate $\mathbf{Q}_2$ even formally since it will be the divergence of $\mathbf{Q}_2$ rather than $\mathbf{Q}_2$ itself that will be important in subsequent arguments. Using (5.12) and (5.13), the dependence of the energy on the time is

$$\frac{\partial \mathscr{E}_k}{\partial t} = -\oint \left([\rho \mathbf{v}(\tfrac{1}{2}v^2 + p/\rho) - \mathbf{Q}_2] . d\mathbf{s}\right) - \mu \int \left(\frac{\partial v_i}{\partial x_k} + \frac{\partial v_k}{\partial x_i}\right) \frac{\partial v_i}{\partial x_k} dV,$$
(5.14)

where the first term on the right-hand side involves a surface integral taken over the surface bounding the volume. This first term is the energy flux across the bounding surface, with $\mathbf{Q}_2$ being the explicit contribution due to the viscosity. The second term on the right-hand side of (5.14), involving a volume integration, represents the decrease of kinetic energy per unit time due to viscous dissipation. This term carries a negative sign (because it is a dissipation); since the integral is a positive quantity it follows that μ also is a positive quantity. Because the fluid velocity normal to a rigid bounding surface is zero, the first integral on the right-hand side of (5.14) vanishes; the dissipation of kinetic energy in the fluid arises entirely from the second term, even though the first one also includes the viscosity.

5.5. Viscous stream function: two-dimensional flow

As for a two-dimensional ideal incompressible fluid flow so also for a two-dimensional viscous incompressible fluid flow, a stream function ψ_V can be defined using the equations (2.7). By substituting this definition for the stream function into the vorticity equation (5.10) there results an equation which must be satisfied by ψ_V, viz. in Cartesian co-ordinates

$$\frac{\partial}{\partial t}(\nabla^2 \psi_V) - \frac{\partial \psi_V}{\partial x}\frac{\partial}{\partial y}(\nabla^2 \psi_V) + \frac{\partial \psi_V}{\partial y}\frac{\partial}{\partial x}(\nabla^2 \psi_V) = \nu \nabla^4 \psi_V. \quad (5.15)$$

This equation does not represent reversible motion; this follows from the fact that the second and third terms on the left-hand side are unaffected when the sign of ψ_V is changed whereas the remaining two terms do then change sign. It should be noted that ψ_V is not now generally a solution of Laplace's equation.

It may happen that the fluid streamline configuration for a given flow system is independent of the fluid viscosity. This will be the case if the motion is either one for which both the velocity and vorticity are constant along each streamline, or else is the superposition of a rigid body rotation and some irrotational motion.

The form of the equation (5.15) for the stream function ψ_V in the limit of small viscosity requires a special mention. It might be thought at first sight that ψ_V for this case can be calculated from the equation which obtains from equating the right-hand side of the (5.15) to zero. But this is not so since this procedure reduces the order of the equation and so makes it impossible to satisfy the full set of boundary conditions applying to the complete initial equation. Instead it is necessary to solve (5.15) as it stands and consider the limiting form of the complete solution as the viscosity becomes small.

The alternative limit of large viscosity can, however, be treated by retaining only the terms involving the viscosity in (5.15) since this does not alter the order of the equation. In this limit ψ_V satisfies the equation:

$$\nabla^4 \psi_V = 0, \tag{5.15a}$$

and the boundary conditions are the same as those applying to (5.15). Because large viscosity has effects which are often indistinguishable from those associated with a low velocity, (5.15a) is the basic equation for low velocity flow, often called creeping motion. The linear equation (5.15a) is the basic equation of the hydrodynamical theory of lubrication.

5.6. Boundary conditions

The equations involving the viscosity must be solved according to boundary conditions that are more stringent than those for an ideal fluid. For an ideal (non-viscous) fluid it is required that at a rigid boundary the relative normal velocity component of the fluid must vanish. It is an experimental fact, however, for a viscous fluid that the tangential velocity component must also vanish. Thus a viscous fluid is at rest where it is in contact with a boundary. At an interface between two immiscible fluids the normal pressure and the viscous stress must be continuous in the absence of any surface tension forces.

The conditions pertaining in the boundary region between a viscous fluid and a rigid boundary will be considered further in a later chapter, using the concept of the boundary layer.

5.7. Stokes-Poiseuille-Hagen flow

The theory of a viscous fluid is considerably simplified if the motion is steady and the fluid velocity small. In such a situation the viscous force will dominate over the inertial force if the fluid velocity is lower than some definite value. For steady flow the momentum equation (5.8) becomes:

$$(\mathbf{v}.\text{grad})\,\mathbf{v} = -\frac{1}{\rho}\text{grad}\,p + \mathbf{F} + \nu\nabla^2\mathbf{v} + \frac{1}{\rho}(\zeta + \tfrac{1}{3}\mu)\,\text{grad div}\,\mathbf{v}.$$

$$(5.16)$$

This equation is non-linear because of the term on the left-hand side: let us suppose that $\mathbf{v}$ is sufficiently small for this term on the left-hand side to be treated as negligible in comparison with the remaining terms of the equation.† For simplicity we will suppose that there is no external applied force $\rho\mathbf{F}$, so that for small $\mathbf{v}$ (5.16) becomes:

$$\text{grad}\,p = \mu\nabla^2\mathbf{v} + (\zeta + \tfrac{1}{3}\mu)\,\text{grad div}\,\mathbf{v}. \qquad (5.17)$$

In this equation the viscous forces predominate over the inertial forces. Fluid flow for which this is so is often referred to as Stokes flow. Possibly the simplest example of Stokes flow is the steady low velocity flow of an incompressible fluid, for which (5.17) reduces to the form

$$\text{grad}\,p = \mu\nabla^2\mathbf{v}. \qquad (5.18)$$

The equations (5.17) and (5.18) are to be solved subject to the condition that $\mathbf{v}$ is exactly zero at the containing boundary surface. The continuity equation is satisfied identically because, the flow being steady ($d\rho/dt = 0$), it follows that div $\mathbf{v} = 0$ from equation (1.11). The important mathematical property of Stokes flow is the simplicity

† In Chapter 7 it will be found that the condition for the left-hand side of (5.16) to be negligibly small is that a certain dimensionless construct involving the ratio of the fluid velocity to the viscosity, and called the Reynolds number, shall be small as compared to unity.

introduced due to the equations (5.17) and (5.18) both being linear in the velocity.

The linear equation (5.18) does not provide an accurate description of the fluid velocity distribution at large distances from a boundary surface. Oseen, in 1910, suggested that for such large distances from a boundary acting as an obstacle to the fluid flow the term $(\mathbf{v} \cdot \mathrm{grad})\mathbf{v}$ appearing in (5.16) should not be neglected entirely but should instead be replaced by the term $(\mathbf{u} \cdot \mathrm{grad})\mathbf{v}$, where $\mathbf{u}$ is the fluid velocity upstream from the obstacle and so uninfluenced by it. The linear equation

$$(\mathbf{u} \cdot \mathrm{grad})\mathbf{v} = -\frac{1}{\rho}\mathrm{grad}\,p + \nu\nabla^2\mathbf{v} \tag{5.19}$$

then results in place of the previous equation (5.18) to describe the fluid velocity at large distances.

A special example of low velocity flow where the viscous forces predominate over the inertial forces was considered by Poiseuille in 1840 and independently by Hagen at about the same time. It is essentially the application of equation (5.18) to the steady flow of an incompressible fluid through a uniform tube of length l and of circular cross-section with radius R, the fluid being driven by a pressure gradient Δp along the tube.

Suppose the axis of the tube to be the x-axis, which is also the direction of the fluid flow; clearly $v = v(y, z)$. The equation (5.18) reduces now to the three component equations:

$$\frac{1}{\mu}\frac{\partial p}{\partial x} = \frac{\partial^2 v}{\partial y^2} + \frac{\partial^2 v}{\partial z^2}, \tag{5.19a}$$

where $v_x \equiv v$;

$$\frac{\partial p}{\partial y} = 0; \tag{5.19b}$$

and

$$\frac{\partial p}{\partial z} = 0. \tag{5.19c}$$

The last two equations show that the pressure is constant over any cross-section of the tube. Although we have in mind a tube of circular cross-section we have not yet used this fact, the equations (5.19) applying to a tube of any cross-sectional shape.

We will, however, restrict our argument to a circular cross-section from this point onwards and replace the Cartesian co-ordinates by polar co-ordinates with origin on the tube axis. Using the distance r as variable, where $r^2 = y^2 + z^2$, and noting that orientation angles do not appear for a circular cross-section, the right-hand side of (5.19a) is rewritten:

$$\frac{\partial^2 v}{\partial y^2} + \frac{\partial^2 v}{\partial z^2} = \frac{1}{r}\frac{\partial}{\partial r}\left(r\frac{\partial v}{\partial r}\right). \qquad (5.20a)$$

On the other hand, by virtue of the relations (5.19b) and (5.19c) we may write

$$\frac{\partial p}{\partial x} = \frac{dp}{dx} = -\frac{\Delta p}{l}. \qquad (5.20b)$$

Consequently the total equation (5.19a) is alternatively

$$\frac{1}{r}\frac{\partial}{\partial r}\left(r\frac{\partial v}{\partial r}\right) = -\frac{\Delta p}{\mu l}. \qquad (5.21)$$

Integrating this expression twice we get for the velocity

$$v = -\frac{\Delta p}{4\mu l}r^2 + A\log r + B, \qquad (5.22)$$

where A and B are integration constants to be determined so that (5.22) satisfies the required boundary conditions. These are two in number: first, that the velocity should remain finite everywhere; and second, that the velocity should vanish at the fluid boundary with the tube. The first condition requires $A = 0$: the second condition (viz. $v = 0$ when $r = R$) requires that

$$B = +\frac{\Delta p \cdot R^2}{4\mu l}.$$

Consequently the appropriate form of (5.22) for the present problem is:

$$v = \frac{\Delta p}{4\mu l}(R^2 - r^2), \qquad (5.22a)$$

showing a parabolic velocity profile across the pipe.

The total volume of fluid flowing through the tube per unit time is also that flowing through any cross-section because the fluid is incompressible. If ΔV is that fluid volume flowing in unit time through an elementary tube formed by the radii r and $r + dr$, then

$$dV = 2\pi r v \, dr$$

so that the total volume of fluid, V, flowing through the tube in unit time is:

$$V = \frac{2\pi \Delta p}{4\mu l} \int\limits_0^R r(R^2 - r^2) \, dr = \frac{\pi \Delta p}{8\mu l} R^4. \tag{5.23}$$

This volume is proportional to the fourth power of the radius; as is to be expected on intuitive grounds it increases with the pressure gradient ($\Delta p/l$), and decreases with increasing viscosity. The equation (5.23), usually called Poiseuille's equation, is the basis of a standard method for measuring fluid viscosity.

5.8. Couette flow

Another type of flow controlled by viscosity and described by equation (5.18) is that in a fluid contained between two surfaces that are not too far apart, with one surface stationary and the other moving, and which arises because, at each surface, the fluid must be at rest with respect to each surface even though the surfaces themselves are in relative motion. Such fluid motion is often called Couette flow. As an example of Couette flow we will consider the two-dimensional case of two parallel flat plates distance L apart, one only of which is moving in its own plane with a velocity v_1. With the origin of co-ordinates in the stationary plane surface, and with the x-axis along the direction of motion of the second plane, while the z-axis is perpendicular to the planes, then the fluid velocity is $v = v(x, z, t)$: for steady shearing motion the equation (5.18) becomes

$$\frac{dp}{dx} = \mu \frac{d^2 v}{dz^2}, \tag{5.24a}$$

where the total derivatives can properly replace the partial derivatives now. The boundary conditions to be satisfied are that the fluid is at rest at each boundary, i.e.

$$v = 0, \text{ when } z = 0; \quad v = v_1, \text{ when } z = L$$

and the solution of the equation (5.24a) is easily found to be:

$$v = \frac{z}{L}v_1 - \frac{L^2}{2\mu} \cdot \frac{dp}{dx} \cdot \frac{z}{L}(1 - z/L). \qquad (5.24b)$$

In the absence of a pressure gradient (i.e. if $dp/dx = 0$) the fluid velocity profile is given by:

$$v = \frac{z}{L}v_1. \qquad (5.24c)$$

This last equation describes the so-called simple Couette flow. The velocity profile is here linear, as opposed to Poiseuille flow where it is

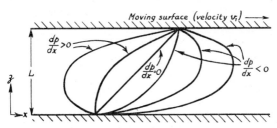

FIG. 8. *Couette flow with pressure decreasing along the flow direction, and with pressure increasing along the flow direction. The case of simple Couette flow, where the pressure gradient is zero, is also shown.*

parabolic. The velocity profile in the presence of a pressure gradient is not so simple. If the pressure gradient is negative, with pressure decreasing along the direction of motion, equation (5.24b) shows that the velocity is positive for all z, and is greater than (5.24c) at all points except at $z = 0$ and $z = L$. On the other hand, if the pressure gradient is positive, increasing along the direction of motion, then there will be a region for small z where v is negative (i.e. there is a fluid back flow in the region of the stationary plate) while for all larger values of z the velocity becomes instead positive, flowing in the direction of the moving plate. The pressure gradient must never be such as to violate the condition $v = v_1$ for $z = L$, on a macroscopic scale. The velocity profiles given by equation (5.24b) are shown in Fig. 8.

More complex geometrical arrangements can also be treated, such as two concentric cylinders one of which is moving. Again the general Couette flow is obtained by solving the complete equation (5.18) including the pressure gradient, while the simple Couette flow (with linear velocity gradient) is obtained by solving (5.18) with $\text{grad}\,p$ equated to zero, i.e. the left-hand side of the equation neglected, the viscosity not explicitly appearing in the solution.

5.9. Wave damping

Waves in a fluid transport energy (cf. Chapters 3 and 4), while the effect of viscosity is to dissipate energy. It might be expected, therefore, that any wave motion in a viscous fluid will be damped whereas waves in an ideal fluid (considered earlier) will not be so damped: we will show now that this expectation is in fact true. While we could show this by using the elementary arguments used in Chapters 3 and 4 we will, in fact, use slightly more sophisticated arguments now, and in the process will derive an expression for the wave velocity in terms of the fluid isothermal compressibility.

The wave disturbance is assumed to be small. Because any wave motion must in fact involve compression effects, the basic equation of motion is (5.8). The viscosity coefficients μ and ζ will both be assumed constant throughout fluid. By invoking the arguments of Art. 3.1., the motion can be assumed irrotational so that the substitution (2.2) may be made. Further, $\rho \mathbf{F}$ is assumed to be a conservative force so that $\rho \mathbf{F} = -\text{grad}\,\Phi$. We are now in a position to rewrite the equation (5.8). First invoke the vector relation.

$$\nabla^2 \mathbf{v} = \text{grad div }\mathbf{v} - \text{curl curl }\mathbf{v}.$$

The momentum equation is then, after a little rearrangement:

$$\rho \frac{d\mathbf{v}}{dt} = -\text{grad}\,[(p + \Phi) - (\tfrac{4}{3}\mu + \zeta)\,\text{div }\mathbf{v}] - \mu\,\text{curl curl }\mathbf{v}. \quad (5.25)$$

Using equation (2.2) this equation involving the velocity is transformed into one involving the velocity potential ϕ:

$$\rho \operatorname{grad} \left(\frac{\partial \phi}{\partial t} \right) = - \operatorname{grad} [(p + \Phi) - (\tfrac{4}{3}\mu + \zeta) \nabla^2 \phi].$$

Here two vector relations have been used, viz. $\operatorname{div} \operatorname{grad} \phi = \nabla^2 \phi$ and $\operatorname{curl} \operatorname{grad} \phi = 0$.

Let us now differentiate this expression with respect to the time:

$$\rho \operatorname{grad} \left(\frac{\partial^2 \phi}{\partial t^2} \right) = - \operatorname{grad} \left[\frac{\partial p}{\partial t} - (\tfrac{4}{3}\mu + \zeta) \nabla^2 \left(\frac{\partial \phi}{\partial t} \right) \right] - \frac{\partial \rho}{\partial t} \operatorname{grad} \left(\frac{\partial \phi}{\partial t} \right),$$

$$(5.26)$$

where we may write $d/dt = \partial/\partial t$ to good approximation since the fluid velocity is small. The second term on the right-hand side of (5.26) is of second order of small quantities and may be neglected; the equation (5.26) can then be integrated to give

$$\rho \frac{\partial^2 \phi}{\partial t^2} = - \frac{\partial p}{\partial t} + (\tfrac{4}{3}\mu + \zeta) \nabla^2 \left(\frac{\partial \phi}{\partial t} \right), \qquad (5.27)$$

remembering that both $\partial^2 \phi / \partial t^2$ and $\operatorname{grad} \rho$ are sufficiently small for the product $(\partial^2 \phi / \partial t^2) \operatorname{grad} \rho$ to be neglected.

To proceed further the pressure term must be considered, and rearranged. The pressure is a function of the density so that

$$\frac{\partial p}{\partial t} = \frac{\partial p}{\partial \rho} \frac{\partial \rho}{\partial t} = - \rho \frac{\partial p}{\partial \rho} \operatorname{div} \mathbf{v}.$$

The last step follows from the continuity equation (1.11) with the term $(\mathbf{v} . \operatorname{grad}) \rho$ neglected. If V is the volume of unit fluid mass then:

$$\rho \frac{\partial p}{\partial \rho} = - V \frac{\partial p}{\partial V}.$$

But the compressibility $\mathcal{K}$ is defined as the inverse of the negative relative volume change with pressure, i.e.

$$\mathcal{K} = - V \frac{\partial p}{\partial V}. \qquad (5.28)$$

Consequently

$$\rho \frac{\partial p}{\partial \rho} = \mathscr{K},$$

so that the time dependence of pressure is:

$$\frac{\partial p}{\partial t} = -\mathscr{K} \operatorname{div} \mathbf{v} = -\mathscr{K} \operatorname{div} \operatorname{grad} \phi = -\mathscr{K} \nabla^2 \phi. \quad (5.29)$$

Combining equations (5.27) and (5.29) we obtain the wave equation

$$\frac{\partial^2 \phi}{\partial t^2} = c^2 \nabla^2 \phi + \left(\frac{4\mu + 3\zeta}{3\rho}\right) \nabla^2 \left(\frac{\partial \phi}{\partial t}\right), \quad (5.30)$$

where the coefficient of the first term on the right-hand side has the dimensions of the square of a velocity and is given by

$$c^2 = \frac{\mathscr{K}}{\rho}. \quad (5.31)$$

If the viscosity vanishes then equation (5.30) reduces to the previous equation (4.7) for an inviscid compressible fluid, and c is now the wave velocity. For adiabatic conditions the pressure and density are related according to $p \propto \rho^\gamma$, and it is easy to deduce that $\mathscr{K} = \gamma p$; consequently the two expressions for c, viz. (4.12) and (5.31), are identical. The relation (5.31) is important in showing explicitly the dependence of the wave velocity on the compressibility. The two limiting cases of the expression are interesting. If the fluid is entirely rigid there is no change in volume (relative or actual) with pressure change so that $\mathscr{K} \to \infty$; in this case the disturbance velocity is indefinitely great, and this agrees precisely with our previous conclusion that a fluid behaves as if it is incompressible if its velocity is small in comparison with the disturbance velocity (i.e. sound velocity) in the fluid. If the fluid is perfectly compressible, then according to (5.28) $\mathscr{K} \to 0$ and the disturbance velocity is zero; in this case the fluid cannot support itself let alone a wave disturbance.

Information about the spatial dependence of the wave described by equation (5.30) is obtained by supposing the equation is applied to the sinusoidal disturbance

$$\phi(r, t) = \phi_1(r) \exp\{-i\omega t\}. \tag{5.32}$$

Using (5.32) and (5.30) we obtain the following equation for the unknown function ϕ_1:

$$\nabla^2 \phi_1 + \frac{3\rho\omega^2(3\rho c^2 + i\omega(4\mu + 3\zeta))}{9\rho^2 c^4 + \omega^2(4\mu + 3\zeta)^2} \phi_1 = 0. \tag{5.33}$$

This equation can be written more simply in the symbolic form

$$\nabla^2 \phi_1 + (a + ib) \phi_1 = 0, \tag{5.34a}$$

where

$$a = \frac{9\rho^2 \omega^2 c^2}{9\rho^2 c^4 + \omega^2(4\mu + 3\zeta)^2}; \quad b = \frac{3\rho\omega^3(4\mu + 3\zeta)}{9\rho^2 c^4 + \omega^2(4\mu + 3\zeta)^2}. \tag{5.34b}$$

As the viscosity vanishes, $a \to \omega^2/c^2$ and $b \to 0$, the coefficient of ϕ_1 in (5.34a) then being real. The solution of (5.34a) in the general case including the viscosity is a lengthy and specialized matter, and will not be pursued here. It does, however, represent a motion having a damped space amplitude. The total wave disturbance has an amplitude factor $\exp\{-2\nu k^2 t\}$ where $k = 2\pi/\lambda$. The damping is stronger the smaller the wavelength so that capillary waves are damped very strongly by the effect of viscosity while gravity waves are hardly affected at all.

5.10. Transverse viscosity disturbance

Although a fluid is incapable of withstanding the sustained passage of a transverse wave system, a viscous fluid can support such a disturbance over very short distances, for example in the immediate neighbourhood of an oscillating body. The transverse viscosity disturbance which results is subject to strong damping of the amplitude. We illustrate this by considering the effect on a viscous incompressible fluid of a completely immersed thin rigid plate which is executing simple harmonic motion. The effect of inertial forces will be neglected (Stokes flow).

Suppose the thin plate to be in the (x–z) plane, and to be undergoing simple harmonic motion in this plane. The fluid in contact with the plate must be at rest with respect to the plate, because of viscosity. Consequently a transverse shear disturbance will move into the fluid, the direction of propagation being perpendicular to the plane of the plate and the wave motion being parallel to that of the plate.

The system is described mathematically using the equations (5.9) and (5.19). If the direction of motion of the plate is parallel to the x-axis then apparently $v_y = v_z = 0$, and further $v_x = v_x(y)$ a function of y only. From (5.19) it follows that $p = $ constant, and from (5.9) it follows that, since $F = 0$ and $(\mathbf{v} . \text{grad})\mathbf{v}$ is negligibly small:

$$\frac{\partial v}{\partial t} = \nu \frac{\partial^2 v}{\partial y^2}, \tag{5.35}$$

making the replacement $v = v_x$ in this expression.

For simple harmonic motion we have

$$v \sim \exp\{i(\omega t + \epsilon)\}, \tag{5.36a}$$

so that (5.35) yields

$$\frac{\partial^2 v}{\partial y^2} = \frac{i\omega}{\nu} v. \tag{5.36b}$$

The solution of this equation is

$$v = A_1 \exp\{(1+i)\beta y\} + A_2 \exp\{-(1+i)\beta y\}, \tag{5.37a}$$

where A_1 and A_2 are constants to be derived from the boundary conditions appropriate to the problem, and

$$\beta^2 = \frac{\omega}{2\nu}. \tag{5.37b}$$

If the fluid extends to infinity on the positive side of the plate (i.e. y may go to $+\infty$), then $A_1 = 0$ in (5.37a), while $A_2 \neq 0$, since v cannot become indefinitely large. In this case the solution of (5.36b) is the real part of the expression (5.37a), viz.

$$v = A \exp(-\beta y) \cos(\omega t - \beta y + \epsilon). \tag{5.38a}$$

This velocity at distance y from the plate into the fluid is the result of the plate periodic motion:

$$v = A \cos(\omega t + \epsilon). \qquad (5.38b)$$

The expression (5.38a) represents a transverse periodic motion propagating with velocity $c = \omega/\beta$ and wavelength $\lambda = 2\pi/\beta$ into the viscous fluid of infinite extent. The amplitude of the wave at point y_1 is $A \exp(-\beta y_1)$; it has suffered a damping within one wavelength by the factor $\exp\{-2\pi/\beta\}$: the amplitude is reduced by the factor $0 \cdot 0019 \beta^{-1}$ over the distance of a wavelength. This represents very strong damping, so that the direct effect of the viscosity on the main body of the fluid is restricted to a very thin layer about the oscillating body. This is the first example of the so-called boundary layer which will be considered in some detail in Chapter 8.

The retarding force per unit area on the plate undergoing the oscillations is given by

$$F_R = -\mu \frac{\partial v}{\partial y}\bigg|_{y=0}, \qquad (5.39a)$$

so that using (5.38a):

$$F_R = \rho A_2 \sqrt{(\nu\omega)} \cos(\omega t + \epsilon + \pi/4). \qquad (5.39b)$$

It is interesting to note that this force has its maximum retarding effect one-eighth of a period *before* the plate passes through its mean position.

If the fluid does not extend to infinity but encounters a bounding, fixed surface plane at $y = h_0$ and parallel to the oscillating plate, then (5.38a) is not complete since $A_1 \neq 0$ in (5.37a). Since the fluid must be at rest on the boundary, A_1 and A_2 appearing in (5.37a) must satisfy the conditions

$$A_1 + A_2 = A; \quad A_1 e^{(1+i)\beta h_0} + A_2 e^{-(1+i)\beta h_0} = 0. \qquad (5.40)$$

Consequently (5.38a) is replaced now by the more general expression

$$v = A \frac{\sinh(1+i)\beta(h_0 - y)}{\sinh(1+i)\beta h_0} \exp\{i(\omega t + \epsilon)\}. \qquad (5.41a)$$

This expression reduces to the previous (5.38a) as $h_0 \to \infty$. The viscous force on the plate which replaces (5.39b) is:

$$F_R = \sqrt{(2)}\,\mu\beta A \times$$

$$\times \frac{\sinh 2\beta h_0 \cos(\omega t + \epsilon + \pi/4) + \sin 2\beta h_0 \sin(\omega t + \epsilon + \pi/4)}{\cosh 2\beta h_0 - \cos 2\beta h_0}.$$

$$(5.41b)$$

For $h_0\beta \gg 1$, (5.41b) reduces to (5.39b): alternatively, for $h_0\beta \ll 1$ it reduces to

$$F_R \to \frac{\mu A}{h_0}\cos(\omega t + \epsilon). \qquad (5.41c)$$

It will be seen that the direct effects of viscosity on the fluid are greatly enhanced by the presence of a rigid plane boundary in the vicinity of the oscillating plate.

CHAPTER 6

Thermal Effects

The irreversible transfer of momentum, manifested macroscopically by the appearance of viscosity, implies also an irreversible transfer of energy. Consequently the heat content and temperature of the fluid volume can be expected to change as it moves with the fluid. In addition, the flow itself will be affected if heat energy is introduced from outside, e.g. by raising the temperature of a boundary wall.

6.1. Thermal conductivity

Any local temperature elevation about a point in the fluid is reduced by an irreversible conduction of heat by the material of fluid from the elevated region to regions of lower temperature. No fluid motion is necessarily involved in this transfer of heat. It is known from experiment that the flow of heat in unit time across unit area of the surface enclosing a region of elevated temperature (i.e. the conduction heat flux) increases with the spatial gradient of the temperature; when the gradient vanishes, conditions are those of equilibrium and the net flux vanishes. Denote the conduction heat flux, which is a vector, by $\mathbf{q}$. Then for a sufficiently small temperature gradient we may write $\mathbf{q}$ as being proportional to $\operatorname{grad} T$ alone. Explicitly

$$\mathbf{q} = -\kappa \operatorname{grad} T. \tag{6.1}$$

Here the positive factor of proportionality κ is called the thermal conductivity; the negative sign is introduced in (6.1) because heat must flow, on balance, from a hotter to a colder body (Second Law of Thermodynamics). The thermal conductivity is in general a function of the temperature and the pressure itself: it is independent of the pressure gradient if this is small. Although it can be expected that κ will vary with position in the fluid, in many situations of interest this variation is sufficiently slight to allow κ to be treated as a fluid constant to good approximation. Further, κ is only weakly dependent upon the temperature so it is essentially a constant of the flow.

6.2. Transfer of heat

The transfer of heat from one fluid region to another can be conveniently reduced to three essentially independent contributions, viz. one associated with the energy transported by the fluid motion; one associated with viscous dissipation; and the third arising from the conduction process. This last contribution involves temperature differences in the fluid, while the other two need not take such an account.

The total energy flux density, written $\mathbf{Q}$, is thus the sum of three fluxes $\mathbf{Q}_1$, $\mathbf{Q}_2$, and $\mathbf{q}$, where $\mathbf{Q}_1$ is given by equation (1.39), $\mathbf{Q}_2$ from equation (5.13), and $\mathbf{q}$ is given by equation (6.1):

$$\mathbf{Q} = \rho\mathbf{v}(\tfrac{1}{2}v^2 + h) - \mathbf{Q}_2 - \kappa\,\mathrm{grad}\,T. \tag{6.2}$$

The term $\mathbf{Q}_2$ contains the effect of viscous momentum transfer, including any effect of fluid compression.

We next construct an equation expressing energy conservation; remembering the previous equation (1.33) we equate the negative space divergence of the sum (6.2) to the time rate of change of the energy per unit fluid volume, written $\mathscr{E}_1$ to distinguish it from the previous non-dissipative energy $\mathscr{E}$. Thus:

$$\frac{\partial \mathscr{E}_1}{\partial t} + \mathrm{div}\,[\rho\mathbf{v}(\tfrac{1}{2}v^2 + h) - \mathbf{Q}_2 - \kappa\,\mathrm{grad}\,T] = 0. \tag{6.3}$$

This is a statement of the conservation of energy including viscosity and thermal conduction.

Because irreversible dissipative effects are accounted for in this expression, thermodynamic equilibrium cannot be rigorously postulated. Although in theoretical discussions even the most infinitesimal movement from equilibrium makes any appeal to the standard thermodynamic relations (e.g. of Chapter 1) quite illegitimate, in experimental usage the correctness of the relations can only be ascertained within a definite margin of accuracy which may, of course, be small. In our present discussion, which is not concerned with micro-physical arguments, and since the motion and attending dissipative processes have been throughout repeatedly assumed to be small, negligible error need result if we neglect the distinction between $\mathscr{E}$ and $\mathscr{E}_1$ in equation (6.3). Remembering the discussion of Art. 1.7, we can write to this approximation

$$\mathscr{E}_1 = \mathscr{E} = \tfrac{1}{2}\rho v^2 + \rho U. \tag{6.4}$$

If this be accepted as sufficient, thermodynamical arguments can still be invoked to obtain a condition for the validity of this substitution under the physical conditions of the flow. This will lead to an equation to be satisfied by the entropy, which will differ from equation (1.28) in that it will include terms relating to energy dissipation. This approach is quite in keeping with the way in which the heat flux arises, namely as a means of allowing the fluid element to reach equilibrium with its immediate environment as it moves along its trajectory. Since the fluid motion is small, deviations from local equilibrium will be small at each point.

The rearrangement of the expression (6.3) for $\partial\mathscr{E}_1/\partial t$ will involve an analysis which will parallel that leading to equation (1.35) almost identically. The difference, in fact, will arise only from the viscous terms of the equation of fluid motion (5.8). The presence of these dissipative forces is to lead to an explicit appearance of the entropy into the final equation. The calculation follows that of Art. 1.7, so closely that the details need not be rehearsed here; it follows directly, using also the thermodynamic expressions of Art. 1.6, that in the absence of external body forces:

$$\frac{\partial}{\partial t}(\tfrac{1}{2}\rho v^2 + \rho U) = -\operatorname{div}\left[\rho\mathbf{v}(\tfrac{1}{2}v^2 + h) - \mathbf{Q}_2\right] + \rho T\left(\frac{\partial S}{\partial t} + (\mathbf{v}.\operatorname{grad})S\right)$$
$$- \sigma_{ik}\frac{\partial v_i}{\partial x_k}. \tag{6.5}$$

This expression is, under the present approximation (6.4), to be identical with the earlier equation (6.3). For this to be so it is immediately clear that the entropy must satisfy the equation:

$$\rho T\frac{dS}{dt} = \operatorname{div}(\kappa\operatorname{grad}T) + \mu\left(\frac{\partial v_i}{\partial x_k} + \frac{\partial v_k}{\partial x_i}\right)\frac{\partial v_i}{\partial x_k} + (\zeta - \tfrac{2}{3}\mu)\left(\frac{\partial v_l}{\partial x_l}\right)^2.$$
$$\tag{6.6}$$

This equation is to replace the previous equation (1.27) applying to ideal fluid flow. It must be remembered that (6.6) applies only when the space gradients of the velocity and temperature are small; such a situation characterizes many practical cases of importance. When the fluid is inviscid, so that $\mu = \zeta = 0$, and $\operatorname{grad} T = 0$, then (6.6) reduces to ideal form (1.27) applying to reversible conditions.

The basic equation (6.6) simplifies to some extent if applied to an incompressible fluid. Because $\operatorname{div} \mathbf{v} = 0$ the last term on the right-hand side of (6.6) vanishes, the entropy satisfying the equation

$$\rho T \frac{dS}{dt} = \operatorname{div}\left(\kappa \operatorname{grad} T\right) + \mu\left(\frac{\partial v_i}{\partial x_k} + \frac{\partial v_k}{\partial x_i}\right)\frac{\partial v_i}{\partial x_k}. \tag{6.6a}$$

The nature of the condition of incompressibility where temperature variations are also involved will be discussed later in Art. 6.5.

The quantity $[\rho T(dS/dt)]$ is the increase in heat energy per unit time of unit fluid volume as it moves with the fluid. The two equations (6.6) are the basic equations of heat transfer in fluids.

6.3. Equation for the temperature

The equations (6.6) can be rearranged to involve the temperature rather than the entropy by using the fact that the entropy itself is a function of the temperature. Explicitly, the fluid specific heat at constant pressure, C_p, divided by the temperature is thermodynamically equal to the temperature rate of change of entropy,

$$\left.\frac{\partial S}{\partial T}\right|_p.$$

Thus at constant pressure (e.g. that of the atmosphere),

$$\frac{\partial S}{\partial t} = \left.\frac{\partial S}{\partial T}\right|_p \frac{\partial T}{\partial t} = \frac{C_p}{T}\frac{\partial T}{\partial t},$$

$$\frac{\partial S}{\partial x_i} = \left.\frac{\partial S}{\partial T}\right|_p \frac{\partial T}{\partial x_i} = \frac{C_p}{T}\frac{\partial T}{\partial x_i}. \tag{6.7}$$

The insertion of these relations into equation (6.6) gives an equation for the temperature distribution appropriate to the flow. For an incompressible fluid the insertion of (6.7) into (6.6a) gives:

$$\frac{\partial T}{\partial t} + (\mathbf{v}.\,\mathrm{grad})\,T = \frac{1}{\rho C_p}\left\{\mathrm{div}\,(\kappa\,\mathrm{grad}\,T) + \mu\left(\frac{\partial v_i}{\partial x_k}+\frac{\partial v_k}{\partial x_i}\right)\frac{\partial v_i}{\partial x_k}\right\}.$$
(6.8)

This equation for $T(r,t)$ takes on its most familiar form when κ is independent of the position. Then

$$\boxed{\frac{\partial T}{\partial t} + (\mathbf{v}.\,\mathrm{grad})\,T = \alpha\nabla^2 T + \frac{\nu}{C_p}\left(\frac{\partial v_i}{\partial x_k}+\frac{\partial v_k}{\partial x_i}\right)\frac{\partial v_i}{\partial x_k}}$$
(6.9)

where

$$\alpha = \frac{\kappa}{\rho C_p}.$$
(6.9a)

α is usually called the thermal diffusivity.

The several limiting forms of this equation are worth writing down explicitly. If the thermal conduction effects predominate over those due to viscosity, (6.9) reduces to:

$$\frac{dT}{dt} = \alpha\nabla^2 T.$$
(6.9b)

This situation arises for a not highly viscous fluid if the flow velocity is small and is of wide practical occurrence. If alternatively the fluid is at rest ($\mathbf{v} = 0$) we may put $dT/dt = \partial T/\partial t$ in this equation and so recover the Fourier equation familiar in the theory of heat conduction in solids. Again, if the flow is steady (i.e. $\partial T/\partial t = 0$), the equation (6.9) becomes instead

$$(\mathbf{v}.\,\mathrm{grad})\,T = \alpha\nabla^2 T + \frac{\nu}{C_p}\left(\frac{\partial v_i}{\partial x_k}+\frac{\partial v_k}{\partial x_i}\right)\frac{\partial v_i}{\partial x_k}.$$
(6.9c)

For certain flows having sufficiently small velocity, or alternatively if a primary temperature gradient is maintained (say, by some external

8

heat source) in a direction at right angles to the flow velocity, equation (6.9c) simplies further to become

$$\nabla^2 T = -\frac{\nu}{\alpha C_p}\left(\frac{\partial v_i}{\partial x_k}+\frac{\partial v_k}{\partial x_i}\right)\frac{\partial v_i}{\partial x_k}. \tag{6.9d}$$

Finally, if the fluid is at rest and the temperature conditions are steady, equation (6.9) reduces to the Laplace equation

$$\nabla^2 T = 0. \tag{6.9e}$$

These various equations apply to incompressible fluids but the corresponding equations for compressible fluids can be obtained by augmenting equation (6.9) with the term

$$\frac{1}{\rho C_p}(\zeta - \tfrac{2}{3}\mu)(\operatorname{div} \mathbf{v})^2.$$

The uncertainties introduced by this term [see Art. 5.2, following equation (5.9b)], make its inclusion dubious, however, if anything other than broadly qualitative argument is pursued. These extended expressions are easily obtained if required, but will not be written down here.

In conclusion it should be noticed that the temperature equation (6.9), which involves the velocity, is coupled to the momentum equation through the velocity; and this is itself coupled to the continuity equation. In this way it is seen that the fluid velocity influences the temperature distribution in the fluid and vice-versa.

6.4. Conditions at the boundaries

The equations derived so far must be solved subject to boundary conditions which involve the temperature in addition to those collected earlier as applying to viscous flow. Several possibilities must be accounted for because in general extended external heat sources are involved which are either located within the fluid or at the bounding surfaces.

For a heat source distribution within the fluid, the equation (6.9) is augmented by the addition of a term $\mathbf{q}_0$ (say) which is a function of the position and perhaps also of the time.

If the source is located on a rigid boundary surface (i.e. if the surface is maintained by external sources at a temperature above that of the fluid), then heat will flow into the fluid. Thus

$$q_0 = -\kappa \frac{\partial T}{\partial n} \qquad (6.10)$$

at the boundary, the temperature gradient here being normal to the surface.

The surface could be one of separation between two fluid media (say, 1 and 2), the heat source being located in one of the two media. The heat flux across the interface must be maintained (since energy is conserved) and this leads at once to the relation at the boundary

$$\kappa_1 \frac{\partial T_1}{\partial n} - \kappa_2 \frac{\partial T_2}{\partial n} = 0. \qquad (6.11a)$$

In addition conduction effects must also be included explicitly: these cause temperature equalization so that for steady conditions of viscous flow

$$T_1 = T_2 \qquad (6.11b)$$

at the boundary. According to (6.11a), the temperature gradients on each side of the boundary will be in the ratio of the appropriate thermal conductivities.

In many practical problems it is found convenient to define the so-called heat transfer coefficient $\mathscr{H}$, for the transfer of heat between a solid boundary surface and the fluid. Let T_1 be the temperature of the solid surface at some point, and T_0 be the fluid temperature at any point downstream. Because the point is downstream, the value T_0 will depend upon T_1. It is found empirically that the temperature difference $(T_1 - T_0)$ is related to the controlling flux density q_0 through the boundary surface according to the linear relation (which is essentially Newton's Law of Cooling) and for steady fluid flow;

$$q_0 = \mathscr{H}(T_1 - T_0). \qquad (6.12)$$

The heat transfer coefficient can be calculated from (6.12) if the temperature distribution is known throughout the flow. For then q_0 follows from (6.10), and $\mathscr{H}$ consequentially from (6.12).

While $\mathscr{H}$ is constant for any given flow it varies with the flow parameters; in particular it is a function of the fluid velocity (see Art. 7.5 (iv)). It should be made clear that the heat transfer coefficient is not a simple physical property, and that the definition given above is not the only one, nor usually the one appropriate to the more complex flow problems met in practice. While the general form (6.12) is always the basis of the definition for $\mathscr{H}$ the difficulty is the exact definition of the temperature difference appropriate to any particular case (see also Art. 6.6).

The form of (6.12) indicates a close analogy between the heat flow per unit area as a function of temperature difference and the electric current density as a function of the potential difference (Ohm's Law). It follows that $1/\mathscr{H}$ can be regarded as a thermal resistance, and in a multicomponent heat transfer system such resistances can be added in series or in parallel, exactly as in the corresponding electrical cases. For instance, for the transfer of heat between two fluids of different temperature separated by a conducting solid barrier it is the reciprocals of the component heat transfer coefficients which are summed, the thermal resistances being in series. Here, the heat transfer coefficient for the heat conducting barrier is to be the thermal conductivity of the material per unit thickness in the direction of the heat flow. On the other hand, for the simultaneous transfer of heat by convection and radiation the thermal resistances are in parallel and the heat transfer coefficients themselves add directly.

6.5. Conditions for incompressibility

It was seen in Chapter 1 that a fluid which is in fact mechanically compressible can be treated in the theory as if it were incompressible provided that its motion is sufficiently slow: more precisely the fluid velocity must be very small in comparison with velocity of sound in the fluid. For then the terms depending upon compression effects are neglibly small in comparison with remaining terms and may be omitted to a good first approximation. In particular, because the motion is now strictly incompressible, the fluid density can be treated as constant.

This situation will not apply if temperature variations are present in the fluid because then relative volume expansions and contractions arise locally in different fluid regions due purely to temperature differences and these need not have negligible effect on the flow. If β is the volume expansion coefficient of the fluid, then the volume V_1 of a fluid element at temperature T_1 is related to the volume V_0 at temperature T_0 according to

$$V_1 = V_0(1 + \beta \Delta T), \qquad (6.13)$$

where $\Delta T = T_1 - T_0$; ΔT is an actual temperature difference and not a gradient. Consequently the mass density of the fluid will not be constant because of local temperature inhomogeneities throughout the fluid. Corresponding pressure variations turn out to be completely negligible. The appearance of the specific heat at constant pressure rather than that at constant volume in the equation (6.9) is seen now to be more than a happy coincidence.

It follows from the relation (6.13) that V can be replaced by V_0 to a certain degree of approximation only if ΔT, the corresponding temperature difference, is sufficiently small. This leads to the conclusion that a fluid which is in motion and which can intrinsically support temperature variations can act as if it were incompressible only if the flow velocity is very small in comparison with the velocity of sound in the fluid *and* simultaneously if the temperature differences between neighbouring fluid points are small enough for $(\beta \Delta T)$ to be small to the desired degree of approximation.

The effect of temperature differences, giving rise to changed volume elements and so to changed density locally, is to introduce effective forces on a fluid element which makes a warmer element rise (see Art. 6.6) relative to its lower temperature (and so higher density) environment. This irreversible buoyancy force must be added to any other external forces which may be acting on the fluid. The inclusion of the buoyancy force into the equations of motion can be achieved very simply if the flow velocity is sufficiently small, and any associated temperature differences are sufficiently small. For now any density variations throughout the fluid are small and any temperature effect on the density can be neglected as an unessential refinement throughout the equations of motion with the exception of the one term in the momentum equation which relates to an externally applied force not depending on the fluid velocity. This force is $\rho_1 F_i$, where ρ_1

is the local fluid mass density, and from (6.13) we can write this as $\rho(1-\beta\Delta T)F_i$ where ρ is chosen to have some constant mean value. The momentum equation is then:

$$\rho\left\{\frac{\partial v_i}{\partial t}+v_k\frac{\partial v_i}{\partial x_k}\right\} = -\frac{\partial p}{\partial x_i}+\rho(1-\beta\Delta T)F_i+\mu\frac{\partial^2 v_i}{\partial x_k\,\partial x_k} \quad (6.13a)$$

to the present approximation, which is usually called the Rayleigh approximation. The density can now be treated as constant if the flow velocity is sufficiently small so that this equation can be applied to liquids or gases to this approximation. The temperature distribution itself is to be determined from equation (6.9).

6.6. Logarithmic mean temperature difference

If a non-uniform fluid system can be regarded as being composed of two separate parts at different temperatures but in full thermal contact, then the problem of specifying the mean effective temperature difference between the two parts must be treated with some care. Such a mean temperature must conform with the theoretical conditions such as the equations (6.1) and (6.12); the logarithmic mean temperature difference, denoted by $\bar{\theta}_L$, is widely used for this purpose as we shall now explain.

Consider a cool fluid flowing along a hotter heated pipe: the fluid temperature will rise as it proceeds along the pipe, and the temperature difference between the fluid and the containing pipe will be less near the exit to the pipe than in the region of the entrance.† Let the heated pipe be of length L and with temperatures $T_1^{(p)}$ and $T_2^{(p)}$ at respectively the entrance and exit ends. Let the corresponding fluid temperature be $T_1^{(f)}$ and $T_2^{(f)}$. It is convenient to introduce the difference in temperature between the pipe wall and the fluid at each point, θ, as a variable parameter: thus $\theta(x) = T^{(p)}(x) - T^{(f)}(x)$, where the x-direction is along the axis of the pipe and is the flow direction.

The mean value of the temperature difference θ over the length of

---

† An alternative system which could also be considered is that of a cool fluid flowing with constant velocity relative to and in thermal contact with a hotter constant moving fluid; again the cooler fluid will heat up at the expense of the hotter fluid.

pipe L can be defined according to the conventions of the statistician as:

$$\bar{\theta} = \frac{1}{L} \int_0^L \theta(x)\,dx, \tag{6.14}$$

where the pipe entrance is at the origin of co-ordinates. An expression for θ at each point along the tube can be obtained from the equations of fluid dynamics, and particularly from the temperature equation (6.9). Neglecting viscous forces and assuming that the steady fluid velocity v is entirely along the axis of the pipe, with the cross-section being essentially constant, then it follows from (6.9) that

$$\frac{\partial \theta}{\partial x} = -C\theta \quad \left(C = -\frac{v}{\alpha} = \text{constant}\right). \tag{6.15}$$

where we have assumed the pipe to be maintained at a constant temperature distribution. The integration of equation (6.15) gives

$$\log \frac{\theta}{\theta_1} = -Cx, \tag{6.15a}$$

so that the temperature difference decreases along the pipe (as is intuitively necessary), and the decrease is exponential to the present approximation. The constant can be determined from (6.15a) by considering the total length of pipe, viz.

$$-C = \frac{1}{L} \log \frac{\theta_2}{\theta_1}. \tag{6.15b}$$

Thus finally, the temperature difference at any point x is given by

$$\theta = \theta_1 \exp \left\{ \frac{x}{L} \log \frac{\theta_2}{\theta_1} \right\}. \tag{6.15c}$$

The mean temperature, defined according to (6.14), can now be calculated: we have in fact

$$\bar{\theta}_L = \frac{1}{L} \int_0^L \theta_1 \exp \left\{ \frac{x}{L} \log \frac{\theta_2}{\theta_1} \right\} dx. \tag{6.16a}$$

Upon integration we get:

$$\bar{\theta}_L = \frac{\theta_2 - \theta_1}{\log(\theta_2/\theta_1)}. \qquad (6.16b)$$

This gives the mean temperature difference in terms of the inlet and outlet temperature differences between the pipe and the fluid. This is the expression for the logarithmic mean and $\bar{\theta}_L$ given by (6.16b) is called the logarithmic mean temperature difference. It is less than the arithmetic mean and greater than the geometric mean. As the pipe length is diminished ($L \to 0: \theta_2 \to \theta_1$) then (6.16b) shows that $\bar{\theta}_L \to \theta_1$, which is a primitive requirement of any formula for the mean temperature.

The reason for the use of the logarithmic formula (6.16b) rather than the direct arithmetic mean is seen by reference to the expression (6.15c). The arithmetic mean is only legitimate if the temperature gradient is linear. While this can be arranged to be the case in the heated pipe, this cannot be so in the fluid, according to (6.15c): consequently the temperature difference θ cannot be a linear function of the distance along the pipe.

It must be emphasized that the expression (6.16b) for the logarithmic mean temperature difference is not generally applicable and must be applied with care. To begin with temperature differences between the pipe and the fluid must be small [so that equation (6.12) is valid], and temperature gradients must be small [so that equation (6.1) is valid]. In addition, both $\mathscr{H}$ and κ must be constant [i.e. C shall be constant in equation (6.15)] so that the temperature difference may be given by (6.15c). Further, the specific heat must be constant so that the temperature equation (6.9) shall remain true and $\mathscr{H}$ be constant; and finally there must not be a phase change in the tube.

6.7. Convection

Although the fluid may be acted upon by no external mechanical forces other than gravity, steady motion can still occur and be maintained by the action of buoyancy forces if the temperature is held non-uniform by some external heat source. The action of the buoyancy forces, which depend for their existence upon the presence of density gradients in a gravitational field, is to cause an irreversible mechanical mixing within the fluid called convection, which augments the action of pure fluid conduction in bringing about conditions of uniform temperature distribution within the fluid. Convection coming about in this way is often referred to as natural or free convection in order to distinguish it from forced convection where fluid circulation and mixing results from mechanical (usually pumping) processes. In what follows we are not concerned at all with forced convection, although forced convection will be considered in Chapter 7. It is obvious that convective heat transfer differs profoundly from conductive heat transfer; in the former case the medium must move in some definite and systematic manner in order that heat should flow along a temperature gradient, whereas in the latter case the medium remains at rest.

(i) Static conditions

For fluid mechanical equilibrium the momentum equation (5.9) reduces to the form:

$$\mathbf{F} = \operatorname{grad} p, \tag{6.17}$$

so that if no external forces are acting p is constant. Consider a horizontal layer of fluid of depth h contained between two planes which need not be at the same temperature. Gravity will act vertically downwards; as usual the positive z-axis will be taken to be vertically upwards. If p_0 is the pressure applied to the fluid at the upper plate, the pressure in the fluid at any depth z is given by

$$p = p_0 + \rho g(h - z). \tag{6.18}$$

Clearly p is a function of z only, and $\partial p / \partial z < 0$. Inserting $\mathbf{F} = -\mathbf{g}$ in (6.17) it follows that ρ is a function z only, and that $\partial \rho / \partial z < 0$: explicitly

$$\rho = -\frac{1}{g} \frac{\partial p}{\partial z}. \tag{6.19}$$

For a unit mass of fluid $\rho = 1/V$, so that $\partial V / \partial z > 0$. For static conditions, therefore, the specific volume must increase with height. This requirement can be rewritten in a more significant form by making an appeal to thermodynamics. For, introducing the entropy as function of the volume

$$\frac{\partial V}{\partial z} = \frac{\partial V}{\partial S}\frac{\partial S}{\partial z} > 0.$$

The entropy increases with the specific volume if the fluid expands when its temperature is raised (which is usually the case): assuming this to be so, the condition for equilibrium becomes, in terms of the entropy

$$\frac{\partial S}{\partial z} = \frac{\partial S}{\partial T}\bigg|_p \frac{\partial T}{\partial z} + \frac{\partial S}{\partial p}\bigg|_T \frac{\partial p}{\partial z} > 0. \tag{6.20}$$

Here account has been taken of the fact that the entropy is a function of the pressure and temperature. According to equation (6.19) we can write $\partial p/\partial z = -g/V$: on the other hand, from Maxwell's thermodynamic relations we have

$$\frac{\partial S}{\partial p}\bigg|_T = -\frac{\partial V}{\partial T}\bigg|_p.$$

Therefore, the condition (6.20) can be expressed alternatively.

$$\frac{\partial T}{\partial z} > -\frac{gTp}{C_p}\left(\frac{\partial V}{\partial T}\bigg|_p\right) \tag{6.21}$$

and this is the condition for the occurrence of both mechanical and thermodynamic equilibrium in the fluid. The interesting result follows from (6.21) that even if the temperature decreases with height, stable equilibrium is still possible if the temperature gradient is less than the critical value

$$\frac{gTp}{C_p}\left(\frac{\partial V}{\partial T}\bigg|_p\right).$$

(ii) Equations for convection

If the temperature gradient existing in a fluid is such as not to satisfy the condition (6.21), either because it is too great in value or because the temperature is not a function of the height alone, then equilibrium is not possible. Free convection spontaneously arises in the fluid due to the presence of gravity. We shall for simplicity assume the fluid to be incompressible under isothermal conditions (remember Art. 6.5).

To conduct our present arguments it is most convenient to refer conditions in the fluid to some standard condition specified by the three corresponding parameters (ρ_0, p_0, T_0): explicitly, ρ_0 is a constant density relevant to the fluid, p_0 is the pressure for static equilibrium, and T_0 is the constant mean temperature of the fluid. The pressure, density, and temperature which actually occur at some arbitrary point in the fluid and at some given time will be written†

$$p = p_0 + p_1; \quad \rho = \rho_0 + \rho_1; \quad T = T_0 + \vartheta. \tag{6.22}$$

Here the three variables (p_1, ρ_1, ϑ), which characterize the fluid conditions at any point, are generally function of (x, y, z, t). The insertion of the expressions (6.22) into the three equations (1.11), (5.9), and (6.9) gives the basic equations for free convection. Noting that $\rho_1 = -\beta\rho_0\,\vartheta$, where β is the temperature coefficient for the density, and restricting discussion to those cases for which (p_1, ρ_1, ϑ) are each small, we are led to the set of equations

$$\frac{\partial v_i}{\partial t} + v_k \frac{\partial v_i}{\partial x_k} = -\frac{1}{\rho_0}\frac{\partial p_1}{\partial x_i} - \beta\vartheta g_i + \nu \frac{\partial^2 v_i}{\partial x_k \partial x_k}, \tag{6.23a}$$

$$\frac{\partial \rho_1}{\partial t} + \rho_0 \frac{\partial v_k}{\partial x_k} = 0, \tag{6.23b}$$

$$\frac{\partial \vartheta}{\partial t} + v_k \frac{\partial \vartheta}{\partial x_k} = \alpha \frac{\partial^2 \vartheta}{\partial x_k \partial x_k} + \frac{\nu}{C_p}\left(\frac{\partial v_i}{\partial x_k} + \frac{\partial v_k}{\partial x_i}\right)\frac{\partial v_i}{\partial x_k}, \tag{6.23c}$$

to the first approximation. α is the thermal diffusivity, defined by (6.9a). It will be seen that the temperature coefficient of expansion for the fluid occurs only in the momentum equation in connection with the acceleration of gravity.

Steady flow is often of interest. In this case the equations (6.23) are open to simplification, especially due to the fact that the conduction of heat predominates over the convection of heat, so that the term

† The use of ϑ here for a temperature must not be confused with the use of θ in Art. 6.6 as a temperature difference.

proportional to ν/C_p in (6.23c) can be omitted. We are then left with the set of five equations

$$v_k \frac{\partial v_i}{\partial x_k} = -\frac{1}{\rho_0} \frac{\partial p_1}{\partial x_i} - \beta\vartheta g_i + \nu\frac{\partial^2 v_i}{\partial x_k \partial x_k},$$

$$v_k \frac{\partial \vartheta}{\partial x_k} = \alpha\frac{\partial^2 \vartheta}{\partial x_k \partial x_k},$$ (6.24)

$$\frac{\partial v_k}{\partial x_k} = 0.$$

These equations are to be solved subject to the boundary conditions that at the rigid boundaries

$$\vartheta = 0, v_z = 0, \frac{\partial v_z}{\partial z} = 0; \quad v_x = v_y = 0 \text{ for all } (x, y).$$

(6.24a)

(iii) Onset of steady convection

Details of the onset of convection can be obtained by an appeal to the equations (6.23) which include the time, as was first shown by Lord Rayleigh. The method most often used involves a study of the perturbation of the fluid conditions which obtain when the upper and lower fluid surface regions are held at different constant temperatures. The various fluid variables appearing in the equations (6.23), and relating to the fluid at rest, are supposed to be perturbed in such a way that the perturbation depends upon the time through the factor $\exp(-i\omega t)$: here $i = \sqrt{(-1)}$ and ω is an angular frequency that is to be found. Thus, for the fluid velocity we write

$$v(x, y, z, t) = \exp(-i\omega t) v_1(x, y, z)$$

while for the temperature we write

$$\vartheta(x, y, z, t) = \vartheta_0 + \exp(-i\omega t) \vartheta_1(x, y, z),$$

where ϑ_0 is constant. The insertion of these expressions, and equivalent ones for the other fluid variables, into the equations (6.23) leads at once to a set of relations between ω and the remaining variables. In general ω will turn out to be an imaginary quantity; it is the exact form of ω that is of interest now. If the imaginary part of ω is positive then the term $\exp(-i\omega t)$ increases with the time: if the imaginary part is negative $\exp(-i\omega t)$ decreases with the time. In the former case the perturbation will grow indefinitely and the fluid conditions are unstable, while in the latter case the reverse is true and the flow conditions are stable. The limiting case of instability is obtained, therefore, when the imaginary part of ω is zero. The real part of ω determines the nature of the motion: this will be oscillatory if the real part does not vanish.

If the convection is to be steady both the real and imaginary parts of ω must vanish. Consequently the equations (6.23) are to be reduced to the set (6.24); in other words, to determine the conditions for the onset of steady convection it is necessary to solve the equations (6.24) in a form appropriate to the physical system under discussion in its perturbed state. In order to do this it is necessary to state explicitly the physical structure of the convection that is of interest. For example, it may have the form of a set of hexagonal cells with axis in the vertical direction: here the fluid may move upwards inside the cell, and downwards in the surface region, or this flow pattern may be reversed. By finding the magnitude of the temperature gradient above which a particular type of convection occurs the conditions for the onset of this convection can be elucidated and the conditions for stability ascertained. The subject is very difficult, and it is not appropriate to pursue it further here; there is still much to be understood in the theory and much of our present knowledge has resulted from empirical deductions arrived at on the basis of experiments.

6.8. Rotation

The equations used so far have not included the possibility of rotation of the fluid, although in many problems where theory is appropriate (for example that of the Earth's atmosphere), the fluid is in fact rotating. The particular co-ordinate axes to be used in any special case are open to choice: suppose the fluid to be rotating about some axis with constant angular velocity Ω. As a consequence of the rotation each fluid element is acted upon by an apparent force, the Coriolis force, of magnitude $2\rho[\boldsymbol{\Omega} \times \mathbf{v}]$. This must be added to the force terms in the momentum equation. For an incompressible fluid, if ρ_0 is the constant mean density in the presence of temperature gradients, then the momentum equation including gravity and rotation which replaces the previous equation (6.23a) without rotation, is†

$$\frac{\partial v_i}{\partial t} + v_k \frac{\partial v_i}{\partial x_k} = \frac{1}{\rho_0} \frac{\partial p_1}{\partial x_i} - \beta \vartheta g_i + \nu \frac{\partial^2 v_i}{\partial x_k \partial x_k} - 2\epsilon_{ijk}\Omega_j v_k. \quad (6.25)$$

Here ϵ_{ijk} is a function which takes only one of the three values $+1$, -1, or zero. Explicitly, ϵ_{ijk} has the value $+1$ or -1 according as to whether the three differing subscripts are permitted in the cyclic order (i, j, k), or not. Thus $\epsilon_{ijk} = +1$ while $\epsilon_{ikj} = -1$, and so on. Repeated suffixes do not occur; thus $\epsilon_{iik} = 0$, and $\epsilon_{ikk} = 0$. The remaining equations of the motion are exactly the equations (6.23b) and (6.23c). The coupling between these equations (6.25), (6.23b), and (6.23c) through the velocity means that the temperature distribution is affected by the rotation at least to some extent.

Conditions for the onset of stable convection are derived, as before, by seeking the time-dependent solutions of the equations of motion, i.e. solutions of the set

$$\frac{1}{\rho_0} \frac{\partial p_1}{\partial x_i} + \beta \vartheta g_i = \nu \frac{\partial^2 v_i}{\partial x_k \partial x_k} - 2\epsilon_{ijk}\Omega_j v_k,$$

$$v_k \frac{\partial \vartheta}{\partial x_k} = \alpha \frac{\partial^2 \vartheta}{\partial x_k \partial x_k}, \qquad (6.26)$$

$$\frac{\partial v_k}{\partial x_k} = 0$$

† There is also a centrifugal force acting which is $\rho [\boldsymbol{\Omega} \times [\boldsymbol{\Omega} \times r]]$. This can be written alternatively $(\rho/2)$ grad $(|\boldsymbol{\Omega} \times \mathbf{r}|^2)$ where $\mathbf{r}$ is the distance of the point from the rotation axis. This term does not involve the velocity and can be absorbed in the pressure term of the momentum equation involving the velocity. Further, because the rotation is constant, the force $\rho [\dot{\boldsymbol{\Omega}} \times \mathbf{r}]$ associated with non-steady rotation does not appear here.

The boundary conditions are again those of Art. 6.7. As a general result the effect of rotation is to inhibit the onset of convection although obviously the exact details for any system depend very critically on the system itself. The mathematics associated with detailed calculations is almost always extremely difficult, so that no applications of the equations (6.26) can be appropriately treated here. It should be pointed out, however, that there is great benefit to be derived from experimental studies of rotating fluids. This aspect will be considered again in the next chapter, both for rotating and also non-rotating fluids, when the utility of certain pure numbers constructed from the various parameters of the physical system will be considered.

CHAPTER 7

Dimensionless Parameters

The equations of fluid dynamics take on their most powerful form when expressed in terms of dimensionless variables. Certain dimensionless parameters can then be recognized which allow the relative effects of the various forces acting on the fluid to be uniquely specified in a way that is very convenient for practical applications of the theory. In order to make our arguments definite we will consider a specific situation. Suppose the simple viscous fluid flows under the action of gravity, with its flow obstructed in some region of space by a small impenetrable obstacle; in addition temperature gradients can be assumed within the fluid due to a distribution of heat sources in the neighbourhood of the surface of the obstacle. Because the obstruction is small, the flow pattern is assumed unaffected by the obstruction at a sufficient distance away: the unaffected flow will be called the free stream.† By using the properties of the free stream and the geometry of the obstructing body as datum variables, the equations of fluid motion can be put into a dimensionless form as we shall now see.

7.1. Dimensionless variables

Let the small obstruction to the flow have some typical linear dimension L. The obstruction may be caused to oscillate by some external force with a time period τ; alternatively the obstacle may suffer forced vibrations due to the fluid flow past it. Let those quantities which refer to the free stream carry a subscript ∞, so that the free stream velocity, density, pressure, temperature, specific heat at

---

† As a matter of nomenclature: an irrotational flow of an incompressible inviscid fluid past a rigid impenetrable obstacle, and which is a unique solution of the equations of motion subject to the appropriate boundary conditions, and which in addition has associated free stream velocity completely unaffected by the presence of the obstacle, is an example of Dirichlet flow.

$$\frac{\partial v_i}{\partial x_k} = \frac{\partial v_\infty v_i^*}{\partial L x_k^*} = \frac{v_\infty}{L} \frac{\partial v_i^*}{\partial x_k^*}$$

constant pressure, thermal conductivity, and shear viscosity will be denoted respectively by the symbols (v_∞, ρ_∞, p_∞, T_∞, $C_{p\infty}$, κ_∞, and μ_∞). The six variables (t, x_i, v_i, ρ, p, and T) can be expressed in terms of the free stream properties together with L and τ by introducing a number of dimensionless variables as follows.

Let any quantity which carries an asterisk as a subscript be dimensionless. Then we write the scheme:

$$t = \tau t^*; \quad x_i = L x_i^*; \quad v_i = v_\infty v_i^*;$$
$$\rho = \rho_\infty \rho^*; \quad p = p_\infty p^*; \quad T = T_\infty T^*. \quad \mu = \mu_\infty \mu^* \tag{7.1}$$

These will be augmented by the two further expressions: $\zeta = \mu_\infty \zeta^*$

$$F_i = g F_i^*; \quad \Omega = \Omega_0 \Omega^*. \tag{7.2}$$

Here Ω_0 is the free stream angular velocity, measured in radians per second.

Using these relations it is a straightforward matter to arrange the expressions for the viscous momentum flux σ_{ik} and the thermal diffusivity α in terms of the dimensionless variables σ_{ik}^* and α^* defined by:

$$\sigma_{ik}^* = \frac{\mu}{\mu_\infty}\left(\frac{\partial v_i^*}{\partial x_k^*} + \frac{\partial v_k^*}{\partial x_i^*}\right) + \left(\frac{\zeta}{\mu_\infty} - \frac{2}{3}\frac{\mu}{\mu_\infty}\right)\delta_{ik}\frac{\partial v_l^*}{\partial x_l^*}, \tag{7.3a}$$

and

$$\alpha^* = \frac{\kappa}{\kappa_\infty}\frac{C_{p\infty}}{C_p}\cdot\frac{1}{\rho^*} \equiv \frac{\kappa^*}{C_p^* \rho^*}. \tag{7.3b}$$

Explicitly, σ_{ik} and α are written

$$\sigma_{ik} = \frac{v_\infty \mu_\infty}{L}\sigma_{ik}^*, \tag{7.4a}$$

$$\alpha = \frac{\kappa_\infty}{\rho_\infty C_{p\infty}}\alpha^*. \tag{7.4b}$$

The force on the fluid which arises from external causes, and which does not depend upon the fluid velocity, is $\rho\mathbf{F}$. Using the Rayleigh approximation explained before, and embodied in equation (6.13a), we write this term displaying the buoyancy force explicitly

$$\rho^* \rho_\infty g F_i^* - (\rho_\infty \beta_\infty T_\infty g)\rho^* \beta^* \Delta T^* F_i^* \tag{7.5a}$$

9

where

$$\beta^* = \frac{\beta}{\beta_\infty}. \tag{7.5b}$$

The dimensionless variables to be used in what follows are now all specified. It should be remembered that measured temperature is actually relative to some chosen scale zero so that T_∞ can always be interpreted as a temperature difference, e.g. between the fluid free stream and some relevant boundary wall.

7.2. Equations containing dimensionless variables

Inserting the relations (7.1) to (7.5) into the equations of motion we obtain a set of equations in which the datum variables are prominently displayed. The equation of continuity gives at once:

$$L\frac{\partial \rho^*}{\partial t^*} + (\tau v_\infty)\frac{\partial}{\partial x_k^*}(\rho^* v_k^*) = 0. \tag{7.6}$$

The momentum equation (5.8a) including steady rotation becomes:

$$\frac{v_\infty}{\tau}\frac{\partial v_i^*}{\partial t^*} + \frac{v_\infty^2}{L}v_k^*\frac{\partial v_i^*}{\partial x_k^*} = gF_i^* - (\beta_\infty T_\infty g)\beta^* \Delta T^* F_i^* - \frac{p_\infty}{L\rho_\infty}\frac{1}{\rho^*}\frac{\partial p^*}{\partial x_i^*} +$$
$$+ \left(\frac{v_\infty\mu_\infty}{\rho_\infty L^2}\right)\frac{1}{\rho^*}\frac{\partial \sigma_{ik}^*}{\partial x_k^*} - (\Omega_0 v_\infty)\,2\epsilon_{ijk}\Omega_j^* v_k^*, \tag{7.7}$$

and finally the equation for the temperature becomes, using (6.6) and (6.7):

$$\frac{T_\infty}{\tau}\frac{\partial T^*}{\partial t^*} + \frac{v_\infty T_\infty}{L}v_k^*\frac{\partial T^*}{\partial x_k^*} = \left(\frac{\kappa_\infty T_\infty}{\rho_\infty C_{p\infty}L^2}\right)\alpha^*\frac{\partial^2 T^*}{\partial x_k^* \partial x_k^*} +$$
$$+ \left(\frac{\mu_\infty v_\infty^2}{\rho_\infty C_{p\infty}L^2}\right)\frac{\sigma_{ik}^*}{\rho^* C_p^*}\frac{\partial v_i^*}{\partial x_k^*}. \tag{7.8}$$

These equations are completely general and apply either to compressible or incompressible fluids.

The set of equations (7.6) to (7.8) is such that the coefficient of each dimensionless term representing a definite physical effect refers to standard conditions, and has dimensions which are the same as any other coefficient appearing in the same equation. Each equation can, therefore, be arranged to have dimensionless coefficients if it is divided throughout by any one coefficient of the equation. The coefficient to be used for this purpose is entirely open to choice and will depend upon which force is to be treated as the datum. For the present we will use the coefficient of the second term on the left-hand side of each equation (the inertial term) for this purpose; other terms for division will be taken later. Our next step, then, after having obtained the equations (7.6), (7.7), and (7.8) is to divide (7.6) throughout by (τv_∞), (7.7) throughout by (v_∞^2/L) and (7.8) throughout by $(v_\infty T_\infty/L)$. In this way the inertia properties are taken as standard. There results the equations of fluid motion in a completely dimensionless form as follows:

$$\left(\frac{L}{\tau v_\infty}\right)\frac{\partial \rho^*}{\partial t^*} + \frac{\partial(\rho^* v_k^*)}{\partial x_k^*} = 0, \tag{7.9}$$

$$\left(\frac{L}{\tau v_\infty}\right)\frac{\partial v_i^*}{\partial t^*} + v_k^*\frac{\partial v_i^*}{\partial x_k^*} = \left(\frac{gL}{v_\infty^2}\right)F_i^* - \left(\frac{\beta_\infty T_\infty gL}{v_\infty^2}\right)\rho^* \beta^* \Delta T^* F_i^* -$$
$$- \left(\frac{p_\infty}{\rho_\infty v_\infty^2}\right)\frac{1}{\rho^*}\frac{\partial p^*}{\partial x_i^*} + \left(\frac{\nu_\infty}{Lv_\infty}\right)\frac{1}{\rho^*}\frac{\partial \sigma_{ik}^*}{\partial x_k^*} +$$
$$- \left(\frac{\Omega_0 L}{v_\infty}\right)2\epsilon_{ijk}\Omega_j^* v_k^*, \tag{7.10}$$

$$\left(\frac{L}{\tau v_\infty}\right)\frac{\partial T^*}{\partial t^*} + v_k^*\frac{\partial T^*}{\partial x_k^*} = \left(\frac{\kappa_\infty}{\rho_\infty C_{p\infty} Lv_\infty}\right)\alpha^*\frac{\partial^2 T^*}{\partial x_k^*\partial x_k^*} +$$
$$+ \left(\frac{\nu_\infty v_\infty}{T_\infty C_{p\infty} L}\right)\frac{\sigma_{ik}^*}{\rho^* C_p^*}\frac{\partial v_i^*}{\partial x_k^*}. \tag{7.11}$$

These are the equations of motion in one possible full dimensionless form.

7.3. Numbers

It is convenient to have a set of symbols which allow for easy reference to the dimensionless coefficients appearing in the dimensionless equations of motion. For this purpose it is now customary to name certain of the dimensionless coefficients (which are in fact simply numbers and whose value is dictated by the exact details of the flow) after the people who realized their especial significance under given conditions of the flow. We will consider the equations in turn, isolating the more obvious of these numbers. For convenience we drop the subscript ∞ upon these numbers on the strict understanding that we are always concerned with the free stream.

(i) Strouhal number, S

In each of the equations (7.9)–(7.11) the coefficient of the term on the left-hand side associated with the time is the same. It will define the Strouhal number according to:

$$S = \frac{\tau v}{L}. \tag{7.12}$$

It has a value other than unity only when the motion is periodic; for non-periodic motion $\tau = L/v$ so that $S = 1$.

Consider the momentum equation (7.10). The left-hand side involves only the number S: the right-hand side involves numbers which we now define by considering the various terms.

(ii) Froude number, Fr

The first term gives the ratio of gravitational to inertial forces acting on the fluid. The coefficient defines the Froude number:

$$Fr = \frac{v^2}{gL}. \tag{7.13}$$

Reference to the gravity wave velocity equation (3.27) shows that the Froude number is pertinent there.

(iii) Reynolds number, Re

The fourth term gives the ratio of the inertial to viscous forces, and defines the Reynolds number:

$$Re = \frac{vL}{\nu}. \tag{7.14}$$

A high Reynolds number is associated with the situation where the viscous forces are weak in comparison with the inertia forces. This may be due to the fact that ν is actually small (i.e. either μ is small or ρ is large) but it may alternatively arise if the free stream velocity is high. Consequently the larger Re the more nearly does the fluid approximate to the ideal, treated in Chapter 1. The viscous forces, however, act in such a way as to damp out instabilities in the flow (indeed also the flow itself in the absence of an external driving force) and it is not surprising that large values of Re are associated with unstable flow. It is found that stable (laminar) flow only occurs for Re less than some critical value which is characteristic of the particular system: for higher values the flow is unstable. Thus for water at ordinary temperatures flowing through a pipe the flow is laminar only if $Re <$ about 2,000 where L is taken to be the diameter of the pipe. It should be noted that for any given set-up L may be chosen as any suitable dimension but which particular dimension is chosen for L must be carefully explained.

(iv) Rossby number, Ro

The fifth term is concerned with the rotational effects and gives the ratio of the inertial to Coriolis forces. This is described by the Rossby number:

$$Ro = \frac{v}{\Omega_0 L}. \qquad (7.15)$$

The smaller Ro, the more important are the effects of rotation.

(v) Grashof number, G

The second term on the right-hand side gives the ratio of the inertial to buoyancy forces. The coefficient as it stands can be written in terms of the Reynolds number, leaving a remainder defined as being the Grashof number. Thus:

$$\frac{\beta \Delta T g L}{v^2} = \frac{\beta \Delta T g L^3 \rho^2}{\mu^2} \cdot \frac{v^2}{L^2 v^2} = \frac{\beta \Delta T g L^3}{v^2} \left(\frac{1}{Re}\right)^2,$$

where the Reynolds number is introduced according to (7.14). Because Re is dimensionless so also is the remainder, which defines the Grashof number:

$$G = \frac{\beta \Delta T g L^3}{\nu^2} \tag{7.16}$$

Remembering the physical interpretation of Re, it follows that G is a measure of the relative importance of the buoyancy and viscous forces acting on the fluid.

(vi) Ruark number, Q

The coefficient of the third term is a measure of the ratio of the pressure force to the inertial force and is often used to define a cavitation number, perhaps more properly called the Ruark number.

$$Q = \frac{\rho v^2}{p}. \tag{7.17}$$

To convert this into a true cavitation number the fluid vapour pressure must be included in the numerator.

(vii) Mach number, M

For a gas the Ruark number can be related directly to the free stream sound velocity, c_s, given by (4.12). The Mach number is defined as being

$$M = \frac{v}{c}, \tag{7.18}$$

so that

$$\frac{\rho v^2}{p} = \gamma M^2. \tag{7.18a}$$

We turn now to the temperature equation (7.11); consider the right-hand-side.

(viii) Peclet number, Pe

The first term gives the ratio of the quantity of heat conducted by the fluid material to that transported by the bulk fluid motion, i.e. the ratio of the heat transfer by conduction to the heat transfer by convection. The coefficient is called the Peclet number so that:

$$Pe = \frac{vLC_p\rho}{\kappa}.$$ (7.19)

(ix) Prandtl number, Pr

The Peclet number can be conveniently broken down by introducing the Reynolds number. For:

$$Pe = \frac{vLC_p\rho}{\kappa} = \frac{vL\rho}{\mu}\cdot\frac{\mu C_p}{\kappa} = (Re)\frac{\mu C_p}{\kappa}.$$

Because the Reynolds number is dimensionless so is the remainder in this expression: it is called the Prandtl number

$$Pr = \frac{\mu C_p}{\kappa}$$ (7.20)

so that $Pe = Re \times Pr$. In molecular terms Pr denotes the ratio of the molecular diffusivity of momentum to the molecular diffusivity of energy. Expressed this way it is quite clear why the Prandtl number must be a characteristic of the fluid rather than of the flow. Pr is unlike the other numbers defined up to this point in that it involves the properties of the fluid alone and does not depend upon the flow. According to the expressions (6.9a) for the thermal diffusivity and (5.9a) for the kinematic viscosity we have the alternative definition for the Prandtl number:

$$Pr = \frac{\nu}{\alpha}.$$ (7.20a)

(x) Eckert number, E

The last term on the right-hand side of equation (7.11), involving the temperature effects and viscosity, can be rewritten by introducing the Reynolds number as follows:

$$\frac{\nu v}{TC_pL} = \left(\frac{\nu}{vL}\right)\left(\frac{v^2}{C_pT}\right) = \left(\frac{1}{Re}\right)\left(\frac{v^2}{TC_p}\right).$$

Since the Reynolds number is dimensionless then so is the quantity (v^2/TC_p) also dimensionless. If T is interpreted as the temperature difference between the boundary wall and the free stream, written ΔT, then the Eckert number is defined as:

$$E = \frac{v^2}{\Delta T . C_p}. \tag{7.21}$$

The numerator of this expression is twice the kinetic energy of unit fluid mass while the denominator is the change of heat content of unit fluid mass when raised through the temperature difference ΔT. If E has its largest value, which is unity (e.g. if the free stream velocity is sufficiently great), then the temperature effects of frictional heating on a surface are not negligible. In incompressible flow $E \ll 1$; $E \approx 1$ for compressible gas flow. It may be mentioned in passing that for compressible flow E is related to the Mach number according to

$$E = (\gamma - 1) M^2, \tag{7.21a}$$

where as usual γ is the ratio of the specific heats at constant pressure and constant volume. The Eckert number is considered again in Art. 7.5 (v).

Using the various numbers defined so far, the five equations (7.9)–(7.11) can be rewritten symbolically in the form

$$\left(\frac{1}{S}\right)\frac{\partial \rho^*}{\partial t^*} + \frac{\partial}{\partial x_k^*}(\rho^* v^*) = 0, \tag{7.22}$$

$$\left(\frac{1}{S}\right)\frac{\partial v_i^*}{\partial t^*} + v_k^* \frac{\partial v_i^*}{\partial x_k^*} = \left(\frac{1}{Fr}\right)F_i^* - \left(\frac{G}{(Re^2)}\right)\beta^* \Delta T^* F_i^* - \left(\frac{1}{Q}\right)\frac{1}{\rho^*}\frac{\partial p^*}{\partial x_i^*} +$$
$$+ \left(\frac{1}{Re}\right)\frac{1}{\rho^*}\frac{\partial \sigma_{ik}^*}{\partial x_k^*} - \left(\frac{1}{Ro}\right)2\epsilon_{ijk}\Omega_j^* v_k^*, \tag{7.23}$$

$$\left(\frac{1}{S}\right)\frac{\partial T^*}{\partial t^*} + v_k^* \frac{\partial T^*}{\partial x_k^*} = \left(\frac{1}{Pe}\right)\alpha^* \frac{\partial^2 T^*}{\partial x_k^* \partial x_k^*} + \left(\frac{E}{Re}\right)\frac{\sigma_{ik}^*}{\rho^* C_p^*}\frac{\partial v_i^*}{\partial x_k^*}. \tag{7.24}$$

It is a very straightforward matter to deduce that the vorticity equation (5.10) can be written in the dimensionless form:

$$\left(\frac{1}{S}\right)\frac{\partial \omega_i^*}{\partial t^*} + v_k^* \frac{\partial \omega_i^*}{\partial x_k^*} = \omega_k^* \frac{\partial v_i^*}{\partial x_k^*} + \left(\frac{1}{Re}\right)v^* \frac{\partial^2 \omega_i^*}{\partial x_k^* \partial x_k^*},$$

and so involves only the Reynolds number if the régime does not involve periodic motion of the obstacle. For periodic flow the Reynolds and Strouhal numbers must both be accounted for.

7.4. More numbers

Other numbers, not all unrelated to those defined so far, arise naturally if the equations (7.6)–(7.8) are each divided throughout by other terms of each equation. It is not necessary to write out all the length equations again; it is sufficient to state some additional numbers which arise and which are important.

(xi) Taylor number, Ta

The ratio of the magnitude of the Coriolis force to that of the viscous force is obtained by dividing the coefficient of the last term on the right-hand side of (7.7) by that of the last but one term, i.e. equals $(\Omega_0 v)(vL^2/v)$. The square of this ratio is often called the Taylor number.

$$Ta = \frac{\Omega^2 L^4}{v^2}. \tag{7.25}$$

This number plays an important rôle in the study of rotating fluids.

(xii) Galileo number, Ga

The ratio of the gravitational to viscous forces according to (7.7) is given by the dimensionless grouping $(\rho L^2 g/v\mu)$. This can be written in terms of the Reynolds number:

$$\frac{L^2 g}{vv} = \frac{L^3 g}{v^2} \cdot \frac{v}{Lv} = \frac{L^3 g}{v^2}\left(\frac{1}{Re}\right).$$

Because Re is dimensionless so also is the remainder which defines the Galileo number

$$Ga = \frac{L^3 g}{v^2}. \tag{7.26}$$

(xiii) Graetz number, Gr

The relative importance of the thermal capacity of the fluid and conductive heat transfer is significant in certain aspects of streamline flow and this is described by the Graetz number. By dividing the first term on the left-hand side of (7.8) by the first term on the right-hand side we obtain

$$Gr = \frac{\rho L^2 C_p}{\tau \kappa}. \tag{7.27}$$

Here, $(\rho L^3/\kappa)$ is the mass rate of fluid flow so that $[\rho L^3(C_p/\tau)]$ is the fluid thermal capacity for the motion.

There remain two important numbers concerning the flow of heat in a fluid which are especially significant at the boundaries.

(xiv) Nusselt number, Nu

The heat transfer per unit area of surface between a fluid and solid boundary is usually expressed in terms of the heat transfer coefficient, $\mathscr{H}$, defined according to (6.12). $\mathscr{H}$ is not a dimensionless quantity but a dimensionless quantity results if it is compared with the fluid thermal conductivity. This is a comparison of heat flux at the boundary in the light of equations (6.1) and (6.12): in dimensionless form the equality of these two expressions gives

$$\frac{\kappa_\infty T_\infty}{L} \kappa^* \frac{\partial T^*}{\partial x_i^*} = \mathscr{H}(T_1^* - T_0^*) T_\infty,$$

so that

$$\kappa^* \frac{\partial T^*}{\partial x_i^*} = \left(\frac{L\mathscr{H}}{\kappa}\right)(T_1^* - T_0^*).$$

The Nusselt number is then defined as:

$$Nu = \frac{\mathscr{H} L}{\kappa} \tag{7.28}$$

and is essentially the ratio of the total heat transfer to the conductive heat transfer at the boundary. Using the Nusselt number, then, the conditions of inflow of heat flux across a boundary can be written in the dimensionless form:

$$q^* = (Nu)(T_1^* - T_0^*) \tag{7.28a}$$

in terms of the datum variables.

Some comment is necessary here. Because the fluid is viscous, the fluid in contact with the boundary wall is at rest relative to the wall. Heat transfer from the boundary into the fluid is, therefore, by conduction in the immediate viscinity of the wall. This indicates a complex situation in the fluid contiguous with the boundary which is considered further in the next chapter (see also Art. 7.5 (iv)).

(xv) Stanton number, St

Alternatively the heat transfer coefficient can be made dimensionless by comparing it with the fluid thermal capacity; this leads to the Stanton number

$$St = \frac{\mathcal{H}}{\rho C_p v}. \tag{7.29}$$

St and Nu are related as is seen by rearranging (7.28). For we can write:

$$\frac{\mathcal{H}L}{\kappa} = \frac{\mathcal{H}L}{\kappa} \cdot \frac{\mu}{\mu} \cdot \frac{C_p}{C_p} \cdot \frac{\rho}{\rho} \cdot \frac{v}{v} = \frac{\mathcal{H}}{\rho C_p v} \cdot \frac{vL\rho}{\mu} \cdot \frac{\mu C_p}{\kappa}.$$

Using the relations (7.28), (7.20), and (7.14) it follows that:

$$Nu = (St) \times (Re) \times (Pr). \tag{7.30}$$

Since $(Re) \times (Pr) = Pe$ we have further:

$$\frac{Nu}{St} = Pe. \tag{7.30a}$$

It will be seen from equation (7.29) that the Stanton number can be regarded as the comparison between the rate of heat transfer by the wall and the fluid convection heat transfer. This is also essentially the ratio of the Nusselt and Peclet numbers which agrees with equation (7.30a).

The Stanton number is related to the logarithmic mean temperature difference $\bar{\theta}_L$ defined by equation (6.16b). Consider a hot pipe of uniform cross-sectional area A carrying a cooler flowing fluid with mean velocity v along the direction of the axis of the pipe (the fluid could alternatively be hotter than the pipe in which case the arguments to follow are simply reversed). Using the nomenclature of Art. 6.6, the fluid is heated as it passes along the pipe, and the heat taken by the fluid from the pipe in unit time per unit length is $\rho v A C_p (T_2^{(f)} - T_1^{(f)})$. If Σ_1 is the cross-sectional area of unit length of the inside of the pipe which is in contact with the fluid, then the heat lost by unit length of pipe in unit time is $\mathscr{H} \Sigma_1 \bar{\theta}_L$, as follows from the definitions of $\mathscr{H}$ and $\bar{\theta}_L$. Consequently

$$\rho v A C_p (T_2^{(f)} - T_1^{(f)}) = \mathscr{H} \Sigma_1 \bar{\theta}_L$$

from which it easily follows using (6.16b) and (7.29) that $\bar{\theta}_L$ and (St) are related according to:

$$\bar{\theta}_L \left\{ (St) + \frac{A}{\Sigma_1} \log \left(\frac{\theta_2}{\theta_1} \right) \right\} = \frac{A}{\Sigma_1} \Delta T^{(p)}.$$

If the temperature difference across the heated pipe and the temperature difference between the pipe and the fluid at the entrance and exit are known, together with the geometry of the pipe, then this information specifies the Stanton number for the flow. It is often more convenient in practice to use the Stanton number rather than the heat transfer coefficient in the description of many fluid heat transport situations.

(xvi) Weber number, W

For a free liquid surface it may be necessary to include the effects of surface tension. Then we invoke the expression (3.49): the equations of liquid motion are to be modified by replacing $1/\rho \, \mathrm{grad} \, p$ by

$$\frac{1}{\rho} \mathrm{grad} \, p_0 - \frac{1}{\rho} \mathrm{grad} \left[\mathscr{T} \left(\frac{\partial^2 \xi}{\partial x^2} + \frac{\partial^2 \xi}{\partial y^2} \right) \right]$$

where the notation is that of Chapter 3. The ratio of surface tension to inertial forces is then readily found to be:

$$\left\{ \frac{\mathscr{T}_\infty}{\rho_\infty L^2} \frac{\partial}{\partial x_i^*} \left[\mathscr{T}^* \left(\frac{\partial^2 \xi^*}{\partial x^{*2}} + \frac{\partial^2 \xi^*}{\partial y^{*2}} \right) \right] \right\} \bigg/ \left(\frac{v_\infty^2}{L} v_k^* \frac{\partial v_i^*}{\partial x_k^*} \right).$$

The dimensionless coefficient appearing here is called the Weber number:

$$W = \frac{\rho v^2 L}{\mathscr{T}}.$$

7.5. Method of dimensions

Dimensionless groupings of the variables relevant to any fluid situation may be derived without the explicit use of differential equations, by using the method of dimensions in the form proposed by Lord Rayleigh. This method, although relying more on intuition than that necessarily using differential equations, is very convenient in practice in deducing functional dependencies between dimensionless groupings such as the Numbers defined in the previous Arts. The method is based on the requirement that any equation describing a physical situation must be dimensionally homogeneous throughout; we illustrate the procedure with examples. It should be made clear that the functional dependencies suggested by dimensional analysis must be checked alternatively experimentally and/or theoretically for correctness and the instances which follow are known to be reliable.

(i) Frictional force

Suppose we wish to know the frictional force exerted on a body immersed in a flowing fluid stream. Let F_t be this force due to friction: we might know from experience (or guess!) that F_t will depend upon the size of the body L, the fluid velocity, v, the fluid density, ρ, and the fluid viscosity, μ. Thus write

$$F_t = f_1(L, v, \rho, \mu). \qquad (7.31)$$

According to the Rayleigh method we write (7.31) as:

$$F_t \sim L^\alpha v^\beta \rho^\gamma \mu^\delta, \qquad (7.31a)$$

where $(\alpha, \beta, \gamma, \sigma)$ are four exponents to be chosen so as to make (7.31a) dimensionally homogeneous throughout. The dimensions of the various quantities appearing in (7.31a) are as follows, in terms of length (L), mass (M), and time (T):

$$F_t \sim [MLT^{-2}]; \ v \sim [LT^{-1}]; \ \rho \sim [ML^{-3}]; \ \mu \sim [ML^{-1}T^{-1}].$$

Thus (7.31a) is written alternatively for the present purpose:

$$F_t \sim MLT^{-2} \equiv L^\alpha (LT^{-1})^\beta (ML^{-3})^\gamma (ML^{-1}T^{-1})^\delta.$$

$$(7.31b)$$

By equating the powers of the corresponding dimensions on each side of this expression dimensional homogeneity is achieved. There are three dimensional units, but four exponents to determine. We, therefore, must determine three exponents in terms of the fourth, and the standard exponent to be left undetermined is that of the term containing all three-dimensional units (viz. δ). Equating the powers of M in (7.31b) leads to the relation

$$1 = \gamma + \delta \qquad \text{i.e. } \gamma = 1 - \delta;$$

equating powers of T:

$$-2 = -\beta - \delta \qquad \text{i.e. } \beta = 2 - \delta;$$

and equating power of L:

$$1 = \alpha + \beta - 3\gamma - \delta \qquad \text{i.e. } \alpha = 2 - \delta.$$

The initial expression (7.31a) is then:

$$F_t \propto \rho v^2 L^2 \left(\frac{\mu}{\rho v L}\right)^{\delta},$$

i.e.

$$\frac{F_t}{\rho v^2 A} = f\left(\frac{1}{Re}\right), \tag{7.32}$$

where A is the surface area of the obstacle relevant to the frictional force. Apparently the frictional force per unit area of the obstacle divided by the product ρv^2 is a function of the Reynolds number alone; dimensional analysis will not give any information about the form of this functional dependence on Re, which must be determined empirically or by a more detailed analysis involving differential equations. The expression (7.32) will be of interest in Chapter 8, Art. 8.9. The ratio $(F_t/\rho v^2 A)$ is sometimes called the Fanning friction factor in those applications where the friction force is being exactly opposed by a pressure difference ('pressure drop').

(ii) Oscillating body

An example of the construction of a relation between dimensionless numbers by using the arguments of the method of dimensions is that of the periodic flow variations in a fluid in non-steady flow past an obstacle. Let τ be the time period of the fluid oscillations: we might intuitively expect

$$\tau = f_2(v, \mu, L, \rho), \tag{7.33a}$$

where the symbols have their usual meanings. By using identical arguments to those leading to the relation (7.32) it follows easily that

$$\tau = \left(\frac{L}{v}\right) f\left(\frac{\mu}{vL\rho}\right),$$

where f is some functional dependence, naturally different from that in (7.32). From the definitions (7.12) and (7.14) it is seen that this expression is a relation between the Strouhal and Reynolds numbers, viz.

$$S = f\left(\frac{1}{Re}\right). \tag{7.33b}$$

(iii) Free convection

Consider a hot body immersed in a cooler fluid; suppose the motion of the fluid to be entirely due to the the presence of the hot body, i.e. the motion is that of free convection. Let us deduce the general form of the expression for the heat lost by the body per unit area and per unit time, so for geometrically similar bodies. There are seven quantities which can be expected to control the system, viz. the temperature excess of the body over the fluid at large distances, ΔT; the linear dimensions of the body, L; the thermal conductivity of the fluid, κ; the kinematic viscosity; the thermal capacity of the fluid per unit fluid volume ρC_p; the temperature coefficient of volume expansion, β; and the acceleration of gravity, g. We can make one simplification if the fluid is incompressible, for in this case β and g will occur only through the product (βg) according to equation (6.13a). Let us, therefore, write the dimensional equation

$$q \equiv L^{\alpha}(\Delta T)^{\epsilon}(\rho C_p)^{\gamma} \kappa^{\delta} \nu^{x}(g\beta)^{y}. \tag{7.34}$$

As usual, we will choose the coefficients $(\alpha, \epsilon, \gamma, \delta, x, y)$ so as to make this expression dimensionally homogeneous throughout; there are six coefficients and only four independent dimensions and so we will select $(\alpha, \epsilon, \gamma, \delta)$ in terms of the two (x, y) as standard. The dimensions of the several quantities appearing in (7.34) are as follows:

$$q \sim [MT^{-3}]; \; \Delta T \sim [\theta]; \; \rho C_p \sim [ML^{-1}T^{-2}\theta^{-1}];$$

$$\kappa \sim [MLT^{-3}\theta^{-1}]; \; \nu \sim [L^2 T^{-1}]; \; g\beta \sim [LT^{-2}\theta^{-1}].$$

These dimensional arrangements are to be inserted into equation (7.34). The result is readily found to be:

$$\alpha = 3y-1; \; \epsilon = 1+y; \; \gamma = 2y+x; \; \delta = 1-2y-x.$$

Consequently, (7.34) reduces to the form

$$q = \left(\frac{\kappa \Delta T}{L}\right)\left(\beta g \Delta T L^3 \cdot \rho^2 \frac{C_p^2}{\kappa^2}\right)^y \left(\frac{\rho C_p \nu}{\kappa}\right)^x. \qquad (7.35a)$$

This dimensionless expression can be rearranged to show explicitly the numbers introduced in Arts. 7.3, and 7.4. Thus from equation (7.20) it is seen that

$$\left(\frac{\rho C_p \nu}{\kappa}\right)^x = (Pr)^x;$$

from equations (7.16) and (7.20) it follows that

$$\left(\beta g \Delta T L^3 \cdot \frac{\rho^2 C_p^2}{\kappa^2}\right)^y = (G \times (Pr)^2)^y.$$

Consequently (7.35a) can be written in terms of the Grashof and Prandtl numbers as follows:

$$q = \frac{\Delta T \kappa}{L}(G)^y (Pr)^{x+2y}. \qquad (7.35b)$$

This shows that the process of free convection is controlled by the Grashof and Prandtl numbers: because the Prandtl number is a constant for a given fluid, q is a function of G alone for a given fluid over a sufficiently limited temperature range. In particular, the Grashof number dictates the onset of instability in this case; the critical value of G is a characteristic of the particular system but values in the general range 10^3–10^5 are typical.

The expression (7.35b) can be reduced further. According to (6.12), the ratio $(q/\Delta T)$ defines the heat transfer coefficient for the system: from the definition (7.27) of the Nusselt number it follows that

$$\left(\frac{q}{\Delta T}.\frac{L}{\kappa}\right) = \frac{\mathscr{H}L}{\kappa} = Nu.$$

Thus (7.35b) is alternatively:

$$Nu \sim G^x(Pr)^{x+2y} \qquad (7.35c)$$

or, more generally,

$$Nu = f(G, Pr), \qquad (7.36a)$$

where f is some function to be determined empirically. For free convection, therefore, the Nusselt number is a function of the Grashof and Prandtl numbers. For steady conditions of free convection a balance between the accelerating force due to gravity and the decelerating viscous force can be expected to exist and this suggests that g and ν will occur always in the form (g/ν) in this case. We can write

$$\left(\beta g \Delta T L^3 . \frac{\rho^2 C_p^2}{\kappa^2}\right) = \left(\beta . \frac{g}{\nu} . \Delta T . \frac{L^3 \rho C_p}{\kappa} . \frac{\mu C_p}{\kappa}\right)$$

so that it can be expected that the Nusselt number for steady free convection can be written in the functional form:

$$Nu = f_1\left(\frac{\Delta T g \beta C_p L^3}{\nu \kappa}\right) f_2(Pr). \qquad (7.36b)$$

This expression has been found useful in many practical cases.

The form of (7.35c) has led a number of authors to assume a relation

$$Nu = AG^n Pr^m \qquad m \geqslant n \qquad (7.36c)$$

where the exponents (n, m) and the constant A are to be determined empirically. For laminar flow it is found empirically that $m \doteqdot n \doteqdot \frac{1}{4}$ and that $0 \cdot 7 < A < 1 \cdot 3$ (i.e. $A \sim 1$) applies for a range of geometrical arrangements such as spheres, cylinders, and plates, to reasonable accuracy. For gases (Pr) is usually not very different from unity so that the exponent m (which consequently cannot be determined very

10

accurately) is often omitted in applications of the theory to atmospheric problems. It should be pointed out that any full mathematical treatment of the problem (when it is possible to overcome the mathematical problems) would yield the functional form in (7.36a) unambiguously.

(iv) Forced convection

In forced convection, where the free convection currents are negligible in comparison with the currents caused to flow by some external energy source (e.g. a pump), the heat lost by a heated immersed body is known to have a different dependence from that associated with free convection. In particular the fluid velocity relative to the body will be important. The significant variables are now six in number, viz. $(\nu, \kappa, L, \rho C_p, \Delta T, v)$ where v is the relative fluid velocity. We write now:

$$q \equiv K^\alpha L^\beta (\rho C_p)^\gamma (\Delta T)^\delta \nu^x v^y \tag{7.37a}$$

and express $(\alpha, \beta, \gamma, \delta)$ in terms of (x, y). It is readily found that for dimensional homogeneity:

$$\alpha = 1 - x - y; \quad \beta = y - 1; \quad \gamma = x + y; \quad \delta = 1. \tag{7.37b}$$

Consequently in functional form

$$q = \frac{\kappa \Delta T}{L} f_1 \left(\frac{\rho C_p v L}{\kappa} \right) f_2 \left(\frac{\mu C_p}{\kappa} \right). \tag{7.37c}$$

Reference to the definitions (7.14), (7.20), and (7.27) show that according to (7.37c) the Nusselt number is a function of the Reynolds and Prandtl numbers: explicitly (7.37c) can be rewritten in the form:

$$Nu = f_1(Re \times Pr) f_2(Pr) \tag{7.38a}$$

i.e. $$Nu = f_1(Re) f_3(Pr) = f(Re, Pr), \tag{7.38b}$$

where again the functional forms must be determined empirically in the present absence of a mathematical analysis. The Nusselt number can be written, according to (7.37c), alternatively as:

$$Nu = B(Re)^x (Pr)^y \tag{7.38c}$$

and the values $B \sim 10^{-1}$; $x \sim \frac{1}{2}$; $y \sim \frac{1}{3}$ apply fairly generally to a wide range of situation.

From equation (7.29) the Nusselt number can be replaced by the Stanton number. Thus (7.38b) can be rearranged to become

$$St = \frac{1}{Re}f_1(Re) \cdot \frac{1}{Pr}f_3(Pr) = f_4(Re, Pr). \qquad (7.38d)$$

This leads to the possibility of using the expression

$$St = CRe^n Pr^m, \qquad (7.38e)$$

where the values for n and m follow from (7.38c) and (7.38d).

At very small values of Re (very low velocities) the functional dependence in (7.38b) is very easily deduced. For now the equations (6.24) reduce to the Laplace equation $\nabla^2 \vartheta = 0$, and Nu cannot depend upon μ or v since the fluid is effectively at rest. Consequently $Nu = $ constant in this limit, and heat transfer reduces to a simple conduction process. Alternatively, in the limit of very large values of Re (in practice this means very high velocities), Nu must be independent of Re otherwise the possibility will exist for increasing the heat transfer indefinitely by a simple velocity increase (or alternatively a density increase), which in fact is not so. These considerations show that any specific functional form such as (7.38c) that may result naturally from dimensional analysis is at best of only limited range of validity: the position and possible extent of this range is not, however, deducible from purely dimensional considerations and must, in the absence of any full mathematical analysis, be found empirically by direct experiment. There is always the possibility, however, that such a specific result from purely dimensional considerations will not be useful in practice. For these reasons the formula (7.38c) cannot be regarded as the proper theoretical basis for the rule $\mathscr{H} = Av^x + B$ (where A and B are constants, and x is some suitable positive number) which is widely used in engineering applications of fluid dynamics and which is a corollary of the expression (7.38c) when the fluid properties remain unaffected by the flow.

(v) Heating of a body by fluid friction

Suppose a viscous fluid in laminar flow with velocity v flows past a rigid obstacle having a typical dimension l. We will now deduce by dimensional arguments the temperature difference ΔT between the obstacle and the fluid when steady conditions prevail. For simplicity the thermal conductivity of the obstacle will be assumed to be negligibly small in comparison with that of the fluid. It should be made clear that thermal equilibrium is assumed not to have been set up. When equilibrium is established the thermal conductivity is, of course, irrelevant.

It can be expected that ΔT will depend not only upon l and v, but also on the fluid parameters C_p, μ, ρ, κ. Explicitly let us write

$$\Delta T \equiv v^\alpha C_p^\beta \mu^\gamma \rho^\delta l^x \kappa^y. \tag{7.39}$$

The dimensions of the various quantities appearing here are known from the previous subsections: the quartet of suffixes $(\alpha, \beta, \gamma, \delta)$ will be determined in terms of the pair (x, y). By requiring dimensional homogenuity throughout (7.39) it is easily found that:

$$\alpha = 2+x; \beta = -1-y; \gamma = -y-x; \delta = x.$$

Thus we have for ΔT

$$\Delta T = \frac{v^2}{C_p}\left(\frac{l\rho v}{\mu}\right)^x\left(\frac{\kappa}{C_p\mu}\right)^y, \tag{7.40a}$$

i.e.

$$\Delta T = \frac{v^2}{C_p}f_1(Re)f_2(Pr), \tag{7.40b}$$

where we have introduced the Reynolds and Prandtl symbols according to the previous definitions. It is seen that the temperature difference is proportional to the square of the fluid velocity, and inversely proportional to the specific heat (i.e. the fluid thermal capacity). The Eckert number, defined according to (7.21), can be introduced into (7.40b) to yield the functional expression

$$E = F_1(Re) F_2(Pr) \tag{7.40c}$$

The functions (f_1, f_2), or their corresponding reciprocals (F_1, F_2), could be determined by solving the equation (6.9d) directly subject to the appropriate boundary conditions. These must involve information about the thermal conductivity of the obstacle relative to that of the fluid. If this conductivity is negligibly small (as was assumed above) then the temperature at each point on the surface of the obstacle must equal that of the fluid in contact with the surface at each point so that there is no heat flux through the surface at any point. On the other hand, if the conductivity of the obstacle is very large then the surface is everywhere at the same temperature; local temperature differences between the obstacle and the fluid in contact will exist, and now it is the *total* heat flux through the surface that must vanish for steady conditions. In each limiting case, however, the thermal conductivity of the obstacle will not appear in solutions such as (7.40). For these cases where the thermal conductivities of the fluid and the obstacle are comparable then both coefficients must appear in the final result.

Although we will not consider the rigorous solutions of these problems here the result may be noted that for conditions of small Reynolds number the expression (7.40c) is found to take the form $E = A(Pr)^{-1}$, where A is a numerical constant determined by the exact shape of the body: alternatively if the Reynolds number is large then $f_1(Re) \to 1$. In each limit, therefore, Re does not appear.

7.6. The Pi theorem

Having treated the examples of the last Article by the method of dimensions we are now in a position to consider a very convenient and general method of isolating the dimensionless groupings relevant to any particular complex physical situation, viz., the so-called Pi theorem of Vaschy and Buckingham. The theorem has been the object of much mathematical substantiation by Buckingham, Riabouchinsky, Martinot-Lagarde, Birkhoff, and others. We give here a statement of the theorem and an example of its application; the complex mathematical foundations would be quite out of place here and will not be considered.

Suppose a given physical situation is properly described by a set of positive dimensional derived variables, written Q_j with $j \leqslant n$ (e.g. fluid velocity, pressure, viscosity, density, thermal conductivity). These variables Q_j are called derived variables because they depend upon a set of fundamental units $q_i (i \leqslant r)$, (e.g. length, mass, time, temperature; for mechanics $r = 3$, while if temperature effects are also included $r = 4$), so that $Q_j = Q_j(q_i)$. As an example, density is defined as being mass per unit volume so that if Q_1 is the density, and

q_1 the fundamental mass unit and q_2 the fundamental length unit, then $Q_1 = Q_1(q_1,q_2)$ in this case. We now assert that it is possible to change units by which we mean that a set of positive numbers can be selected, written α_i, which on simple multiplication convert the fundamental unit q_i into the new fundamental unit $\alpha_i q_i$. Thus in converting a standard length in inches into a standard length in centimetres, $\alpha = 2 \cdot 54001$, and so on. Any change in the fundamental units will affect the derived units Q_j: the new derived unit will be

$$Q_n' = \alpha_1^{a_{n1}} \alpha_2^{a_{n2}} \alpha_3^{a_{n3}} \ldots \alpha_r^{a_{nr}} Q_n(q_1, q_2, q_3, \ldots, q_r),$$

where the a_{ni} are called the dimensions of Q_n. The function Q_n is dimensionless if all the a_{ni} vanish exactly. This is nothing other than a rather formal way of expressing what has been used in the last Article. The Pi theorem itself moves on from this point.

If a geometrically similar set of systems is considered, then a consistent description of the behaviour of each system of the set can be written in the general functional form

$$f(Q_1, Q_2, Q_3, \ldots, Q_n) = 0 \qquad (7.41)$$

and this relation can be arranged to be free of dimensional units. The Pi theorem states, in fact, that this functional relation, which is itself dimensionally homogeneous as an entity and therefore *in toto* unit free, is fully equivalent to the relation

$$F(\Pi_1, \Pi_2, \Pi_3, \ldots, \Pi_{n-r}) = 0 \qquad (7.42)$$

where the quantities $(\Pi_1, \Pi_2, \Pi_3, \ldots, \Pi_{n-r})$ are a set of suitable dimensionless products of the dependent variables Q_j. These dimensionless products are to be formed by combining a chosen set of $s = n-r$ specific variables Q with each of the remaining Q_j taken separately. Thus:

$$\left.\begin{aligned}
\Pi_1 &= \Pi_1(Q_1, Q_2, Q_3, \ldots, Q_{n-r}; Q_{n-r+1}) \\
\Pi_2 &= \Pi_2(Q_1, Q_2, Q_3, \ldots, Q_{n-r}; Q_{n-r+2}) \\
&\;\; \cdot\;\;\cdot\;\;\cdot\;\;\cdot\;\;\cdot\;\;\cdot\;\;\cdot\;\;\cdot\;\;\cdot\;\;\cdot\;\;\cdot\;\;\cdot\;\;\cdot\;\;\cdot \\
\Pi_{n-r} &= \Pi_{n-r}(Q_1, Q_2, Q_3, \ldots, Q_{n-r}; Q_n)
\end{aligned}\right\} \qquad (7.43)$$

This is a statement of the Pi theorem, given without proof. The theorem may look very complicated in this form, but in fact it is very easy to use in practice. As an example we will reconsider the case of forced convection treated earlier in 7.5 (iii); it will be easy to follow the theorem in use in a case where we know the answer.

We know from 7.5 (iii) that there are seven variables for the problem, viz: $(q, v, \kappa, L, \rho C_p, \Delta T, v)$. These seven variables could alternatively be isolated from the equations of motion describing the system. In the nomenclature of the Pi theorem, this means that $n = 7$. We use the fundamental units (M, L, T, θ), i.e. $r = 4$ in the nomenclature above. Consequently $(n-r) = 3$, so that we are able to construct three dimensionless groupings Π_1, Π_2, and Π_3. In constructing these groupings, four (remember $r = 4$) of the derived variables are used as the basis for representing the remaining three. The four chosen as standard must contain between them each of the four fundamental units: we choose $(\kappa, \Delta T, L, v)$ as the datum quartet while the functions $(q, \rho C_p, v)$ form the remainder. The functions represented in (7.43) become for the present force convection problem

$$\left.\begin{aligned}
\Pi_1 &= \Pi_1(\kappa, \Delta T, L, v; q) \\
\Pi_2 &= \Pi_2(\kappa, \Delta T, L, v; \rho C_p) \\
\Pi_3 &= \Pi_3(\kappa, \Delta T, L, v; v).
\end{aligned}\right\} \qquad (7.44)$$

Each of these functions is to be made dimensionless. Remembering the dimensions of these several derived variables from the last Article it is easily found that the dimensionless groupings Π_i are:

$$\left.\begin{aligned}
\Pi_1 &= \frac{q}{\kappa L \Delta T} = \frac{\mathscr{H}}{\kappa L} = Nu, \\
\Pi_2 &= \frac{\rho C_p v}{\kappa} = Pr, \\
\Pi_3 &= \frac{vL}{v} = Re.
\end{aligned}\right\} \qquad (7.45)$$

Consequently, the Pi theorem leads to the conclusion that the fluid flow in forced convection is described by a relation between the dimensionless numbers Nu, Re, and Pr of the form

$$F(Nu, Re, Pr) = 0. \qquad (7.46)$$

This is exactly the result derived in 7.5 (iii), equations (7.38).

7.7. Use of models

The arrangement of the equations of fluid motion into a dimensionless form, of which the scheme (7.9), (7.10), and (7.11) is typical, is the correct first step in any mathematical solution procedure. Because no steps of analysis are involved in this dimensionless rearrangement the mathematical problems to be faced are, however, exactly the same as those originally applying. With the boundary conditions also arranged in a dimensionless form the solution, when found, is simply intrinsically indeterminate as regards to scale.

Although the mathematics is still difficult the fact that the equations are intrinsically indeterminate as regards to scale can be used to great advantage by employing suitably constructed laboratory models to gain approximate empirical information which is nevertheless sufficient for many practical purposes in the absence of a full mathematical theory. This alternative practical approach is of immense value in the application of the arguments of fluid dynamics to physico-engineering problems.

According to the scheme of equations (7.9), (7.10), and (7.11) any two similar fluid flows around geometrical identical obstacles (i.e. flows which can be made identical by the manipulation of the units of length, mass, time, and temperature, and not involving any change of obstacle shape whatsoever), and which have the same values of the dimensionless numbers (S, Fr, G, Q, Re, Ro, and Pe), are indistinguishable. It is not necessary that the two flows should involve the same fluid, provided that the basic classical continuum requirements of the macroscopic fluid structure are not violated in either case. If the characteristics of the flow for one of the fluids are once determined experimentally to a given accuracy, then, through the scaling scheme of the dimensionless numbers, those of the second fluid can be inferred to essentially the same accuracy. The utility of the method in design studies arises solely from the possibility of the choice of scale: the design of large-scale structures (e.g. buildings, bridges, ships, aeroplanes) can be facilitated by measurements made on geometrically similar constructs of laboratory size under controlled conditions.

Although of wide intrinsic validity the method meets practical limitations due to the fact that molecular properties cannot be scaled. Thus while it is easy to vary geometrical size or temperature distributions it is not possible to vary fluid properties such as density, viscosity, thermal conductivity, and specific heat. As a result model experiments are best conducted under restricted variation of parameters; this is, anyway, very convenient because information can easily become obscured by the sheer weight of data. We consider now a few scaling procedures which are important in some common practical problems.

(i) Inertial modelling

The most elementary modelling is that involving proportional changes in the scale of mass, length and time only. This scaling has some utility when (Re) is large, and gives significant information about the frictional flow in pipes of given roughness, and to the resistance of projectiles in air for speeds up to about one-quarter the speed of sound.

(ii) Reynolds modelling

If temperature effects are neglected (so that $G = 0$) and gravitational effects are negligibly small, then the equations (7.9), (7.10), and (7.11) when applied to the non-periodic flow of an incompressible non-rotating fluid lead to a velocity field which is very nearly that predicted by the single equation for the velocity:

$$\frac{\partial v_i^*}{\partial t} + v_k^* \frac{\partial v_i^*}{\partial x_k^*} = -\left(\frac{1}{Q}\right)\frac{1}{\rho^*}\frac{\partial p^*}{\partial x_i^*} + \left(\frac{1}{Re}\right)\frac{1}{\rho^*}\frac{\partial \sigma_{ik}^*}{\partial x_k^*}.$$

If the boundary walls are fixed then the flow can be expected to be invariant to changes of scale which leave the Reynolds number unaffected. For Reynolds scaling it is required that $(Lv)/\nu = $ constant. For a given fluid over a temperature range where ν is essentially constant this requires that the fluid velocity must scale as the inverse size, and the time scales as the square of the size. For different fluids, $v \sim \nu/L$, and time $\sim L^2/\nu$. Models based on Reynolds scaling have wide practical value. It allows for the determination of the critical Reynolds number for the breakdown of the laminar régime, such as for Poiseuille-Stokes flow through a pipe, provided care is taken to scale surface roughness, or better to effectively eliminate it altogether. This scaling is also very valuable in the experimental study of skin friction; thus the friction factor $(F_t/\rho v^2 A)$ of equation (7.32), being a function only of Reynolds number, is confirmed by experiment to scale in this way over a wide range of fluids for speeds not in excess of about one-third the speed of sound. By suitably choosing a fluid for its value of ν, Reynolds modelling for large Reynolds number can be achieved, within limits. Water is often useful as a scaling fluid for air in this case.

(iii) Froude modelling

When gravity forces predominate over all others scaling which preserves the Froude number has its value. This situation occurs quite generally when a fluid has a free surface, the density appearing in the Froude number being that of the fluid of interest (very often water) relative to the other one (usually then air). If the fluid is incompressible and non-rotating, the equation (7.10) reduces to:

$$\frac{\partial v_i}{\partial t^*} + v_k^* \frac{\partial v_i^*}{\partial x_k^*} = \left(\frac{1}{Fr}\right) F_i^* - \frac{\partial}{\partial x_i^*} \frac{1}{\rho^*} \left(\frac{p^*}{Q^*}\right),$$

since the viscosity is also negligible. For the Froude number to be constant it follows that $(gL)/v^2 = $ constant, so that (if g is constant), L/v^2 must be constant. Thus the velocity must scale as $\sqrt{L}$, and the time also as $\sqrt{L}$, independently of any fluid properties. Reference to equation (3.27) shows that Froude scaling will be useful in the study of long gravity waves, though not of surface waves and ripples. It is useful in the determination of the wave resistance of ships (a use that goes back about 130 years in practice), and in the general study of the effect of waves on harbours, beaches, and so on. It is also appropriate in turbine studies. In erosion problems, however, capillary waves make the interpretation of the results difficult. Because it is usually not possible to scale Re as well as Fr simultaneously, Froude scaling distorts viscous effects, such as the viscous attenuation of waves.

(iv) Further modelling

Other modelling schemes, possibly of limited range, may be constructed from the dimensionless groupings extracted from the theory in the present chapter. For instance rotational scaling can result from using Ro [equation (7.15)], or Ta [equation (7.24)]. Heat transfer effects can be studied using (7.35c) (free convection) or (7.38) (forced convection).

The use of model situations greatly extends the useful practical scope of the equations of fluid dynamics to cover complex everyday problems. Even so the limitations and difficulties of modelling techniques must be clearly remembered in experimental applications.

CHAPTER 8

The Laminar Boundary Layer

8.1. The problem stated

Consider the steady flow of a fluid past an immersed stationary small obstacle, or the fully equivalent opposite movement of an obstacle through a stationary fluid. Suppose that both gravitational and buoyancy forces have negligible effect: according to equation (7.23) of Art. 7.3, this fluid situation can be discussed by using the equation (in dimensionless form)

$$\frac{\partial v_i^*}{\partial t^*} + v_k^* \frac{\partial v_i^*}{\partial x_k^*} = -\frac{1}{Q}\frac{1}{\rho^*}\frac{\partial p^*}{\partial x_i^*} + \frac{1}{Re}\cdot\frac{1}{\rho^*}\frac{\partial \sigma_{ik}^*}{\partial x_k^*}. \tag{8.1}$$

If now the fluid velocity is increased relative to the immersed obstacle (or equivalently, the opposite velocity of the obstacle is increased relative to the fluid) then the Reynolds number becomes progressively larger and there will be a velocity beyond which the inertial force becomes so great relative to the viscous force that the inequality

$$\frac{1}{\rho^*}\frac{1}{Q}\frac{\partial p^*}{\partial x_i^*} \gg \frac{1}{Re}\cdot\frac{1}{\rho^*}\frac{\partial \sigma_{ik}^*}{\partial x_k^*} \tag{8.2}$$

becomes progressively more exact as the velocity increases further. Then, the equations of fluid motion become indistinguishable from those applying for an ideal fluid. Consequently the arguments of Chapter 1 become valid to higher approximation *within the main body of the fluid* even though the fluid is actually viscous.

The boundary conditions, however, present a grave difficulty. While for an ideal fluid (which has exactly zero viscosity) it is only the normal velocity component that must be zero relative to any impenetrable boundary, for a viscous fluid it is the total velocity (i.e the transverse components as well as the normal component) that must vanish. These conditions are quite independent of the fluid velocity at points away from the boundary. For a pseudo-ideal fluid (having a high free-stream velocity) this means that the viscous forces are of vital consequence in the boundary region even though they are swamped by the inertial forces in the main fluid volume. There is an obvious contradiction here if the total fluid volume including the boundaries is treated as a single entity.

8.2. Resolution of the problem

One way of resolving this difficulty, and a way that has proved most fruitful and important in practice, is to divide the fluid volume into two unequal parts for the purposes of mathematical discussion, viz. one region where the viscous forces have a completely negligible effect; and another region where their effect is important. The region where viscosity is important must clearly include the regions of any boundary surfaces: the important empirical result which makes this fluid division valuable is that the effect of viscosity is confined more or less to the neighbourhood of the boundary unless the fluid viscosity is very high and usually does not involve the main fluid volume. One small example of this has already been met with in Art. 5.9, where it was seen that the transverse viscosity disturbance caused by the oscillation of a body in a viscous fluid is so rapidly damped that it hardly penetrates into the fluid at all for normal fluids. Because the region where viscosity effects are important is restricted to the immediate neighbourhood of a boundary it is permissible to refer to this region as a boundary layer. In the boundary layer as contemplated now strong velocity gradients will exist and the associated flow may be either stable with a profile which follows that of the boundary (parallel flow) or be unstable (turbulent). It appears empirically that unstable flow is to be expected in the boundary layer for a fluid flowing past a flat plate at zero angle of incidence when $Re > \sim 10^5 - 10^6$ in the boundary layer itself: the exact value for other systems depends upon the system. In what follows we consider only the stable régime that exists below this critical limit. The main stream outside the boundary layer can be regarded as an ideal fluid to very good, and sufficient, approximation.

There is no actual sharp region of division between the boundary layer and the mainstream in the sense of a near-discontinuity, so that the boundary layer region is not open to exact definition. Usually the layer is regarded as ending when the fluid velocity has risen from zero at the boundary itself up to some specific fraction of the main stream velocity, say up to 99% of it. The exact fraction chosen does not, however, have critical consequence.

The concept of the boundary layer, first treated seriously and consistently by Prandtl and Blasius, gains strong support from experiments conducted on fluids with small friction (low viscosity) where the measured pressure distribution is only very little different from that as calculated for a perfect fluid. If the viscosity is large then the boundary layer is not necessarily thin and the situation is not usually simple from a mathematical point of view. It is found in practice that for the flow of fluids of low viscosity past an obstacle (or equivalently, for the motion of an obstacle through such a fluid) a thin region of flow can be easily distinguished near the front of the obstacle which gradually widens along its length. The region where viscous effects are important is not always confined to the vicinity of the obstacle surface along the whole length. Under certain conditions the boundary layer thickens considerably downstream, and the flow in the boundary layer becomes directed oppositely to that of the main stream. The result of this is to cause the boundary layer to move away from the surface; when this happens we say that boundary layer separation has occurred. Boundary layer separation is always associated with the breakdown of laminar flow in the layer and the formation of vortices. Separation usually occurs near blunt surfaces or generally where a surface has considerable curvature or a complex angular profile. Behind the obstacle (downstream) the boundary layer also persists, at least to some degree, and is then called the wake. If the geometrical profile of the obstacle is such that separation occurs at or near the trailing end of the obstacle then the wake is small and of only limited effect. This is the case in a streamlined body: a body is said to have a streamlined shape (or to be streamlined) if its profile is such as to lead to only small pressure gradients in the surrounding fluid flow at each point of its surface. An aeroplane wing cross-section is a good example of a streamlined profile. For a streamlined obstacle separation will occur well towards the downstream region of the surface, or even as far back as the trailing end. If the obstacle is not streamlined then the boundary layer can become quite wide and the wake become substantial, persisting well downstream of the obstacle. The pressure distribution in the wake behind an obstacle is quite different from that to be expected from the theory of an ideal fluid. It should be pointed out that it is usually not possible in practice to construct an obstacle which is streamlined over a large range of velocity, especially if the upper velocity limit is high (i.e. of the order of, or greater than, the sound velocity).

8.3. The describing equations

Prandtl very largely pioneered the boundary layer field and much of the basic mathematical theory is due to him and his student Blasius: the following treatment leans heavily on their work. Even now, however, no completely final theory has been developed, so that much of the discussion must be qualitative and be based ultimately on the authority of direct experiment and observation. Our arguments here will be restricted to the steady flow of an incompressible fluid past a smooth obstacle with a velocity small enough for separation not to occur. The boundary will be regarded as at rest and the fluid will flow past it with a main stream velocity $\mathbf{v}_m$; the free stream flow will be supposed to be irrotational, even though this is not so in the boundary layer.

To make the arguments quite definite we consider a specific situation, and for simplicity make this two-dimensional. Consider a plane finite in the x-direction (which is also the direction of the undisturbed upstream fluid flow) and of length L: the y-axis is to lie also in the plane and y can have any value in the fully infinite range

$$-\infty \leqslant y \leqslant \infty.$$

The plane will be regarded as of negligible thickness, i.e. to have no extension in the z-direction. The origin of co-ordinates can be conveiently placed on the leading (upstream) edge of the plane: then for $x < 0$ (upstream with respect to the plane obstruction) the fluid streamline flow is unaffected by the obstacle; for $x > 0$ the obstacle divides the flow symmetrically about the x-axis.

The Navier-Stokes (momentum) equation for this problem can be separated into two component equations, viz.

$$v_x \frac{\partial v_x}{\partial x} + v_z \frac{\partial v_x}{\partial z} = -\frac{1}{\rho}\frac{\partial p}{\partial x} + \nu\left(\frac{\partial^2 v_x}{\partial x^2} + \frac{\partial^2 v_x}{\partial z^2}\right), \tag{8.3a}$$

$$v_x \frac{\partial v_z}{\partial x} + v_z \frac{\partial v_z}{\partial z} = -\frac{1}{\rho}\frac{\partial p}{\partial z} + \nu\left(\frac{\partial^2 v_z}{\partial x^2} + \frac{\partial^2 v_z}{\partial z^2}\right), \tag{8.3b}$$

and the continuity equation is

$$\frac{\partial v_x}{\partial x} + \frac{\partial v_z}{\partial z} = 0. \tag{8.3c}$$

There are no variations with respect to y here, variations being restricted to the $(x-z)$ plane. The equations (8.3) are exact. They will, however, need to be modified to account for the concept of the boundary layer already considered by the introduction of approximations dictated by our insistence on the boundary layer being always thin and without separation.

Because the boundary layer is always thin with the flow contained in it essentially parallel to the plane surface it follows that $v_z \ll v_x$. Further it follows from the picture built up in Art. 8.2 that v_x will vary only slightly with x, and that v_z will vary only slightly with z. On the other hand, v_x must vary strongly with z since it must increase from zero at $z = 0$ to essentially the main stream velocity when $z = h$, if h is the thickness of the boundary layer. In general h will be a function of x, the distance downstream from the leading edge of the plate. Expressed mathematically these conditions are:

$$\frac{\partial v_x}{\partial x} \ll \frac{\partial v_x}{\partial z}; \; \frac{\partial^2 v_x}{\partial x^2} \ll \frac{\partial^2 v_x}{\partial z^2}; \; v_z \ll v_x, \tag{8.4a}$$

$$\frac{\partial v_z}{\partial z} \sim \frac{\partial^2 v_z}{\partial z^2} \sim \epsilon \quad \text{where } \epsilon \ll 1. \tag{8.4b}$$

By inserting these approximations into the exact equations (8.3) we obtain the equations

$$v_x \frac{\partial v_x}{\partial x} + v_z \frac{\partial v_x}{\partial z} = -\frac{1}{\rho} \frac{\partial p}{\partial x} + \nu \frac{\partial^2 v_x}{\partial z^2} \qquad (8.5a)$$

$$\frac{\partial p}{\partial z} = 0 \quad \text{(virtually)}. \qquad (8.5b)$$

which are to be augmented by the continuity equation (8.3c). It will be seen that the pressure is essentially only a function of x: this follows immediately from the neglect of the velocity component v in comparison with the component v_x. Expressed alternatively, the pressure in the laminar boundary layer is almost exactly equal to that of the main stream.

The equations (8.5) are to be solved subject to the boundary conditions $v_x = 0$ for $z = 0$ and $v_x = v_m$ outside the boundary layer, where v_m is the main stream velocity. (The main stream is not to be confused with the free stream of Chapter 7.)

8.4. Boundary layer thickness for a thin plate

It is convenient now to express the equations (8.5) for the laminar boundary layer in dimensionless form. Because the pressure in the boundary layer is virtually that of the main stream, and because the main stream flow is by assumption irrotational with the Bernoulli equation being valid, then the pressure in the boundary layer is given by

$$p = \text{constant} - \tfrac{1}{2}\rho v_m^2$$

so that

$$-\frac{1}{\rho} \frac{\partial p}{\partial x} = v_m \frac{\partial v_m}{\partial x},$$

where $v_m(x)$ is the main stream velocity, a function of position with respect to the obstructing plane. Equation (8.5a) then becomes

$$v_x \frac{\partial v_x}{\partial x} + v_z \frac{\partial v_x}{\partial z} - \nu \frac{\partial^2 v_x}{\partial z^2} = v_m \frac{\partial v_m}{\partial x}. \qquad (8.6)$$

11

This equation is to be made dimensionless and arranged into a specific form, which is best done in two steps. First introduce the dimensionless variables x^*, z_1^*, v_x^*, and v_{1z}^* according to:

$$x = Lx^*; z = Lz_1^*; v_x = v_\infty v_x^*; v_z = v_\infty v_{1z}^*; v_m = v_\infty v_m^* \quad (8.7)$$

Here L is a characteristic length, e.g. the length of the plate. Inserting these relations into (8.6) gives the equation in a first dimensionless form:

$$\frac{v_\infty^2}{L} v_x^* \frac{\partial v_x^*}{\partial x^*} + \frac{v_\infty^2}{L} v_{1z}^* \frac{\partial v_x^*}{\partial z_1^*} - \nu \frac{v_\infty}{L^2} \frac{\partial^2 v_x^*}{\partial z_1^{*2}} = \frac{v_\infty^2}{L} v_m^* \frac{\partial v_m^*}{\partial x^*},$$

i.e.

$$v_x^* \frac{\partial v_x^*}{\partial x^*} + v_{1z}^* \frac{\partial v_x^*}{\partial z_1^*} - \left(\frac{\nu}{L v_\infty} \right) \frac{\partial^2 v_x^*}{\partial z_1^{*2}} = v_m^* \frac{\partial v_m^*}{\partial x^*}. \quad (8.8)$$

We now rearrange this equation into a form which has every coefficient equal to unity: the reason for this will be clear in a moment. To do this we make the substitutions

$$\sqrt{(Re)} \cdot z_1^* = z^* \quad \text{and} \quad \sqrt{(Re)} \cdot v_{1z}^* = v_z^*, \quad (8.9)$$

where z^* and v_z^* are new dimensionless numbers. Then, equation (8.8) becomes

$$v_x^* \frac{\partial v_x^*}{\partial x^*} + v_z^* \frac{\partial v_x^*}{\partial z^*} - \frac{\partial^2 v_x^*}{\partial z^{*2}} = v_m^* \frac{\partial v_m^*}{\partial x^*}. \quad (8.9a)$$

The continuity equation becomes now

$$\frac{\partial v_x^*}{\partial x^*} + \frac{\partial v_z^*}{\partial z^*} = 0. \quad (8.9b)$$

These equations give as their solution v_x^* and v_z^* as function of $v_m^*(x^*)$. The important point about the dimensionless form (8.9a) and (8.9b), where all the coefficients are unity, is that it can be expected that two unknown functions v_x^* and v_z^* will be of comparable magnitude for all free stream velocities. Indeed, the only effect of varying the velocity is to change the scale of the flow and the boundary regions.

The conclusion that $v_x^* \sim v_z^*$ can be used to derive an expression for the thickness of the boundary layer. For if these two velocity components are comparable then it follows from the definitions (8.7) and (8.9) that

$$v_x \sim \sqrt{(Re)} \cdot v_z. \qquad (8.10)$$

Suppose, now, we choose to apply this relation to a streamline very close to the surface of the boundary layer, but just inside the layer. Then a fluid particle starting at the front (upstream) edge of the plate will take the time τ to travel the distance L of the plate, where $\tau = L/v_x$. In this same time the fluid particle will have moved a distance $h(L)$ in the direction perpendicular to the plane surface, where $h(L) = v_z \tau$. But the streamline is very close to the thickness of the boundary layer at the rear of the plane. Consequently taking h as the boundary layer thickness

$$\frac{h}{L} \sim \frac{v_z}{v_x} \sim \frac{1}{\sqrt{(Re)}} \quad \text{i.e. } h(L) \sim \sqrt{\left(\frac{Lv}{v_\infty}\right)}. \qquad (8.11)$$

The boundary layer at the downstream end of the plate is, apparently the thicker the longer the plane plate surface in the flow direction and the more viscous the fluid; it is thinner the greater the free stream velocity. Because the axis of plane symmetry (i.e. $z = 0$) is a plane of

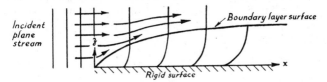

FIG. 9. *Schematic velocity profiles for the boundary layer bordering a flat plate, with incident parallel flow at zero angle of incidence (see equation (8.12).*

zero velocity, the laminar boundary layer flow at some point x depends only upon the length of the plane plate upstream and not at all (at least to very good approximation) on that downstream. Consequently the variable L in (8.11) can be replaced by the continuous variable x where $0 \leqslant x \leqslant L$:

$$h(x) \sim \sqrt{\left(\frac{xv}{v_\infty}\right)}. \qquad (8.12)$$

It seems, therefore, that the boundary layer thickness increases along the surface as the square root of the distance from the leading edge. Also the boundary layer becomes very large in extent if the free stream velocity is very small: this agrees with what is intuitively reasonable since for very slow motion of a viscous fluid (Re very small) the viscous forces can predominate throughout the fluid.

The associated Reynolds number is $Re = (v_x x)/\nu$, and this is a function of x. As x increases (i.e. as we go along the surface downstream) so does Re increase linearly; at some critical value of $Re(\sim 10^5$ if the plate is very smooth but lower if it is not) the stable flow breaks down and the formula (8.12) is no longer valid. Apart from this, remember that it has also been assumed that the boundary layer is thin (i.e. $h \ll L$) everywhere along the surface so that (8.12) may break down if this condition is not fulfilled even though the flow is still laminar (e.g. if the velocity is very low). However, (8.12) is anyway only claimed to be valid as to an order of magnitude estimate and refinements such as those just mentioned need not be troublesome on this basis.

In conclusion it should be noticed that if the plate is rotating about the z-axis (which is perpendicular to the plane of the plate) relative to the fluid which is now stationary then $v_\infty = x\Omega_0$ where x is now measured from the rotation axis, so that for the boundary layer surrounding the plate:

$$h \sim \sqrt{\left(\frac{\nu}{v_\infty}\right)}. \tag{8.13}$$

The laminar boundary layer is apparently of constant thickness across the plate.

The approximate arguments present above apply strictly to a flat plate only, although they are broadly indicative of more complex surfaces. Also the formulae such as (8.12) are order of magnitude estimates and are not exact. Blasius has, in fact, solved the problem of the laminar boundary layer for a flat plate exactly: we will not go into the analysis in detail here but only quote the exact expression to replace (8.12):

$$h(x) = 5\sqrt{\left(\frac{x\nu}{v_\infty}\right)} \tag{8.14}$$

As to numerical values, the boundary layer thickness for the flow of air at the downstream end of a plate of length $L = 1$ ft, and with a mainstream velocity of 50 ft/sec, [with an associated Reynolds number of a little less than 5×10^5 and so still laminar flow (just)] is about one-tenth of an inch. It is most important to notice that none of the arguments given here apply in the immediate neighbourhood of the leading edge of the plate (i.e. $x \sim 0$), since then $\partial^2 v_x/\partial x^2$ is not $\ll \partial^2 v_x/\partial z^2$. Consequently the equation (8.5a) does not apply: the full Navier-Stokes equation must be solved in this region. The expression (8.13), therefore, applies only for (Re) greater than some non-zero, though small, value.

8.5. Displacement thickness

In the last Article the thickness of the boundary layer was approached from a purely mathematical point of view. It is useful to consider the thickness of the layer from a more physical point of view. This can be done very simply by introducing the so-called displacement thickness, δ_d.

Consider a plane surface (of effectively infinitely extent) in the $(x$–$y)$ plane: suppose an incompressible fluid to flow in plane flow past it in the x-direction. For a viscous fluid a boundary layer will form of thickness h, and v_z is a function of z for $z < h$. For $z = h$ the fluid velocity is effectively that of the main stream unaffected by the boundary viscosity, i.e. $v = v_m$ for $z \geqslant h$. If, however, the viscous fluid were to be replaced by an ideal fluid moving with main stream velocity v_m, no boundary layer is formed, the velocity near the boundary remaining uninfluenced by the boundary. In the neighbourhood of the boundary the flow in the two cases is different but could be made the same if the boundary were physically displaced for the ideal case. Explicitly, the decreased fluid velocity in the viscous case means that a smaller fluid volume flows near the boundary than in the ideal case: the two cases are made equivalent if the boundary for the ideal flow is moved into the fluid by some appropriate amount, thus suitably decreasing the flow volume available to the ideal fluid. Expressed alternatively, the presence of the boundary layer with its associated decrease of the fluid velocity in the surface region, causes the stream lines of the main stream to be displaced outwards into the fluid. The distance of such displacement defines the displacement thickness.

The decrease in the flowing fluid volume due to the surface viscous effects per unit area of surface is clearly

$$\int\limits_0^\infty [v_m - v_x(z)]\, dz.$$

The integrand vanishes outside the boundary layer, by the definition of the layer, so that the effective upper limit for integration is $z = h$. According to the above arguments, define the displacement thickness δ_d according to:

$$\delta_d v_m = \int\limits_0^h [v_m - v_x]\, dz, \qquad (8.15)$$

i.e.

$$\delta_d = \int\limits_0^h \left[1 - \frac{v_x(z)}{v_m}\right] dz. \qquad (8.15a)$$

Detailed analysis, associated with the determination of v_x as function of z in the boundary layer, leads to the result

$$\delta_d = 1\cdot 73 \sqrt{\left(\frac{x\nu}{v_m}\right)} \qquad (8.15b)$$

at some distance x downstream. Reference to equation (8.14) shows that the displacement thickness is about one-third of the boundary layer thickness at each point along the surface. The expression (8.15b), like the previous (8.14), does not apply in the region $x \to 0$.

If the fluid is compressible, the definition (8.15a) can be modified to include density variation: then we can take

$$\delta_d = \int\limits_0^h \left[1 - \frac{\rho(z)\, v_x(z)}{\rho_m v_m}\right] dz. \qquad (8.15c)$$

Other thicknesses can be defined in analogous ways. Thus the decrease in momentum in the boundary region for an incompressible, viscous fluid in comparison with that for reversible (ideal) flow is

$$\rho \int_0^h v_x(z)[v_m - v_x(z)]\,dz$$

and this allows for the momentum thickness, δ_m, to be defined by

$$\delta_m = \int_0^h \frac{v_x(z)}{v_m}\left[1 - \frac{v_x(z)}{v_m}\right]dz. \tag{8.15d}$$

For a flat plate detailed calculation shows that, for zero fluid angle of incidence

$$\delta_m = 0 \cdot 664 \sqrt{\left(\frac{x\nu}{v_m}\right)}$$

i.e. that $\delta_d = 2 \cdot 6\,\delta_m$ in this case.

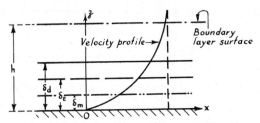

FIG. 10. *Relative arrangement of the several boundary thicknesses in a typical case (not to scale).*

Similarly and energy thickness, δ_E, can be defined by

$$\delta_E = \int_0^h \frac{v_x(z)}{v_m}\left[1 - \left(\frac{v_x(z)}{v_m}\right)^2\right]dz. \tag{8.15e}$$

Compressibility effects can be included, but this will not be done here.

8.6. Flow between parallel plates

Suppose the single plate of length L considered so far is replaced by a pair of parallel plates separated by a distance D. Each plate will have a boundary layer about it of the type already considered and the formula (8.12) will apply on each of the surfaces containing the flow. For the two facing surfaces, the two associated boundary layers will overlap if L is sufficiently great and D is suitably small. Downstream of the point of complete overlap the flow will be that showing marked viscous effect, i.e. Poiseuille flow. The distance downstream x_D from the leading edges of the plates ($x = 0$) at which overlap can occur is obviously given as to order of magnitude by the condition

$$2h(x_D) \sim D \quad \text{i.e. } x_D \sim \frac{v_\infty D^2}{\nu}. \tag{8.16}$$

This distance increases with both v_∞ and D, but decreases as ν increases. It gives a measure of the distance downstream from the

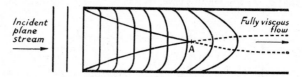

Fig. 11. *Overlap of the two boundary layers bordering two parallel plates. The point A marks the point of complete overlap. The velocity profiles are shown.*

opening of the planes (i.e. from $x = 0$) at which the features of the initial plane stream flow are all lost due to the plates. Equation (8.16) can be expressed in the convenient form

$$\xi \sim Re(D), \tag{8.16a}$$

where $\qquad \xi = \dfrac{x_D}{D} \quad \text{and} \quad Re(D) = \dfrac{v_\infty D}{\nu}.$

These formulae can also apply to a pipe of circular cross-section and of diameter D (cf. Art. 5.7).

Detailed analysis, while confirming these general conclusions, shows one significant feature that must be mentioned. The fluid in the boundary layer is moving more slowly than that in the main stream: as the fluid moves downstream between the plates the extent of the boundary layers increases (cf. Art. 8.4), and the extent of the fluid volume suffering retardation increases. The condition of fluid conservation, however, requires that the flow of fluid across a plane perpendicular to the flow direction must be the same at all points along the flow. This condition can be satisfied in the presence of increasing boundary layers only if the remaining main stream accelerates appropriately as its extent diminishes. Consequently the flow between parallel plates is actually accelerating flow.

8.7. Wake behind a flat plate

The character of the boundary layer encasing a plane moving in a not too viscous fluid has been traced downstream to the trailing edge of the plane. Clearly the flow pattern cannot stop there abruptly, the fluid behind the plane being affected by its presence. This downstream disturbance is least if the plane moves at zero incidence angle to the undisturbed fluid.

The equations for the boundary layer can, in fact, be applied to fluid regions away from rigid boundary surfaces provided that the effects of viscosity are still significant. In particular they apply in the region downstream of the plane where the fluid which has been separated by the passing obstacle reunites. The flow in the wake is essentially rotational, as it is in the boundary layer. Taking the situation previously considered in Art. 8.3 it is found experimentally that the wake is confined to a rather narrow region about the x-axis, and is a trail of dead fluid whose mean velocity decreases with the distance downstream. The width of the wake increases downstream as the following simple argument suggests.

The equation (8.6) will apply in the wake if the flow is laminar. With v_m as the main stream velocity say upstream of the plate causing the wake, suppose v to be the fluid velocity in the wake. In the wake $|v| \ll |v_m|$: this need not apply in the immediate vicinity of the obstruction, but will hold beyond some relatively small downstream distance. Beyond this distance it is a sufficient approximation to regard the fluid pressure as constant so that the right-hand side of equation (8.6) can be equated to zero here. If we concern ourselves with orders of magnitude only and retain only terms of the first order of small quantities we can conclude that:

$$v_x \frac{\partial v_x}{\partial x} \sim \frac{v v_m}{x}; \; v_z \frac{\partial v_x}{\partial z} \sim 0; \text{ and } v \frac{\partial^2 v_x}{\partial z^2} \sim \frac{v v}{\delta_W^2},$$

where δ_W is the width of the wake at a distance x downstream. Then (8.6) leads to the relation:

$$\frac{v v_m}{x} \sim \frac{v v}{\delta_W^2},$$

i.e.

$$\delta_W \sim \sqrt{\left(\frac{v x}{v_m}\right)}. \tag{8.17}$$

Apparently the laminar wake thickness increases as the square root of the distance downstream from the obstacle. The result (8.17) is

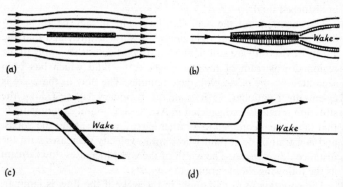

Fig. 12. *The Wake associated with a flat plate at various incident angles of the incident plane fluid stream: (a) ideal flow–very low velocity; (b) zero incidence, boundary layer and wake; (c) incidence angle of about 60° to the incident flow direction; (d) plane at right angles to the incident plane.*

formally the same as the previous result (8.12) for the boundary layer thickness. If the plane has a non-zero angle of incidence to the oncoming stream, then the situation is more complicated: both cases of zero and non-zero incidence are sketched in Fig. 12.

8.8. Flow past a real body: separation

The arguments developed so far for a thin plate apply qualitatively also for a general obstacle which is not thin throughout its length. The boundary layer and wake encase the obstacle as before; however, the wake is now more pronounced than for a flat plate, and the boundary layer will usually separate at some point along the surface. To illustrate this new situation we consider a definite situation and for this purpose consider the obstacle to be a long rigid cylinder of circular cross-section, with its axis perpendicular to the direction of the incident plane flow. The problem is again essentially two-dimensional.

If an irrotational fluid flow moving in the x-direction is incident on the cylindrical obstruction, whose axis is the y-axis, then a sectional cut is in the $(x-z)$ plane and has the same appearance as Fig. 1 of Art. 2.4. The blunt profile met with by the fluid will cleave it, and the diameter XY of Fig. 1 is the natural axis of symmetry whether the fluid is ideal or not. There will be a stagnation point on the upstream side of this axis: for an ideal fluid this will be the point X on the surface but for a real fluid the stagnation point will be upstream of the surface to some extent, due to the presence of the boundary layer. A boundary layer will form around the surface and the upstream half (the region M_1XM_2 of Fig. 1) will generally be laminar. The downstream half (the region M_1YM_2 of Fig. 1) will not be so simple. We can see this as follows.

For an ideal fluid which has no viscosity there is no boundary layer, and the flow conditions are straightforward. On the upstream half of the obstacle the fluid particles suffer acceleration (i.e. between X and M_1 or M_2), the pressure decreasing according to the Bernoulli formula. On the downstream half of the profile the reverse happens, the fluid velocity decreasing, and the pressure increasing correspondingly, until the upstream values are reached again at the point Y, which is a stagnation point. These velocity/pressure changes become less marked for streamlines further away from the body, and at large distances are imperceptible. The presence of viscosity complicates the picture, however, due to the dissipative effect of the viscous force. It is known from the equations (8.5) that the fluid pressure in the boundary layer is the same as that for the corresponding fluid point outside it; that is, the pressure due to the main stream fluid flow is impressed onto the boundary layer. Consequently the primitive pressure distribution in the boundary layer is essentially that for an ideal fluid flow. The flow pattern for the viscous fluid past the upstream half of the cylindrical profile is essentially the same as that shown in Fig. 1 for the ideal fluid excepting for the presence of the boundary layer. The stagnation point is pushed upstream by the amount δ_s: detailed calculations not to be given here lead to the result that δ_s is proportional to $\sqrt{v}$. As the viscosity decreases so the kinematic viscosity v decreases and the stagnation point moves towards the surface. As for

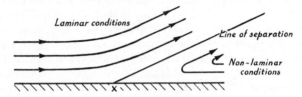

FIG. 13. *Schematic representation of the fluid flow in the region of separation: the point of separation on the surface (see equation (8.18)) being marked by point X.*

the ideal flow so now also for the viscous flow with boundary layer, the fluid particles in the layer on the upstream side of the obstacle suffering an increase in velocity and the pressure consequently falling. The effect of the viscosity, which is important in the boundary layer, is to oppose the fluid flow with the consequence that the energy of the fluid particles on the line M_1M_2 is now lower than for that corresponding to ideal flow in the region of the boundary. Because the pressure in the main fluid is impressed on the boundary layer the downstream flow in the neighbourhood of the boundary for viscous flow differs profoundly from that applying to ideal flow: this is because the fluid particles at the points M_1M_2 have in viscous flow insufficient energy to surmount the pressure gradient downstream of the obstacle which is effectively the same as that for ideal flow. Consequently the fluid particle motion is stopped by the adverse pressure gradient at some point downstream before the region of Y is reached. The pressure external to the layer then becomes the accelerating force for the boundary layer fluid particles, and the fluid moves in the opposite direction, in sympathy with the local pressure gradient. The fluid particles are also forced outwards away from the wall with the result that the boundary layer separates from the wall, the thickness of the layer increasing at the same time. It is seen that the occurrence of separation is associated with appearance of vorticity in the fluid.

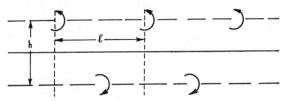

FIG. 14. *The structure of the Kármán vortex street. In real flow the vortices become more diffuse with time, and are usually joined by a set of filaments. The street profile shown here could be an idealized wake formed by a fluid flowing to the left, due to an obstruction to the flow (with dimensions a little less than h perpendicular to the flow direction) located off the figure to the right.*

The mathematical criterion for the onset of separation is readily deduced from the above arguments. Before separation occurs the flow direction is downstream at all distances from the body so that (with the downstream direction taken as positive) it follows that

$$\frac{\partial v_x}{\partial z}\bigg|_{z=0} > 0,$$

where the z-direction is normal to the surface at any point and directed into the fluid. On the other hand, after separation has occurred the flow direction near the wall is reversed although that further out is unaffected; thus, when separation has occurred

$$\frac{\partial v_x}{\partial z}\bigg|_{z=0} < 0.$$

The point of separation itself is therefore characterized by the condition

$$\left.\frac{\partial v_x}{\partial z}\right|_{z=0} = 0. \tag{8.18}$$

At the point of separation a streamline intersects the boundary surface at a definite angle, and the velocity gradient in the direction normal to the wall vanishes on the surface. The point on the surface

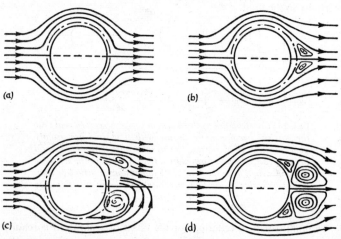

FIG. 15. *Development in time of boundary layer and separation about a circular cylindrical obstacle, the axis of the cylinder being perpendicular to the flow direction. (a) Flow immediately after fluid starts moving – essentially frictionless flow but with restricted boundary layer; (b) later – two vortices clearly visible on the downstream size of the cylinder, beginning to break away; (c) symmetry of flow and stability largely lost as fluid velocity builds up further; after a long time the stability is re-established (after photographs by Prantdl and Tietjens).*

at which the condition (8.18) occurs can be calculated only by solving the full set of boundary layer equations.

The appearance of separation greatly affects the wake in that its size is considerably increased, and its structure becomes more complicated. The vortices formed in the separated region of the boundary break away from the obstacle and are carried downstream. Upper and lower eddies may break away alternately and form a regular wake pattern of vortices downstream of the body. This system is known as a Kármán vortex street and is shown in Fig. 14. The

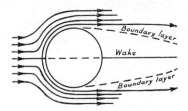

FIG. 16. *The fluid separation about a spherical obstacle. The dotted line marks the boundary layer to be found within the profile, and the inner region is the wake.*

vortices rotate alternately clockwise and anti-clockwise. If l is the distance in the downstream direction between the centres of consecutive vortices showing the same direction of rotation, and if h is

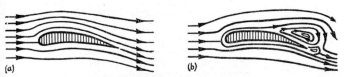

FIG. 17. *Boundary layer and separation associated with an airplane wing (fluid velocity less than the velocity of sound): (a) Low velocity (potential) flow; (b) higher velocity (after Prandtl).*

the distance across the stream between the two lines of vortex centres (see Fig. 14) then Von Kármán showed that the street arrangement is in neutral equilibrium if $h/l = 0\cdot281$, otherwise the system is unstable to small disturbances. The vortex street moves downstream with a velocity which is less than that of the main stream: this velocity relative to the main stream is $(\pi/l)\tanh \pi h/l$.

The appearance of separation and its development in time as the main stream velocity increases is shown clearly in Fig. 15 derived from experimental data using a circular cylindrical obstacle. The

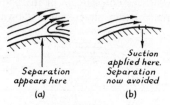

Fig. 18. *Showing the effect of suction on an established boundary layer: (a) no suction: (b) suction applied.*

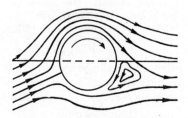

Fig. 19. *An example of the effect of rotation of the boundary layer conditions. A cylinder (with axis perpendicular to the flow direction) is rotated in a clockwise sense at such a rate that the upper surface moves with exactly the adjoining fluid velocity. No boundary layer appears on the upper surface (since there is no relative velocity between the cylinder and the contiguous fluid there) but a boundary layer with separation appears at the lower surface where there is an enhanced relative motion (after Prandtl).*

separation about a sphere is shown in Fig. 16. The appearance of separation for a streamlined body (in this case an aeroplane wing profile) is shown in Fig. 17.

The details of an adverse pressure gradient which gives rise to separation can be modified, and the gradient even eradicated, if the fluid in the boundary layer can be sucked into the obstacle through sets of small holes instead of being allowed to proceed normally downstream. This boundary layer suction (as it is called), first demonstrated by Prandtl for a sphere, can be arranged to prevent separation altogether. It will be found in the next Article that separation of the boundary layer considerably increases the energy necessary to maintain the conditions of flow: it is understandable, then, that attempts have been made to develop a practical, cheap, and reliable suction system, e.g. for use with aeroplanes for decreasing drag. The effect of boundary layer suction on separation is shown in Fig. 18, based on experimental measurements.

8.9. Resistance to flow

Any relative motion between a real fluid and an obstacle takes place with an irreversible loss of energy. The motion can be maintained only if this loss is replaced continuously by some external source of

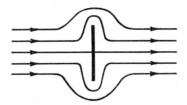

FIG. 20. *Ideal fluid flow about a flat plate held broadside on to a plane steady flow. (Compare this case with Fig. 12 (d) for dissipative flow.)*

energy; expressed alternatively, there is resistance to the flow. This resistance arises partly from the effect of viscosity, but partly also from the energy transported by wave motion if there is a free fluid surface. In what follows we neglect the wave resistance. The theory of an ideal fluid is quite unable to account by itself for the observed

12

fact of resistance to flow: one of the great achievements of the boundary layer theory is that of accounting for flow resistance.

It has been known for a hundred years that a flat rigid plate held in a moving incompressible inviscid fluid of essentially infinite volume (no free surfaces or boundaries) (Dirichlet flow) should offer no resistance to the flow even if held broadside onto the stream. The streamlines for this case are sketched in Fig. 20. It is seen that the flow shows a complete symmetry relative to the plate, and the fluid velocity at the edges of the plate must be indefinitely large (i.e. there is an infinite negative pressure there). This result for a flat plate is repeated for any shape: the general result that the motion of an obstacle through a perfect fluid without free surfaces occurs without resistance is a paradox in the light of everyday experience and is usually known as the d'Alembert paradox. Of course there is no ideal fluid known, but it is not the case that the resistance to flow approaches zero as the viscosity decreases. The paradox was resolved (by Kirchoff) by introducing a flow pattern involving a wake, being a region of constant pressure: this is sketched in Fig. 12(d) for the case of a flat plate perpendicular to the flow direction. There is, however, one very important qualification to be made about the stationary wake. If it is of finite length then the obstacle and the finite wake can be treated as a single entity with d'Alembert's paradox remaining valid: if resistance is to appear even for an ideal fluid then the wake must be of infinite length. The same general arguments apply also for obstacles of other shape.

It is a general result for the laminar wake in a viscous fluid that the drag, F_W, caused by the fluid on a body directed parallel to the fluid flow direction (i.e. to the x-direction) is given by

$$F_W = -\rho v_\infty \iint v_x \, ds \tag{8.19}$$

where the integral is to be taken over the cross-sectional area of the wake at a substantial distance downstream. Although this expression carries a negative sign, F_W is in fact a drag since $v_x < v_\infty$, the fluid material of the wake moving more slowly when the body is present than when it is not. Two companion expressions to (8.19) can be derived in which v_x is replaced by each of the remaining velocity components v_y and v_z. These forces tend to move the obstacle transversely and are usually called the lift forces, due to their lifting action in aerodynamics.

The tangential frictional force, F_t, acting per unit surface area treated as plane is

$$F_t = \mu \frac{\partial v_x}{\partial z}\bigg|_{z=0}. \tag{8.20}$$

By averaging this expression over the whole surface the total frictional force on the surface is arrived at. The difficulty in such a calculation is that of deriving the expression for the appropriate velocity gradient in analytic form.

Perhaps the simplest case to study is the steady plane flow of fluid past a thin plate of downstream length L and with its surface parallel to the flow direction. A solution was early given by Blasius who derived $(\partial v_x/\partial z)$ by a numerical solution of the momentum equation. If the Reynolds number is not too small the force is found to be

$$F_t = 1{\cdot}328\sqrt{(\mu\rho L v_\infty^3)} = 1{\cdot}328\rho L v_\infty^2 (Re)^{-1/2}. \tag{8.21a}$$

In this case the force is proportional to $v_\infty^{3/2}$, or alternatively to $(Re)^{-1/2} v_\infty^2$. Both sides of the plate are included in (8.21a), but if the flow is past one side only this result is to be halved. We may, on the basis of (8.21a), for the force on a general body of cross-sectional area A write the expression

$$F_t = \rho v_\infty^2 \, A f(Re) \tag{8.21b}$$

where $f(Re)$ is some function still to be derived for the general case. It is conventional to call the ratio $(F_t/\rho v_\infty^2 A)$ the drag coefficient and to denote it by C. In this notation (8.21b) becomes simply

$$C = f(Re) \tag{8.21c}$$

Although the exact dependence of C on (Re) cannot be analytically determined for all (Re) the two limiting cases of (Re) small, and of (Re) large, can be treated exactly. If (Re) is large (but still not large enough to vitiate the laminar régime) the inertial forces predominate over the viscous forces and the equation is pseudo-ideal. The Reynolds number cannot now properly appear in the solution, i.e. C = constant in this limit. For small values of (Re) the viscous forces predominate and we have Stokes flow according to (5.18): the value of the constant of proportionality differs from one shape to another. For a single sphere of radius R (so that $A = \pi R^2$), Stokes showed long ago that

$$f(Re) = \frac{6}{(Re)}. \tag{8.21d}$$

The insertion of (8.21d) into (8.21b) gives at once the well-known formula for the resistance to a sphere moving at slow speed through a viscous fluid. The use of the Oseen equation (5.19) in place of the equation (5.18) gives for the viscous resistance in place of (8.21d):

$$f(Re) = \frac{6}{(Re)}[1 + \tfrac{3}{8}(Re)]. \tag{8.21e}$$

This expression differs from (8.21d) in including one term more in the expansion of $f(Re)$ in powers of (Re). For a cylinder of circular cross-section with its axis perpendicular to the direction of fluid flow, and

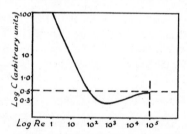

FIG. 21. *The drag coefficient as function Reynolds number for laminar flow, for a sphere.*

starting from the equation (5.19), the force per unit length of cylinder (which has radius R) is such that

$$f(Re) = \left[\tfrac{1}{2} - \gamma - \log\left(\frac{Re}{4}\right)\right]^{-1} \cdot \frac{1}{Re} \tag{8.22}$$

where $\gamma = 0.5772$ (Euler's constant).

The form of the function $f(Re)$ for intermediate values of (Re), where the velocity is neither large nor small, must at the present time be determined empirically. For a sphere the data is sketched in Fig. 21, but other geometrical shapes show a similar curve. From Fig. 21 for a sphere it is seen that the drag at first diminishes as the fluid velocity increases (Re increases) but later increases again tending to a constant value. If the fluid velocity increases further, so that (Re) exceeds a certain critical value (for a sphere this is about 10^5), then a very remarkable thing happens in that the drag coefficient suddenly drops; this effect is usually called the drag crisis (see Fig. 22). The

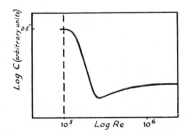

FIG. 22. *The drag crisis shown by plotting the drag coefficient as function of the corresponding Reynolds number.*

resistance only partially recovers its previous value, approaching a constant value some 5 times smaller than that applying when (Re) is below the critical value. The crisis is that the decrease in C is usually sufficiently great in the region $Re \sim 3 \times 10^5$ (for a sphere) for the resistance to motion to *decrease* as the velocity increases in this region. The explanation of the crisis is found to be the appearance of turbulent flow in the downstream areas of the boundary layer and a consequential readjustment of the wake: the wake contracts and this leads to a temporary reduction of the drag. A further increase of velocity leaves the wake relatively unaffected so that the drag force changes little from this cause.

An important point to notice is that as the Reynolds number increases indefinitely the drag factor does not vanish. But as the

Reynolds number increases the fluid becomes more nearly 'ideal'. There is, then, a critical difference between the conclusions to be drawn from the equations of fluid motion including the viscosity but with the effective viscosity very small or asymptotically vanishing in its effect, and the equations which ignore the viscosity altogether. This is one example of the fact that small perturbations do not always produce small effects: the order of the controlling differential equation may have to be changed to account for the perturbation and the number and form of the boundary conditions may also be affected.

If the fluid is compressible the expression (8.21b) is not sufficient to describe the drag: dimensional arguments now lead to an expression of the form

$$F_t = \rho v_\infty^2 \, Af(Re, M^2)$$

where M is the Mach number.

8.10. Temperature boundary layer

If the obstruction to the flow is maintained at a temperature which differs from that of the fluid in the main stream then the obstacle will be bordered by a region of strong temperature gradients provided the fluid thermal conductivity κ is not too large. We forget now convective effects in this temperature boundary layer. For a plane obstacle lying in the flow direction the temperature equation for the boundary layer for steady conditions is, according to (7.23):

$$v_x^* \frac{\partial T^*}{\partial x^*} + v_z^* \frac{\partial T^*}{\partial z^*} = \frac{\partial^2 T^*}{\partial z^{*2}} \alpha^*, \qquad (8.23a)$$

in dimensionless form with unit coefficients where:

$$Lz^* = \sqrt{(Pe)}.z; v_\infty v_z^* = \sqrt{(Pe)}.v_z; Lx^* = x; v_x = v_\infty v_x^*;$$
$$T = T_\infty T^*. \qquad (8.23b)$$

By analogy with the previous equation (8.9a), together with its associated arguments, the width of the boundary layer relating to the temperature variation, δ_T, will be as to order of magnitude

$$\delta_T \sim \frac{L}{\sqrt{(Pe)}} \quad \text{i.e. } \delta_T \sim \sqrt{\left(\frac{\kappa L}{\rho v_\infty C_p}\right)} = \frac{L}{\sqrt{(Pr)}} \cdot \frac{1}{\sqrt{(Re)}} \quad (8.24)$$

Remembering the order of magnitude expression (8.11) for the velocity boundary layer it follows that

$$\frac{\delta_T}{h} \sim \frac{1}{\sqrt{(Pr)}}. \tag{8.25}$$

It is seen that the thickness of the temperature boundary layer will be different from that of the velocity layer. If $Pr > 1$, then $\delta_T < h$; such is the case for water and alcohol: if $Pr < 1$, then $\delta_T > h$; such is the case for air and mercury. Because (Pr) appears through the square root the difference between δ_T and h will not usually be very great. Also, because (Pr) is a characteristic of the fluid and not of the flow, the ratio of δ_T and h is independent of the relative velocity between the fluid and the heated obstacle. The heated fluid in the boundary layer will pass downstream into the wake.

The separation of the velocity and temperature boundary layers as has been done here for incompressible flow is possible because the ratio (δ_T/h) is a function of the Prandtl number only. The temperature field surrounding a hot body is dependent on the velocity field [see equation (6.9)], but the velocity field is very largely uninfluenced by the temperature field [see equation (5.9)]. This is true if frictional heating is negligible; expressed in terms of the Eckert number, E, defined by equation (7.21) it means that $E \ll 1$. If this is not so, i.e. if $E \sim 1$, the situation is more complex. The temperature effect of the viscosity must now be properly included in the calculations using equation (5.8) or (5.9) and the velocity field becomes dependent upon the temperature distribution in the fluid, because the viscosity is temperature dependent and the equations (5.8) and (6.9) are coupled in both v and T. This more general situation, which is found in practice, e.g. in rocket flight at high altitudes and offers a bewildering complexity of alternatives, will not be considered here.

8.11. Effect of viscosity on fluid temperature distribution

We will conclude this chapter with two examples of the temperature distribution within a fluid where viscosity is important, chosen because they allow for exact solutions and yet remain mathematically elementary. The temperature dependence of the viscosity itself will be neglected entirely.

(a) Flow between parallel plates

Consider a flow channel formed by two parallel planes distance D apart and maintained at the same temperature T_0. Let the x-axis be along the symmetry axis of the plates (i.e. parallel to them), and the z-axis be perpendicular to the plates (see Fig. 23). Consider steady Poiseuille flow between the plates in the x-direction, and let us enquire as to the temperature distribution in the fluid. The velocity and temperature profiles are now independent: the velocity is then derived from equation (5.18) (see Art. 5.7)*while the temperature is to be derived from equation (6.9d). In addition to the usual boundary conditions, there is for the present problem the temperature condition that $T = T_0$ when $z = + D/2$ and $z = - D/2$.

The velocity profile for the flow follows immediately from the arguments previously given in Art 5.7, but adapted to the present plane geometry. The profile is parabolic and is described by the equation

$$v(z) = v_m\left[1 - \frac{4z^2}{D^2}\right] \quad \text{where } v_m = \frac{D^2}{8\mu}\left(\frac{\Delta p}{l}\right). \tag{8.26}$$

Here l is the length of the flow channel and Δp is the pressure difference which drives the fluid along the channel. Clearly v_m is the fluid velocity along the x-axis.

With the velocity distribution known, the corresponding temperature distribution including viscous heating can be deduced from equation (6.9d). Because T and v are both independent of x this equation becomes now

$$\kappa \frac{\partial^2 T(z)}{\partial z^2} = -\frac{64\mu v_m^2}{D^4}z^2. \tag{8.27a}$$

This equation is very readily solved under the boundary conditions set out above with the result that the temperature at the distance z from the central symmetry plane is

$$T(z) - T_0 = \frac{1}{3}\frac{\mu v_m^2}{\kappa}\left(1 - \frac{16z^4}{D^4}\right). \tag{8.27b}$$

T_0, it will be remembered, is the constant temperature of either plate. The maximum temperature, T_m, occurs when $z = 0$, i.e. along the

x-axis; thus $T_m = T_0 + \frac{1}{3}(\mu v_m^2)/\kappa$. The equation (8.27b) can be arranged to show T_m explicitly:

$$\frac{T(z) - T_0}{T_m - T_0} = 1 - \frac{16z^4}{D^4}. \qquad (8.27c)$$

The temperature profile is plotted in Fig. 23. It is seen to be much flatter than the velocity profile with the temperature remaining approximately constant over the central region. It follows from

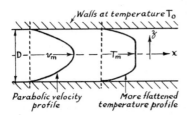

FIG. 23. *Velocity and temperature distribution in plane Poiseuille flow. Viscous heating is included, and the two walls have the same temperature.*

(8.27b) that when the viscosity is zero ($\mu = 0$) then $T(z) = T_0 = $ constant for all z. The heating effect due to viscosity is therefore described by the quantity

$$\frac{1}{3}\left(\frac{\mu v_m^2}{\kappa}\right)\left(1 - \frac{16z^4}{D^4}\right);$$

the maximum heating is along the centre line ($z = 0$) where the temperature is T_m.

The equation (8.27b) can be rearranged into a non-dimensional form involving the numbers of Chapter 7. Writing $T_m - T_0 = \Delta T_m$, (8.27b) can be written

$$\frac{T(z) - T_0}{\Delta T_m} = \frac{1}{3}\frac{\mu v_m^2}{\kappa \Delta T_m}\left(1 - \frac{16z^4}{D^4}\right).$$

But

$$\frac{1}{3}\frac{\mu v_m^2}{\kappa \Delta T_m} = \frac{1}{3}\left(\frac{v_m^2}{C_p \Delta T_m}\right)\left(\frac{\mu C_p}{\kappa}\right).$$

Now $[(\mu C_p)/\kappa]$ is the Prandtl number, and $[v_m^2/(C_p \Delta T_m)]$ can be regarded as an Eckert number, E_m. Thus:

$$\frac{T(z) - T_0}{\Delta T_m} = \frac{1}{3}(E_m)(Pr)\left[1 - \frac{16z^4}{D^4}\right]. \tag{8.27d}$$

Reference to equation (8.27c) shows that $E_m = 3/Pr$.

(b) Simple Couette flow

The velocity profiles for this flow were discussed previously in Art. 5.8; we are concerned now with the associated temperature profiles. We use the same set-up as in Art. 5.8 with the one difference that the two planes are held at different temperatures. The bottom stationary plane will be given the temperature T_0 while the top moving plane will have temperature T_1. The velocity profile is again to be derived from equation (5.24a) with the same boundary conditions as before; the temperature equation (6.9d) is now to be solved subject to the boundary conditions $T = T_0$ when $z = 0$ and $T = T_1$ when $z = L$. For simple flow in the x-direction, when there is no pressure gradient, equation (5.24a) reduces to $\mu(\partial^2 v/\partial z^2) = 0$, and the velocity itself is given by $v = (z/L)v_1$. The equation to be satisfied by the temperature is consequently

$$\frac{\partial^2 T}{\partial z^2} = -\frac{\mu}{\kappa} \cdot \frac{v_1^2}{L^2} \tag{8.28a}$$

where v_1 is the velocity of the moving upper plate. The solution of this equation is

$$T - T_0 = \frac{z}{L}(T_1 - T_0) + \frac{\mu v_1^2}{2\kappa} \cdot \frac{z}{L}\left(1 - \frac{z}{L}\right), \tag{8.28b}$$

and it will readily be verified that, as required, $T = T_0$ when $z = 0$ and $T = T_1$ when $z = L$. If the viscosity vanishes ($\mu = 0$), then the temperature distribution is linear, i.e. $T - T_0 = (z/L)(T_1 - T_0)$. The remaining parabolic term, viz.

$$\frac{\mu v_1^2}{2\kappa} \cdot \frac{z}{L}(1 - z/L),$$

is proportional to μ and describes the viscous heating for the flow. If the two planes are at the same temperature only the viscous heating can affect the fluid temperature, and this is shown by (8.28b). The temperature distribution in the fluid is now parabolic, and is reminiscent of the velocity distribution in Poiseuille flow. The Eckert number can be introduced into (8.28b) if this equation is divided throughout by $T_1 - T_0 (\neq 0)$. Then we have:

$$\frac{T - T_0}{T_1 - T_0} = \frac{z}{L} + \frac{v_1^2}{(T_1 - T_0)} \cdot \frac{\mu}{2\kappa} \cdot \frac{z}{L}\left(1 - \frac{z}{L}\right)$$

$$= \frac{z}{L} + \frac{v_1^2}{C_p(T_1 - T_0)} \cdot \frac{\mu C_p}{\kappa} \cdot \frac{z}{2L}\left(1 - \frac{z}{L}\right). \qquad (8.29a)$$

Reference to Chapter 7 allows this equation to be written in terms of the Prandtl and Eckert numbers:

$$\frac{T - T_0}{T_1 - T_0} = \frac{z}{L} + \frac{(E)(Pr)}{2} \cdot \frac{z}{L}\left(1 - \frac{z}{L}\right). \qquad (8.29b)$$

The direction of the flow of heat is along the negative temperature gradient, and whether a surface bathed by a real fluid will become hotter or cooler will depend upon whether the temperature in the viscous fluid is increasing or decreasing towards the surface. From equation (8.29b) it is seen that in absence of friction

$$\left.\frac{\partial T}{\partial z}\right|_{z=L} = \frac{(T_1 - T_0)}{L}$$

The temperature gradient at the upper (moving) surface is constant (as it is in fact throughout the fluid), and the sign depends upon that of $(T_1 - T_0) = \varDelta T$. In the presence of viscosity, however, the situation is more complex.

From equation (8.29b) the expression for the temperature gradient at the upper surface is:

$$\left.\frac{\partial T}{\partial z}\right|_{z=L} = \frac{\varDelta T}{L}\left\{1 - \frac{(E)(Pr)}{2}\right\}. \qquad (8.30a)$$

The sign of the gradient depends upon both the sign of ΔT and also of the sign of the expression in the bracket. If $\Delta T > 0$ (upper surface hotter than the lower) then

$$\left.\frac{\partial T}{\partial z}\right|_{z=L}$$

is positive if $1 > [(E)(Pr)/2]$, i.e. if $(E)(Pr) < 2$. In this case heat flows from the upper surface into the fluid. Alternatively, if $1 < [(E)(Pr)/2]$ [i.e. if $(E)(Pr) > 2$] the temperature gradient at the upper wall is

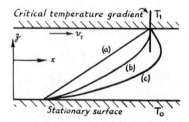

FIG. 24. *Temperature distribution in simple plane Couette flow. Viscous heating is included, but the walls have different temperatures ($T_1 > T_0$): curve (a) refers to the product (E)(Pr) which is zero; curve (b) refers to the condition (E)(Pr) < 2; curve (c) refers to the condition (E)(Pr) > 2.*

negative and heat flows from the fluid into the surface. It is seen, therefore, in extrapolation that when frictional heating is taken into account a hot surface need not lose heat to a flowing fluid in contact with it but with a lower mainstream temperature if the fluid velocity is greater than a definite critical value. For the present case of Couette flow, the upper surface loses heat if the upper surface velocity v_1 satisfies the inequality

$$v_1^2 < \frac{2\kappa(T_1 - T_0)}{\mu}. \tag{8.30b}$$

The upper surface will *gain* heat from the fluid, on the other hand, if

$$v_1^2 > \frac{2\kappa(T_1 - T_0)}{\mu}. \tag{8.30c}$$

This viscous effect, which does not occur if the two surfaces have equal temperature ($T_1 = T_0$), is of great importance in the cooling of surfaces by fluids, particularly at high velocity. It is also of importance in problems of lubrication. The appropriate temperature profiles are shown in Fig. 24.

CHAPTER 9

Turbulent Conditions

9.1. Introduction

The discussion so far has hinged upon only the approximate inclusion of the inertial term $(\mathbf{v}.\mathrm{grad})\mathbf{v}$ into the momentum equation or more often its complete neglect altogether. This approximation, introduced primarily as a mathematical device for linearizing the equation, is permissible if the velocity is not too large. The fluid flow is stable and the fluid parameters, such as pressure and velocity, are uniquely and immediately determined by the boundary conditions. As the fluid velocity steadily increases, the neglect of the inertial terms becomes steadily more suspect and finally is completely inadmissible. The momentum equation cannot then be linearized but must be used in its full non-linear form. The greatly increased mathematical complexity can be expected, however, to be associated with new and interesting phenomena.

Systematic experiments (starting with the now classical work of Osborne Reynolds in the last century concerning the flow of water in a pipe) have shown that the stable laminar flow possible for the smaller fluid velocities is not possible beyond a fairly definite velocity. This defines a critical Reynolds number, Re_c, where the laminar régime breaks down. The value of Re_c for any particular case depends upon the fluid properties and the geometrical structure of the flow. For water through a smooth pipe it is of the order 10^3, and it is found to be of the same order for flow through parallel plates† : for flow past a smooth flat plate it may be as high as 10^5. These values are reduced by the presence of surface roughness.

As the fluid velocity increases further (so that Reynolds number increases) the laminar structure becomes increasingly unstable and

† The length appearing in the Reynolds number is usually taken as the pipe diameter, or the plate separation. Any suitable characteristic geometrical length can be used for this purpose, however, but whatever length is chosen must be rigorously adhered to and quoted explicitly.

when the Reynolds number has increased by about an order of magnitude above Re_c the ordered flow has completely broken down. The flow parameters, such as pressure and velocity, are now subject to fluctuations that have every appearance of being random and it is not immediately obvious that the flow is dictated uniquely by the boundary conditions. It is now recognized, however, that the apparently unstable régime arises from the action of viscous shear stresses in the fluid and not from pure pressure forces. Fluid flow which is characterized by essentially randomly fluctuating flow parameters and in which the relative velocity of neighbouring fluid elements arises from the action of shear stresses is called turbulent flow. Because shear stresses are involved, turbulent flow is strictly rotational. Quite apart from the problem of dealing with non-linear equations (due to the importance of the inertial term) the theoretical study of turbulence is forced to have a statistical form by the fluctuating nature of the flow parameters, which is a fundamental turbulence feature.

Turbulent flow conditions are found to occur as a general rule in a wide range of naturally occurring fluid flow. The study of this flow is still very much in the fore front of present-day research; in the present chapter we restrict our arguments to a certain small range of topics which would seem to be assured of some place in any final theory. We are concerned here with the fully developed flow, where $Re \gg Re_c$, and will not consider the transition region where $Re \sim Re_c$. This means effectively that we shall be concerned more with describing the already existing turbulent field than with the problem of the origin of the turbulence. One further restriction will be placed on our arguments. It is known experimentally that the fluid flow velocity for which turbulence is fully established is usually still low enough for any possible fluid compressibility effects to remain negligible. It is, therefore, permissible for us to consider the turbulence of incompressible flow only in what follows.

9.2. Averages and the mean flow

Turbulent motion must conform to the conservation requirements of mass, momentum, and energy. The equations of Chapter 7 (i.e. the density and temperature equations, and the Navier-Stokes equation) are the most powerful expression of the conservation rules as applied to continuous incompressible fluid flow that is yet available, and they are to be applied also to turbulent conditions.

These equations have been seen to be applicable immediately to laminar flow with the several variables being those directly measured experimentally. Although the actual turbulent flow parameters at any point fluctuate in a random way with the time it is asserted that certain average values can be derived from the experimental data which play the same rôle in the turbulence theory as that of the direct parameters in laminar flow. It is these average values that are assumed to satisfy the usual equations of fluid motion, such as the Navier-Stokes equation, and which are controlled by the boundary conditions. Any measured quantity is now represented as the sum of a steady average value and a non-steady fluctuating term. The definition of the average value is a cardinal point of the theory.

Suppose $Q(x_i, t)$ is some macroscopic turbulent fluid property which is a function of the position and the time, whose average value is sought at some point. By measuring Q over a range of known time intervals a time averaged quantity $\bar{Q}$ can be constructed according to the formula:

$$\bar{Q}(x_i, t) = \operatorname*{Lt}_{\tau \to \infty} \left\{ \frac{1}{2\tau} \int_{t-\tau}^{t+\tau} Q(x_i, t') \, dt' \right\}. \tag{9.1}$$

We see that in general $\bar{Q}$ will be a function also of the time at which the average is taken, although under steady flow conditions $\bar{Q}$ will be independent of this time. If this is so for all the relevant averages computed from (9.1) then the mean conditions are steady and the time average of measured data is the natural expression to employ.

An alternative and apparently equivalent means of defining an average in place of (9.1) is that using the concept of the ensemble familiar in the theory of statistical mechanics. For this purpose a very large number of identical flow systems are observed simultaneously or more possibly the same system is observed on a very large number of occasions under identical situations. A distribution function can then be defined at each point for any given fluid quantity at a given time, essentially equal to the number of times a given property is observed to occur divided by the total number of observations made, in the limit of a large number of observations. A distribution function of this type which is of great utility in the theory is that describing the velocity distribution since it is in practice more easy to measure the fluctuations of fluid velocity at any point than, for instance, those of the turbulent pressure. Let

$$F(x_i, v_i, t) \, dv_i, dx_i$$

be the probability that a turbulent velocity in the elementary range v_i to $v_i + dv_i$ will be found in the elementary position range x_i to $x_i + dx_i$, at some time instant t. Since some velocity must by definition be found in the fluid volume it follows that, for F to be a true probability it must satisfy the normalization condition

$$\int \int F(x_i, v_i) \, dx_i \, dv_i = 1. \tag{9.2}$$

Mean quantities can then be defined applying to a specific fluid point: thus the mean value at some time t of the product of velocity components v_x and v_y at a given point is given by:

$$\overline{v_x v_y} = \int \int \int v_x v_y F(x_i, t; v_x, v_y, v_z) \, dv_x \, dv_y \, dv_z, \tag{9.3}$$

which refers to the point x_i. This expression can be generalized to apply to properties involving fluid points separated by a distance. Thus the mean value of the product of the x-components of the velocities at two points, x_i and x_i', separated by the distance $r = |x_i - x_i'|$ will be defined by

$$\overline{v_x(x_i) v_x(x_i')} = \int \ldots \int v_x(x_i) v_x(x_i') F(v_i', v_i, x_i', x_i, t) \, dv_i(x_i) \, dv_i(x_i')$$

$$\tag{9.4}$$

at the time t. The evaluation of the integral involves a knowledge of the distribution function $F(v_i', x_i', v_i, x_i, t)$. More than two points can be included by an obvious generalization of this expression, and quantities other than the velocity can be averaged if required.

The equivalence of the ensemble and time averages, ultimately to be demonstrated by experimental measurement, requires for its justification a discussion analogous to that associated with the ergodic

13

theorem in statistical mechanics. We will not enter into these very complicated matters here but will assert the correctness of the equivalence.

The experimentally inferred *single* distribution $F(v_i, x_i, t)$ would appear in many cases of interest to be often well represented by the Gaussian distribution: thus for the velocity;

$$F(v_i) = A \exp\{-B(v_i - \overline{v_i})^2\} \tag{9.5}$$

where A and B are related constants to be chosen in conformity with normalization requirements. It should be stressed that this is an experimental result for some cases and need not be theoretically exact. There is some experimental evidence to suggest that the Gaussian form is also applicable approximately to the probability distribution relating to two points in a isotropic turbulent field where the statistical properties of the motion are independent of the direction from any point but depend only upon the distance. For such joint probability functions it is possible to determine the adequacy of the Gaussian distribution in quantitative terms by introducing the so-called flatness factor $\mathscr{F}$ and the skewness factor $\mathscr{S}$. For the velocity correlation for two points separated by a distance r in an isotropic field these two factors are defined respectively by the expressions

$$\mathscr{F}(r) = \frac{\overline{(v_i' - v_i)^4}}{[\overline{(v_i' - v_i)^2}]^2} \quad \text{and} \quad \mathscr{S}(r) = \frac{\overline{(v_i' - v_i)^3}}{[\overline{(v_i' - v_i)^2}]^{3/2}}, \tag{9.6}$$

where the bars denote average values. For a strictly Gaussian distribution, $\mathscr{F} = 3$ and $\mathscr{S} = 0$, both being independent of the separation distance. These values are often found experimentally to some 10% accuracy if r is not too small.

If the turbulent field is homogeneous (so that the statistical properties are the same for all points of the fluid) and isotropic (so that they are also independent of the orientation) then the mean square value of the three components of velocity at each point are equal. Thus:

$$\overline{v_x^2} = \overline{v_y^2} = \overline{v_z^2} = \overline{v^2}; \quad \overline{v_x} = \overline{v_y} = \overline{v_z} = \tfrac{1}{3}\overline{v}. \tag{9.6}$$

The averaging procedures outlined above have two properties which are especially important for our subsequent discussion, viz.

$$\overline{\frac{\partial Q}{\partial x_i}} = \frac{\partial \bar{Q}}{\partial x_i}, \quad \text{and} \quad \overline{\frac{\partial Q}{\partial t}} = \frac{\partial \bar{Q}}{\partial t} \tag{9.7a}$$

and

$$\overline{\bar{Q}_1 Q_2} = \overline{Q_1 Q_2}, \tag{9.7b}$$

where Q, Q_1, Q_2 are any fluid properties that may be averaged.

9.3. The Reynolds stresses

Let our arguments be restricted to incompressible flow. The Navier-Stokes equation (5.9) can be written in the following alternative form:

$$\rho \frac{\partial v_i}{\partial t} = \frac{\partial}{\partial x_k} (_0\sigma_{ik} - \rho v_i v_k), \tag{9.8}$$

using also the equation (5.7) and the incompressibility condition $\partial v_k / \partial x_k = 0$. In (9.8),

$$_0\sigma_{ik} = -p\delta_{ik} + \mu \left(\frac{\partial v_i}{\partial x_k} + \frac{\partial v_k}{\partial x_i} \right). \tag{9.8a}$$

The equation (9.8) will now be averaged using the expressions (9.7). If $\bar{v}_i$ is the mean flow velocity, and u_i is the non-steady turbulent velocity, then we can write

$$v_i = \bar{v}_i + u_i; \quad \bar{u}_i = 0 \tag{9.9}$$

where v_i is actual fluid velocity. Then averaging (9.8) we have

$$\rho \frac{\partial \bar{v}_i}{\partial t} = \frac{\partial}{\partial x_k} (\overline{_0\sigma_{ik}} - \rho \overline{v_i v_k}) \tag{9.10}$$

But from the expressions (9.8a) and (9.9) it follows first that

$$\overline{_0\sigma_{ik}} = \mu \left(\frac{\partial \bar{v}_i}{\partial x_k} + \frac{\partial \bar{v}_k}{\partial x_i} \right) - \bar{p}\delta_{ik}, \tag{9.11a}$$

and then that

$$\overline{v_i v_k} = \overline{(\bar{v}_i + u_i)(\bar{v}_k + u_k)}$$

$$= \overline{(\bar{v}_i \bar{v}_k + \bar{v}_i u_k + \bar{v}_k u_i + u_i u_k)}. \tag{9.11b}$$

Remembering the averaging formulae (9.7) we get:

$$\overline{v_i v_k} = \overline{\overline{v_i}\,\overline{v_k}} + \overline{\overline{u_k}\,v_i} + \overline{\overline{v_k}\,u_i} + \overline{u_i u_k} = \overline{v_i}\,\overline{v_k} + \overline{(u_i u_k)}. \quad (9.11c)$$

Therefore, equation (9.10) can be written alternatively

$$\rho \frac{\partial \overline{v_i}}{\partial t} = \frac{\partial}{\partial x_k}({}_0\overline{\sigma_{ik}} - \rho \overline{v_i}\,\overline{v_k} - \rho\overline{(u_i u_k)}). \quad (9.12)$$

This expression takes on a more significant form if the symbol τ_{ik} is introduced such that

$$\tau_{ik} = -\rho\overline{(u_i u_k)}. \quad (9.13)$$

τ_{ik} is a mean stress which arises from the fluctuating (non-steady) turbulent contribution to the velocity. This term was first discussed by Osborne Reynolds in 1895, and is now called the Reynolds stress after him. In (9.12) it augments the term ${}_0\sigma_{ik}$ which is the mean stress arising from pressure and viscous effects. In physical terms, τ_{ik} represents the mean rate of momentum transfer in the k-direction across unit area of surface perpendicular to the i-direction, due to the random fluctuations of velocity. Writing:

$$_1\sigma_{ik} = \overline{{}_0\sigma_{ik}} + \tau_{ik} \quad (9.14)$$

the equation (9.12) becomes

$$\boxed{\rho \cdot \frac{\partial \overline{v_i}}{\partial t} = \frac{\partial}{\partial x_k}({}_1\sigma_{ik} - \rho\overline{v_i}\,\overline{v_k}).} \quad (9.15)$$

This equation for the mean flow is the same as the equation (9.8) for the actual flow subject to the substitutions $_1\sigma_{ik} \equiv {}_0\sigma_{ik}$, and $\overline{v_i} \equiv v_i$. The fluid represented by (9.15) differs from that represented in (9.8), however, due to the turbulent momentum transfer. Momentum transfer is recognized macroscopically as a dissipative viscosity, and the Reynolds stress can also be interpreted this way. The corresponding viscosity is usually called the eddy viscosity (for reasons which will appear later), and depends upon the rate of shear (non-Newtonian fluid). Also the viscosity may vary very strongly with position over some regions of the turbulent field, while it is essentially constant over other regions. Further, the eddy viscosity increases with size of the flow volume, and increases with the flow velocity. The eddy viscosity is larger than the normal viscosity, and this is interpreted as meaning that the turbulent momentum transfer greatly exeeds the molecular momentum transfer. Because momentum transfer also involves energy transfer it is not surprising that a turbulent field is an efficient transporter of energy.

9.4. Conditions at the boundary

It is asserted on experimental authority that the condition of no-slip of a viscous fluid past a rigid boundary applies to turbulent conditions just as to non-turbulent conditions. Thus the boundary condition of the vanishing of the normal and tangential velocity components at a boundary surface applies to the equations describing turbulence. This immediately implies a complex fluid region near such a surface. Because the fluid is at rest at the boundary there is always a region in the immediate vicinity of the boundary where the flow velocity is small, even though its space gradient is likely to be large. The associated Reynolds number will have a value below the critical value Re_c, and the flow will be laminar. This region is often referred to as the laminar sub-layer and here the simple viscous stresses dominates the turbulent stress. Encasing this sub-layer will be a region for which $Re \sim Re_c$, the flow here being in transition between laminar and turbulent flow. Beyond this, where $Re \gg Re_c$, is the true turbulent region.

9.5. Spectral analysis of the velocity

Turbulent flow is rotational; because the fluid is always continuous the streamlines must take circular paths forming eddies and this is observed to be the case in practice. Although the collective structure of these eddies may be relatively simple when laminar flow has just broken down ($Re \sim Re_c$), there will be a wide range of eddy sizes when the turbulence is fully developed ($Re \gg Re_c$). The appearance of viscous stresses in the fluid implies the existence of turbulent pressure gradients. By analogy with the arguments of kinetic theory, where the pressure arises from molecular interaction, for the macroscopic theory of turbulence the pressure is assumed to arise from the interaction being neighbouring fluid elements. It is natural to represent this interaction explicitly as an interaction between the characteristic turbulence eddies, and the properties of the turbulent field is then controlled by the details of this interaction. The degrees of freedom possessed by the molecules in the kinetic theory are now mirrored by the eddy sizes which represent the turbulent degrees of freedom. A knowledge of the distribution of the total energy of turbulence throughout the eddies of different sizes, and called the turbulent energy spectrum, is vital to the argument. The mathematical process by which the equations of turbulent flow are arranged into a form of displaying such an energy spectrum is called spectral analysis. Spectral analysis has been widely employed in many branches of physics, e.g. electromagnetic theory. Because the turbulent fluid velocity is more easily measured in practice than the turbulent fluid pressure, it is customary to develop the theory in terms of the velocity.

Consider first a cube of side L (which is finite) containing a turbulent field. Later the cube size will be allowed to become indefinitely large (i.e. $L \to \infty$). Focus attention on an eddy having the dimensions in the Cartesian directions (x, y, z) of values respectively $(L/l, L/m, L/n)$. Then we can construct a vector $\mathbf{k}$ having components:

$$k_x = \frac{2\pi l}{L}; \ k_y = \frac{2\pi m}{L}; \ k_z = \frac{2\pi n}{L}.$$

The vector $\mathbf{k}$ can, if we wish it, be interpreted as a wave number vector referring to a wavelength λ, and with a wave-front whose direction cosines are (l, m, n) with respect to the Cartesian axis. According to the rules of spectral analysis, the fluid velocity at the point $\mathbf{r}$ and at time t is written as the Fourier sum

$$u_i(\mathbf{r}, t) = \sum_{\mathbf{k}} u_{ik}(\mathbf{k}, t) \exp\{ik_i x_i\}. \tag{9.16}$$

Here u_{ik} are the components of the amplitude vector $\mathbf{u}_k$ for any given $\mathbf{k}$, and the summation is to be made over all wave numbers (i.e. degrees of freedom) available to the turbulent fluid. The velocity involved here is, of course, the turbulent velocity defined in equation (9.9).

The velocity is an actually measurable quantity and so must be real. If an asterisk as a superscript denotes now the complex conjugate we have:

$$u_i(\mathbf{k}, t) = u_i(-\mathbf{k}, t) = u_i^*(\mathbf{k}, t). \qquad (9.17)$$

The turbulent kinetic energy is clearly

$$\rho V \mathscr{E} = \int_V \tfrac{1}{2}\rho(\mathbf{u}.\mathbf{u}^*)\, dV = \tfrac{1}{2}\rho \int_V (\mathbf{u}.\mathbf{u}^*)\, dV, \qquad (9.18)$$

where $\mathscr{E}$ is the kinetic energy per unit mass. Remember that ρ is constant (incompressible flow); the integration in (9.18) is over the total fluid volume. Using equation (9.16) and (9.17) we can expand (9.18) as follows:

$$\rho V \mathscr{E} = \tfrac{1}{2}\rho \int_V \sum_{\mathbf{k}} \mathbf{u}_i(\mathbf{k}, t) \exp\{ik_i x_i\} \sum_{\mathbf{k}} u_i^*(\mathbf{k}, t) \exp\{-ik_i x_i\}\, dV,$$

i.e.
$$\mathscr{E} = \sum_{\mathbf{k}} \mathscr{E}_k = \tfrac{1}{2} \sum_{\mathbf{k}} |u_i(\mathbf{k}, t)|^2. \qquad (9.19)$$

This implies that
$$\mathscr{E}_k = \tfrac{1}{2}|u_i(k, t)|^2,$$

The quantity $\mathscr{E}_k$ can be called the spectrum of the turbulent energy.

The fluid is incompressible so that

$$\partial u_j/\partial x_j = 0.$$

The insertion of (9.16) into this equation leads at once to the condition

$$u_i k_i = 0, \qquad (9.20)$$

which is an expression of the statement that the vectors $\mathbf{u}$ and $\mathbf{k}$ are orthogonal. Although it is possible to speak formally of a transverse wave in this connection (since the velocity vector is perpendicular to the direction of energy propagation), the wave here will not propagate in time and the transverse characteristics are instantaneous only. This is fully in accord with the known inability of a fluid to withstand shear over an extended volume other than instantaneously.

9.6. Viscous decay

Consider a viscous, incompressible fluid in the absence of body forces. The Navier-Stokes equation (5.9) for the turbulent field is

$$\frac{\partial u_j}{\partial t} + \frac{\partial}{\partial x_l}(u_l u_j) = -\frac{\partial P}{\partial x_i} + \nu \nabla^2 u_j \qquad (9.21)$$

where, with $\rho = $ constant, we may introduce the so-called kinematic pressure P according to $p = \rho P$. Let us expand each term in a Fourier series by using (9.16) and the expansion

$$P = \sum_k P_k(\mathbf{k}, t) \exp\{ik_j x_j\}. \qquad (9.22)$$

Then the equation (9.21) becomes

$$\sum_k \frac{\partial}{\partial t} u_{jk} \exp\{ik_j x_j\} +$$

$$+ \frac{\partial}{\partial x_l}\left[\sum_{k'} u_j(\mathbf{k}', t) \exp\{ik_j' x_j\} \sum_{k''} u_l(k'', t) \exp\{ik_l'' x_l\} \right]$$

$$= -\frac{\partial}{\partial x_j}\left[\sum_k P(\mathbf{k}, t) \exp\{ik_j x_j\} \right] +$$

$$+ \nu \frac{\partial^2}{\partial x_j^2}\left[\sum_k u_j(\mathbf{k}, t) \exp\{ik_j x_j\} \right].$$

Equating term by term in this equation for a given $\mathbf{k}$ we obtain a series of equations of which the typical member is

$$\left(\frac{\partial}{\partial t} + \nu k^2 \right) u_j(\mathbf{k}, t) = -iP(\mathbf{k}, t)k_j - ik_l \sum_{k=k'+k''} u_j(\mathbf{k}', t) u_l(\mathbf{k}'', t). \quad (9.23)$$

It will be seen that the second term on the right-hand side of this expression involves a coupling between the two wave numbers $\mathbf{k}'$ and $\mathbf{k}''$, since these two numbers must be such as to equal the wave number appearing in each of the remaining terms, i.e. $\mathbf{k} = \mathbf{k}' + \mathbf{k}''$.

By remembering the orthogonality condition (9.20) it is possible to derive from the full equation (9.23) an explicit expression for the kinematic pressure. For this purpose multiply in a scalar fashion equation (9.23) throughout by k_j. The left-hand side of the resulting equation is

$$\left(\frac{\partial}{\partial t} + \nu k^2\right) u_j k_j.$$

But according to (9.20) this is zero. On the other hand the corresponding right-hand side of the equation is

$$iPk^2 + ik_j k_l \sum_{k=k'+k''} u_j(k', t) u_l(k'', t),$$

where we have used the relation $k^2 = k_j^2$. Because the left-hand side of the equation must vanish then so also must this expression for the right-hand side. There follows, then, the expression for the kinematic pressure

$$P(k, t) = -\frac{k_j k_l}{k^2} \sum_{k=k'+k''} u_j(k' t) u_l(k'', t). \tag{9.24}$$

This expression can be inserted into the original equation (9.23) to yield an equation for the velocity which does not involve the pressure, viz.

$$\left(\frac{\partial}{\partial t} + \nu k^2\right) u_j(k, t) = -ik_m Q_{jl}(k) \sum_{k=k'+k''} u_l(k', t) u_m(k'', t), \tag{9.25a}$$

where

$$Q_{jl}(k) = \delta_{jl} - \frac{k_j k_l}{k^2}. \tag{9.25b}$$

The problem of solving the set of equations exemplified by (9.25) is in general extremely complicated and rigorous solutions for this set are not yet known. For one set of special conditions, however, solutions have been obtained, viz. when the right-hand side vanishes. For the right-hand side to vanish it is necessary that the coupling between the eddy wave numbers k' and k'' should vanish. The term itself arises from the inertial term in the Navier-Stokes equation, and would not be present if this non-linear term were omitted from the Navier-Stokes equation. The only other force acting is that due to viscosity, so that it can be concluded that the right-hand side of (9.25a) will be negligibly small when the turbulent viscous forces overwhelm the inertial forces. The viscous shear is greater the smaller the eddy; the right-hand side of (9.25a) can, therefore, be expected to be negligibly small in the region of very small eddies ($\mathbf{k}$ large) and this surmise has been confirmed experimentally. For very small eddies, then, the equation (9.25a) will be replaced by the approximate and simpler equation

$$\frac{\partial}{\partial t}u_j(\mathbf{k}, t) + \nu k^2 u_j(\mathbf{k}, t) = 0. \qquad (9.26)$$

The solution of this equation is very easily found to be

$$u_j(\mathbf{k}, t) = u_j(\mathbf{k}, t = 0)\exp\{-\nu k^2 t\} = u_j(\mathbf{k}, t = 0)\exp\{-t/\tau\}, \quad (9.27a)$$

where τ is the decay time defined by

$$\tau = \frac{1}{\nu k^2} \sim \frac{\lambda^2}{4\pi^2 \nu}. \qquad (9.27b)$$

The time τ is that time which is required for u_j to be reduced by viscosity by the factor (e^{-1}). This time is seen to be smaller the greater the kinematic viscosity and the smaller the eddy size. The rôle of the very small eddies must be considered a little further. The arguments developed so far have been based on the continuum approximation according to which the ultimate fine-grained molecular (discrete) structure of matter is not to be accounted for explicitly. For this approximation to be valid now it is necessary to verify that (9.27a) is compatible with a lower cut-off in eddy size which is very large on a microscopic length scale but which may be macroscopically small. Take water and air as two broadly representative fluids for the application of the theory. At a temperature of 20°C the kinematic viscosity of water is of the order 10^{-1} cm^2 sec^{-1}, while for air it is of the order 10^{-2} cm^2 sec^{-1}. Thus, from (9.27b) it follows that eddies having the general dimension 10^{-2} cm (where the conditions are definitely still macroscopic) the corresponding decay times are of the order 10^{-2} sec. (water) and 10^{-4} sec (air). These times are small when compared with times which are usually characteristic of the flow, so that such small eddies give a virtual lower cut-off to the eddy size. Apparently the continuum approximation is sufficient for describing turbulent conditions, and kinetic theory arguments need not be explicitly introduced.

Although the equation (9.26) can be expected to hold over a range of smaller eddy sizes, as the eddy size increases there will come a point when this equation is an insufficient approximation to the full equation (9.25a) due to the right-hand side of the latter equation ceasing to be vanishingly small. The simple viscous dissipation described by the equations (9.27) is now not the complete story, contributions also appearing from the inertial term which may, in fact, dominate the viscous contribution This leads us to draw the tentative theoretical conclusion that the smaller eddies lose energy almost entirely by viscous dissipation but that the larger eddies are not significantly disturbed by this mechanism.

9.7. Eddy size

Full knowledge of the distribution of turbulent energy throughout the range of eddy sizes appearing in the fully turbulent field can be obtained by solving the equations (9.25). Because of mathematical difficulties such knowledge can be inferred at the present time only on the basis of plausible assumptions made using empirical deductions from experiment. For this purpose the simplification is introduced of dividing the actual continuous distribution of eddy sizes into three essentially distinct groups, characterized by physical criteria involving energy and size.

Turbulence arises from secondary instabilities ultimately to be traced to the mechanism generating the flow, and is associated with motions perpendicular to the direction of the applied shear. The local spontaneous breakdown of laminar flow produces local turbulence which is carried downstream like any other fluid property. The laminar flow which is left after the movement of the turbulence downstream must again become turbulent if turbulent conditions are to be maintained continuously.

Because it is an observed fact that a field of turbulence can be maintained over long periods of time it follows that turbulence must include within itself some self-sustaining mechanism. Such a mechanism must be powerful enough to counter exactly the losses due to fluid convection and viscous damping, and also the general diffusion loss implied by the vorticity equation (5.10) which is applicable now. This sustaining mechanism is usually expressed in terms of shear pressure gradients associated with turbulent shear stresses and involving interactions between eddies of different size.

The largest eddies have the general dimension of the fluid volume itself, and these are followed by a continuous distribution of decreasing eddy size through to a limit of essentially vanishing magnitude on a macroscopic scale (see Art. 9.6). As the turbulence builds up (i.e. as Re becomes equal to and then bigger than Re_c) the large eddies appear first, the smaller eddies progressively appearing as Re increases further. The strongest interaction with the source generating the flow is associated with the largest eddies; on the other hand, viscous dissipation has been seen to be stronger the smaller the eddy. The picture therefore emerges in which the energy sustaining the turbulence enters the field through the largest eddies and leaves through the smallest eddies. It is axiomatic that the eddies of intermediate size must be involved in the passage of energy from the largest to the smallest eddies through some cascade-type process. The number of cascade steps is always large even if Re is only slightly above the critical value for the breakdown of laminar flow, although the number would seem to increase with increasing (Re) to some extent. Individual eddies break down with time, the largest eddies breaking down into smaller eddies due to inertial forces, and the smaller eddies themselves breaking down into still smaller eddies until viscous dissipation destroys the progression. For a turbulent field which is maintained exactly steady in a given region by some external energy source it is often convenient, however, to picture the field from a hypothetical quasi-static point of view. The various eddy sizes can be pictured as permanent features (as in fact they are in some average sense) and the energy transfer through the eddies of various sizes can be pictured crudely as the 'excitation' of a smaller eddy by a slightly larger eddy through an essentially inertial mechanism (e.g. by slight distortion).

It is natural, and now also conventional, to divide the fully developed turbulence into three distinct sub-divisions, viz. one containing the large eddies and also the bulk of the energy sustaining the turbulence; one involving the main cascade process (often called the inertial range); and finally one containing the smallest eddies controlled by viscous damping (see Art. 9.6). As a matter of nomenclature, the eddy size below which viscous effects are important but above which they are not defines what is called the internal scale (see Art. 9.10 (d)). The inertial range and the viscous régime can be distinguished in the theory from the region of large eddies in that for the first two ranges conditions are often very nearly homogeneous (independent of location) and isotropic (independent of the direction from any location), where as in the range of large eddies this will not be so. The condition of isotropy (which implies also homogenuity) allows for the introduction of significant simplifications into the theory. It is found experimentally that the turbulent motion a little way downstream of a wire mesh is homogeneous and isotropic to reasonable approximation.

9.8. The energy equation

The terms appearing on the right-hand side of (9.25), representing inertial effects, must be included in any account of the cascade process by which energy is passed from the largest to the smallest eddies. This equation can, therefore, be applied to derive an energy equation relating to energy cascade.

Let us scalar multiply equation (9.25) throughout by the vector velocity $u_j(\mathbf{k}, t)$ to convert it into an equation involving the energy; then

$$u_j(\mathbf{k}, t)\left(\frac{\partial}{\partial t} + \nu k^2\right) u_j(\mathbf{k}, t) = i k_m Q_{jl}(\mathbf{k}) \sum_{\mathbf{k}=\mathbf{k}'+\mathbf{k}''} u_l(\mathbf{k}', t) u_m(\mathbf{k}'', t) u_j(\mathbf{k}, t).$$

Remembering the relations (9.19), this can be written alternatively

$$\left(\frac{\partial}{\partial t} + 2\nu k^2\right) \mathscr{E}_k = W_{jkl}(\mathbf{k}, \mathbf{k}'), \qquad (9.28)$$

where

$$W_{jkl}(\mathbf{k}, \mathbf{k}') = -ik_m Q_{jl}(\mathbf{k}) u_j(\mathbf{k}, t) \sum_{\mathbf{k}'} u_l(\mathbf{k}', t) u_m(\mathbf{k} - \mathbf{k}', t). \quad (9.28a)$$

The physical significance of the quantity W is seen immediately by rewriting equation (9.28) as

$$\frac{\partial \mathscr{E}_k}{\partial t} = W_{jkl}(\mathbf{k}, \mathbf{k}') - 2\nu k^2 \mathscr{E}_k. \quad (9.28b)$$

The left-hand side of the equation tells how the energy of an eddy changes with the time; the second term on the right-hand side refers to viscous dissipation in the eddies. Consequently the first term on the right-hand side must refer to the net gain of energy by the k-th eddies in this period. For steady conditions

$$W_{jkl}(\mathbf{k}, \mathbf{k}') = 2\nu k^2 \mathscr{E}_k, \quad (9.28c)$$

while if the viscous loss is also negligible

$$W_{jkl}(\mathbf{k}, \mathbf{k}') = 0. \quad (9.28d)$$

From these considerations, and those of Art. 9.7, the right-hand side of equation (9.28) can be rearranged on the basis of physical criteria.

To begin with we notice that W_{jkl} as defined in (9.28a) changes sign when $\mathbf{k}$ and $\mathbf{k}'$ are interchanged, i.e. W_{jkl} is antisymmetric in $\mathbf{k}$ and $\mathbf{k}'$:

$$W(\mathbf{k}, \mathbf{k}') = -W(\mathbf{k}', \mathbf{k}). \quad (9.28e)$$

Further, it is readily apparent from the definition of Q according to (9.25a) that Q_{jl} is either zero (when $j = l$), or negative (when $j \neq l$) but never positive. Consequently, for $\mathbf{k} > \mathbf{k}'$, W is positive, while for $\mathbf{k} < \mathbf{k}'$, W is negative. Now according to (9.28a), W is the net energy increase in the k-th eddies due to interaction with all the other eddies, so that we may say that W is positive for interactions with eddies of large size and negative for interactions with eddies of smaller size. The equation (9.28), therefore, is able to describe the energy cascade process outlined in Art. 9.7. We may separate W into two components W_1 and W_2 according to

$$\sum_{\mathbf{k}} W(\mathbf{k}, \mathbf{k}') = \sum_{\mathbf{k}' < \mathbf{k}} W_1(\mathbf{k}, \mathbf{k}') - \sum_{\mathbf{k}' > \mathbf{k}} W_2(\mathbf{k}', \mathbf{k}). \quad (9.29)$$

W_1 describes the gain of energy by the k-th eddies at the expense of the larger eddies ($\mathbf{k'} < \mathbf{k}$), whilst W_2 describes the loss of energy by the k-th eddies to the smaller eddies ($\mathbf{k'} > \mathbf{k}$). The insertion of (9.29) into (9.28b) gives the formal equation for the k-th eddies:

$$\frac{\partial \mathscr{E}_k}{\partial t} = \sum_{k' < k} W_1(\mathbf{k}, \mathbf{k'}) - \sum_{k' > k} W_2(\mathbf{k'}, \mathbf{k}) - 2\nu k^2 \mathscr{E}_k. \quad (9.30)$$

When $\mathbf{k}$ is very small (large eddies) the viscous term is negligibly small; because there are now fewer larger eddies to supply energy to the k-th eddies than there are smaller eddies to accept energy from them, the second term on the right-hand side of (9.30) can be expected to predominate over the remaining first term. Alternatively, when $\mathbf{k}$ is very large (smaller eddies) the term $(-W_2)$ is likely to be negligible in comparison with the term W_1; but the term $(-2\nu k^2 \mathscr{E}_k)$ will still predominate over all provided W increases less quickly with k than k^2. For sufficiently large (though still finite) $\mathbf{k}$ there can be expected to be a range of k (perhaps fairly restricted) where the second term on the right-hand side of (9.30) is negligible in comparison with the other two. Then, for steady conditions

$$\sum_{k' < k} W_1(\mathbf{k}, \mathbf{k'}) = 2\nu k^2 \mathscr{E}_k,$$

and all the energy entering this eddy size is entirely dissipated by viscous effects. It follows also from equation (9.30) that no energy is gained or lost in the processes of energy redistribution among the various eddy sizes where viscosity is unimportant.

So far our discussion has been centred around an essentially restricted turbulent region contained in a cube of size L which allows the spectral analysis which we have employed. As the volume of the turbulent region increases it becomes permissible to replace the summation in the equations by an integration over all wave numbers present. The use of a Fourier sum implies the validity of certain periodic properties of the boundary conditions which seem to be met with in practice but which cannot be gone into here. Suffice it to say that in passing to the limit of large volume no features are introduced which invalidate the physical interpretation of the theory outlined so far.

In passing to the large volume limit it is convenient to introduce a slightly modified notation. For isotropic conditions we write

$$\mathscr{E}(k)\,dk = 4\pi \mathscr{E}_k k^2\,dk; \int T(k',k)\,dk' = W(k',k)\,4\pi k'^2\,dk'. \quad (9.31a)$$

The total kinetic energy of the turbulence per unit fluid mass is $\int \mathscr{E}(k)\,dk$. This has the effect of making $\mathscr{E}(k)\,dk$ the energy contained by eddies having wave numbers in the range k to $k+dk$; and $T(k',k)\,dk'$ is the net energy gain by the eddies of wave number k from all eddies in the range k' to $k'+dk'$.

The basic equation (9.28) then becomes

$$\left(\frac{\partial}{\partial t}+k^2\nu\right)\mathscr{E}(k,t) = \int T(k',k)\,dk', \quad (9.31b)$$

where the integration is over all values of k' excluding the single value $k = k'$.

In attempting to use the equation (9.31b) for finding the energy distribution in the eddies, T must be known as function of k. This is the direct consequence of the need in using the previous equation (9.28) of knowing W as function of k in the calculation of $\mathscr{E}_k$. Because this information cannot at the present time be derived explicitly from the theory it is necessary to invoke some further approximation if progress is to be made beyond this point.

9.9. Heisenberg theory

In the absence of any exact information which gives T as function of k for insertion into equation (9.31b) it is natural to appeal to an assumed relation between these two quantities, constructed from physical arguments, in the hope of repeating experimental data by perhaps fortuitous means. If successful this approach may provide some hints in the evolution of the correct theory. A number of authors [for instance Obukhoff (1941), Von Kármán (1948), Kovásznay (1948), and Heisenberg (1948)] have suggested plausible relations between $\mathscr{E}$ and T; of these that due to Heisenberg is perhaps the simplest and so far also the most successful. The approach centres around the concept of a turbulent viscosity. More specifically the inertial term appearing on the right-hand side of (9.31b) is represented as a fictitious eddy viscosity which is a function of the eddy size.

Following Heisenberg, let us assume that the quantities $\mathscr{E}$ and T in (9.31b) are proportional one to the other and write

$$T(k',k) = g(k)\,\mathscr{E}(k')\,k'^2 \qquad \text{when } k' < k, \qquad (9.32a)$$

$$T(k',k) = -g(k')\,\mathscr{E}(k)\,k^2 \qquad \text{when } k < k', \qquad (9.32b)$$

where $g(k)$ is a function to be defined in a moment. The first expression considers the energy gained by eddies of a chosen size k from the large ones, while the second expression considers the energy lost by the chosen eddies to the smaller ones. We must next define the function g. On purely dimensional grounds assume

$$g(k) = 2Ak^{-3/2}\sqrt{[\mathscr{E}(k)]}, \qquad (9.33)$$

where A is a constant of the order unity. Thus:

$$T(k',k) = 2A\mathscr{E}(k')\,k'^2 \sqrt{\left(\frac{E(k)}{k^3}\right)} \qquad \text{for } k' < k, \qquad (9.34a)$$

$$T(k,k') = -2A\mathscr{E}(k)\,k^2 \sqrt{\left(\frac{E(k')}{k'^3}\right)} \qquad \text{for } k < k'. \qquad (9.34b)$$

Accepting these expressions, their insertion into the energy equation (9.31b) leads to an equation which involves the single unknown function $\mathscr{E}(k)$. Consider the rate of loss of energy by eddies with wave numbers less than some particular number, say k_1. Because the present arguments are based on isotropy requirements the formulae cannot apply over the whole range of k. It is, therefore, only the expression (9.34b) which applies in the present arguments because k' must be greater than k to satisfy our earlier statement of energy cascade.

The energy equation (9.31b) then shows that the rate at which energy is gained by the smaller eddies from the larger ones up to k_1, is proportional to the expression

$$\int_0^{k_1} \frac{\partial \mathscr{E}(k)}{\partial t}\,dk = -2\nu \int_0^{k_1} \mathscr{E}(k)\,k^2\,dk -$$

$$-2\int_0^{k_1} dk\,\mathscr{E}(k)\,k^2 \int_{k_1}^{\infty} A\sqrt{\left(\frac{\mathscr{E}(k')}{k'^3}\right)}\,dk'.$$

14

If, now, an effective eddy viscosity ν_k is defined according to

$$\nu_k = A \int\limits_k^\infty \sqrt{\left(\frac{\mathscr{E}(k)}{k^3}\right)} \, dk, \tag{9.35}$$

then the energy equation becomes finally

$$-\int\limits_0^{k_1} \frac{\partial \mathscr{E}(k)}{\partial t} \, dk = 2(\nu + \nu_{k_1}) \int\limits_0^{k_1} \mathscr{E}(k) \, k^2 \, dk. \tag{9.36}$$

This, according to the Heisenberg theory, is the rate at which energy is lost by eddies of a chosen size to the smaller eddies. The expression (9.36) treats the energy transfer mechanism as being virtually the same as that for viscous dissipation, the smaller eddies behaving for energy transfer in a way analogous to that of the movement of molecules for viscosity. For this to be so the smaller eddies receiving the energy must be small in comparison to the eddies giving the energy.

For large values of k (small eddies) the rate of loss of energy to still smaller eddies (larger values of k) will, on the cascade notions, be expected to be small. It may then be a reasonable approximation to equate the left-hand side of (9.36) to zero:

$$0 = 2(\nu + \nu_{k_1}) \int\limits_0^{k_1} \mathscr{E}(k) \, k^2 \, dk. \tag{9.37}$$

Chandrasekhar has given analytical solutions of this equation. The solution is

$$\mathscr{E}(k_1) = \mathscr{E}_0 \left(\frac{k_0}{k_1}\right)^{5/3} \frac{1}{[1 + (k_1/k_s)^4]^{4/3}}, \tag{9.38}$$

where $\mathscr{E}_0$, k_0, and k_s are constants related closely to the ratio (ν/A). As the kinematic viscosity becomes effectively smaller the functional form of k_s is such that $k_s \to \infty$, as $\nu \to 0$. Consequently in this limit

$$\mathscr{E}(k_1) \propto k_1^{-5/3},$$

an expression which will arise again later [see Art. 9.10 (c)]. Equation (9.37) is also the form taken by (9.36) for steady conditions.

The wave number k_1 is very large in the dissipative region and since k_s is not here also very large it turns out that $k_1^4/k_s^4 \gg 1$. Equation (9.38) then shows that $\mathscr{E}(k_1) \sim k_1^{-7}$ a result that has some experimental support. For extremely large wave numbers, however, it seems from both theoretical and experimental considerations that $\mathscr{E}(k)$ there decreases rather faster than the inverse seventh power of the wave number. Chandrasekhar has given also numerical solutions of the full time dependent equation (9.36) describing the full viscous decay, but these solutions are too lengthy and specialized to consider here.

9.10. Dimensional considerations

In the absence of a full theory of turbulence dimensional considerations can be applied to the turbulence problem with some profit. It is convenient at the outset to introduce the following notation:

L = size of the largest eddies, which is also the characteristic length of the total turbulent region. L is often called the fundamental eddy size, or alternatively the external scale.

λ = size of a typical eddy smaller than the fundamental size ($L > \lambda$).

λ_0 = eddy size below which viscous dissipation becomes important. By definition, λ_0 is the internal scale of the turbulence.

u_λ = mean velocity of an eddy of size λ.

Δu = order of magnitude of the variation of the mean turbulent velocity over the distance L, which is the fundamental eddy size.

Δp = total variation of the fluid pressure over the region of turbulent flow.

Δu_λ = variation of the turbulent velocity (relative to the mean eddy velocity) across an eddy of size λ.

Δu_τ = variation of the turbulent velocity at any given point in the turbulence during some time interval τ.

ϵ = mean energy input into an eddy of each size λ per unit time and per unit fluid mass. On the cascade picture, this is also the mean dissipation of energy per unit fluid mass in the viscous régime.

In addition, a set of Reynolds numbers can be defined in terms of the eddy properties. Thus, the Reynolds number associated with an eddy of size λ will be defined by $Re_\lambda = [\lambda(\Delta u_\lambda)/\nu]$, while that for the total turbulent region is $Re = (L\Delta u/\nu)$. Clearly,

$$Re_\lambda = \left(\frac{\lambda}{L}\right)\left(\frac{\Delta u_\lambda}{\Delta u}\right) Re.$$

(a) Fully developed turbulence

When the Reynolds number of the flow is sufficiently high, the full range of eddy sizes is established and the turbulence is fully developed. On the basis of the cascading of energy through the eddies it follows that, although the turbulent energy is ultimately dissipated by viscosity in the régime where $\lambda \ll \lambda_0$, the energy available for dissipation is that provided by the largest eddies. There are then three quantities which specify the largest eddies, viz. $(\rho, L, \Delta u)$. From these quantities three combinations have some significance for the total turbulent régime. First notice that $\rho(\Delta u)^2$ has the dimensions of a pressure variation; for the fully turbulent region it is suggestive to write

$$\Delta p \sim \rho(\Delta u)^2 \tag{9.39}$$

Second, notice that $(\Delta u)^3 L^{-1}$ has the same dimensions as ϵ. Since ϵ must depend on the properties of the largest eddies we may write

$$\epsilon \sim \frac{(\Delta u)^3}{L}. \tag{9.40}$$

Third, the quantity $(\rho L\Delta u)$ has the dimensions of viscosity, defined as being a turbulent viscosity μ_t. The corresponding turbulent kinematic viscosity ν_t is:

$$\nu_t = \frac{\mu_t}{\rho} \equiv L\Delta u. \tag{9.41}$$

Consequently:

$$\nu_t = \nu(Re). \tag{9.42}$$

These relations would suggest that, unlike the shear viscosity, the turbulent viscosity becomes greater the larger region of turbulence and the greater the variation of the mean turbulent velocity. Such an effect is, in fact, found in practice. The expression (9.41) can be reconciled with expressions such as the previous (9.35). A relation between ϵ and ν_t follows from the combination of equations (9.40) and (9.41): thus:

$$\epsilon \sim \frac{1}{L}\left(\frac{\nu_t}{L}\right)^3 = \frac{\nu_t^3}{L^4} = \nu_t\left(\frac{\varDelta u}{L}\right)^2. \qquad (9.43)$$

We shall use later the knowledge that the ratio (ν^3/ϵ) has the dimensions of (length)^4, while the product $(\nu\epsilon)$ has the dimensions of (velocity)^4.

(b) Local turbulence

Those turbulent properties of the eddies whose size is small compared with the fundamental eddy size L are usually collectively called the local properties of turbulence and the associated turbulence itself is called local turbulence. Regions of local turbulence are separated from the boundaries of the total turbulent region by distances very large in comparison with the extent of the local turbulence. Written alternatively, we assume now $\lambda \ll L$: this does not necessarily imply that $\lambda \sim \lambda_0$, and such an equivalence will not hold for large (Re) where it is known experimentally that $\lambda_0 < \lambda \ll L$. For local turbulence, therefore, the energy equation (9.31b) can be simplified to some extent by omitting the second term on the left-hand side which involves the viscosity. The problem of finding T as function of k still, however, remains so that dimensional arguments are still important. One very important characteristic of local turbulence is that it is isotropic. Consequently the turbulent flow properties within a region of local turbulence are independent of the mean velocity direction. Just as for large-scale turbulence so also for local turbulence we may assume, on the basis of energy cascade through the eddies that conditions are strongly influenced by the properties of the large eddies, i.e. depend on the three quantities $(\rho, \varDelta u, L)$. Because normal viscosity is not now significant the 'collective' properties of interest can only be the fluid density and the energy dissipated through eddy viscosity (i.e. cascaded) ϵ. If this situation is accepted then it can be expected that the two velocity variations $\varDelta u_\lambda$ and $\varDelta u_\tau$ over the distance λ can depend upon at least some of the variables $(\rho, \Delta u, L, \epsilon, \lambda)$. From dimensional arguments it follows that, as to order of magnitude, Δu_λ is given by:

$$\Delta u_\lambda \sim (\epsilon\lambda)^{1/3}. \qquad (9.44)$$

This relation between velocity variation over a small distance in local turbulence and the distance itself was first proposed by Kolmogorov and Obukhov in 1941: these authors further interpret Δu_λ as the velocity of those turbulent eddies whose size is λ.

Consider now Δu_τ, the variation of the turbulent velocity at a given point during the time interval τ. The turbulent field as a whole is moving with a mean velocity, say u, so that during the time interval τ which is short compared with the bulk turbulent time (L/u) the region of the fluid containing the local turbulence will move a mean distance $l = u\tau$. The velocity variation *at a given point* but during the time interval, can, on the cascade theory, depend at most upon $(l, \Delta u, L, \rho, \epsilon)$. Kolmogorov and Obukhov suggest, on dimensional arguments, that as to orders of magnitude:

$$\Delta u_\tau \sim (\epsilon l)^{1/3} \sim (\epsilon u\tau)^{1/3}. \qquad (9.45)$$

Since the eddies of local turbulence must not approach a boundary to the main turbulence during τ it follows that (9.45) is true only if $u\tau \ll L$.

(c) Kolmogorov similarity principles

Consider again local turbulence. The dimensional arguments used so far have indicated general relations; by setting down two similarity principles an expression for the distribution of energy in eddies of different sizes can be constructed which it can be hoped will apply in that part of the inertial range where conditions are isotropic independently of whether the large-scale turbulence is or is not isotropic. These principles were enunciated by Kolmogorov in 1941, and are to apply at large Reynolds numbers of turbulent motion. We closely follow now the formulation given by Obukhoff.

The first similarity principle states that the statistical distribution of energy in the eddies can depend only upon the rate of energy input per fluid mass unit, and on the fluid (shear) kinematical viscosity. Thus

$$\mathscr{E}(k) = f_1(\epsilon, \nu, k), \qquad (9.46)$$

where f_1 is some function yet to be defined. From dimensional arguments it follows that the only combination of ϵ and ν with the required dimensions is $(\epsilon\nu^5)^{1/4}$ so that (9.46) is to be written:

$$\mathscr{E}(k) = \nu^{5/4}\,\epsilon^{1/4}\,\Phi[k(\nu^3/\epsilon)^{1/4}]. \qquad (9.47a)$$

Here Φ is some universal function independent of the source of the turbulence, and $(k^4\nu^3\epsilon^{-1})$ is dimensionless since it was noticed earlier that (ν^3/ϵ) has the dimensions of (length)^4. This is as far as the first principle will take us: any region in which (9.47) is true is said to be a region of universal turbulence.

The second similarity principle states that in the inertial range of local turbulence the energy distribution must be such that at sufficiently large Reynolds number the effect of viscosity is negligible. Thus as $Re \to \infty$, $\mathscr{E}(k) \to f_2(\epsilon, k)$ where f_2 is some function yet to be specified. This requirement dictates the form of the function Φ for very large Reynolds numbers. In order that (9.47a) shall be independent of ν at high Reynolds number then, at high Re, $\Phi \propto \nu^{-5/4}$. Since Φ is dimensionless we can say further that,

$$\Phi \propto \frac{\epsilon^{5/12}}{\nu^{5/4}k^{5/3}}, \qquad (9.47b)$$

because the dimensionless quantity $k(\nu^3/\epsilon)^{1/4}$ must appear explicitly. The simplest form of (9.47b) is to replace the proportionality sign by some suitable constant of proportionality. Thus write

$$\Phi[k(\nu^3/\epsilon)^{1/4}] = A\frac{\epsilon^{5/12}}{\nu^{5/4}k^{5/3}} \quad (Re \to \infty) \qquad (9.47c)$$

so that the energy distribution (9.47a) becomes, in the limit of very large Reynolds number

$$\mathscr{E}(k) = Ak^{-5/3}\epsilon^{2/3}. \qquad (9.48)$$

This is the Kolmogorov energy spectrum in this limit. This expression can be shown to be fully compatible with the viscous dissipation occurring almost entirely with the smaller eddies; this is very largely in the universal range. It is seen that most of the energy lies in the largest eddy sizes. The distribution (9.48) has the same dependence on k as does (9.38) derived from Heisenberg's theory in the limit Re very large.

Although these expressions have certain experimental support the experimental accuracy is not high and alternative expressions have been proposed by other authors. Thus Kraichnan has suggested that conditions may not be independent of the mean fluid velocity since this must affect the shear. His arguments lead to the law

$$\mathscr{E}(k) \propto k^{-3/2} \epsilon^{1/2}$$

in place of (9.48). Unfortunately present experimental data do not allow any decisive comparison between these formulae to be made although (9.48) is generally preferred.

(d) Internal scale

Finally it is necessary to estimate the value of λ_0 in any turbulent system thus specifying the internal scale. On dimensional grounds we would expect

$$\lambda_0 \sim (\nu^3/\epsilon)^{1/4} = \frac{L}{(Re)^{3/4}}. \tag{9.49}$$

It is easy to demonstrate that (9.49) is equivalent to choosing λ_0 as being that value of λ for which Re_λ equals unity. Apparently, λ_0 decreases with increasing Reynolds number.

In concluding this chapter it should be pointed out that an equivalent approach to the turbulent problem is that based on correlation functions rather than on spectral analysis. The later approach has been used here exclusively only for reasons of lack of space: it gives perhaps a clearer picture of the turbulent mechanism than does the correlation approach although the latter has many mathematical advantages. Both approaches are, however, known to be mathematically equivalent in all ways.

CHAPTER 10

Hydromagnetics

It has been tacitly assumed thus far that any electrical properties of the fluid are irrelevant to the flow. If, however, the fluid is able to conduct electricity, expressed by specifying an electrical conductivity σ, then a new and interesting field of study is opened up if the fluid is in addition permeated by a magnetic field.† The study of an electrically conducting fluid moving relative to a magnetic field is called magneto-hydrodynamics; the importance of such a study in astrophysics was first discussed by Alfvén in 1942 and this date can with some reason be taken as being the birth of the subject. It has now grown into a major branch of physics and no more than a brief indication of some of its more elementary and interesting features can be given here. It is now customary to separate magnetohydrodynamics into two parts, viz. that for which it is sufficient to assume the fluid to have a continuous structure, and which is usually called hydromagnetics; and that for which the discrete (atomistic) structure must be accounted for, and which is usually called plasma dynamics. In the present chapter we restrict our discussion to continuum hydromagnetics and will generally consider incompressible flow only.

10.1. Fluid-field coupling

It is a well-known effect in electromagnetism that the relative motion between an electrically conducting medium and a permeating magnetic field gives rise to electric currents within the medium which are directed at an angle to the direction of the magnetic field. The magnitude of the electric currents so produced, which arise in fact from an induced electric field in the medium, depends upon the size and nature of the electrical conductivity of the medium.

The induced electric currents in the medium interact with the initial permeating magnetic field. There results in consequence a body force

† The use of σ for the electrical conductivity is conventional and must not be confused with the notation used previously for the viscous stresses which are, of course, completely unrelated.

on the medium containing the electric current which perturbs the motion of the medium that initially gave rise to the current, and so changes the current induced by the motion. At the same time the induced electric current has an associated magnetic field which also affects the motion, at least to some extent. The permeating magnetic field itself does not remain unaffected by the changed conditions in the conducting medium through which it passes, and these changes again affect the induced electric currents. The result is the presence of a complicated mutual interaction between the conducting medium and the permeating magnetic field. If the conducting medium is a fluid, this mutual interaction is a direct coupling between the fluid and the magnetic field which affects the initial flow pattern to a degree which depends upon the strength of the coupling.

We can express these arguments in mathematical terms as follows. Let $\mathbf{j}$ be the electric current vector at a given fluid point and at a time t, and let $\mathbf{B}$ denote the permeating magnetic field. Then if the fluid velocity is $\mathbf{v}$ it is a result of electromagnetism that (using Gaussian units):

$$\mathbf{j} = \frac{\sigma}{c_L}[\mathbf{v} \times \mathbf{B}] + \sigma E, \tag{10.1}$$

where c_L is a constant having the dimensions of velocity and a magnitude equal to the speed of light. The electric field $\mathbf{E}$ arises from any time change of the magnetic field according to the equation:

$$\operatorname{curl} \mathbf{E} = -\frac{1}{c_L}\frac{\partial \mathbf{B}}{\partial t}. \tag{10.2}$$

Clearly there will be a component of the electric current perpendicular to both the vectors $\mathbf{v}$ and $\mathbf{B}$. In general the electrical conductivity σ will not be constant throughout the fluid; no new features are introduced, however, by such a variation and since the mathematics is more simple if σ is constant throughout the fluid we will assume this to be so in what follows.

The body force on the fluid which arises from the interaction between the current and magnetic field, written $\mathbf{F}_L$, is given by

$$\rho \mathbf{F}_L = \frac{1}{c_L}[\mathbf{j} \times \mathbf{B}], \tag{10.3}$$

and so acts in a direction which is perpendicular to both $\mathbf{j}$ and $\mathbf{B}$. The action of the force is to oppose the motion to which it is due in accordance with the requirements of energy conservation.

The electric current and magnetic field are themselves not un-related: it is known that they satisfy the equation

$$\text{curl}\,\mathbf{B} = \frac{4\pi}{c_L}\eta\mathbf{j} \tag{10.4}$$

where η is the magnetic permeability.

Accordingly (10.3) can be written alternatively:

$$\rho\mathbf{F}_L = \frac{1}{4\pi\eta}[\text{curl}\,\mathbf{B} \times \mathbf{B}]. \tag{10.5}$$

For non-magnetic fluids (such as mercury or liquid sodium), $\eta = 1$, and only such fluids will concern us in what follows.

The equations (10.2) and (10.4) are actually two of Maxwell's equations of electromagnetism applicable to the special case where electric currents flow only in closed circuits (i.e. the displacement current $(1/c_L)(\partial\mathbf{E}/\partial t)$ has been neglected). This does not mean that accumulations of electric charge may not in some case be important but any such accumulations have only a negligible effect on the general continuity of charge in the system.

The values of the electrical conductivity for various fluids vary over an enormous range; clearly the fluid-field coupling is perfect if σ is indefinitely large. For this ideal case any electric field experienced by the fluid would give rise to indefinitely large electric currents, but this is physically impossible. The equation (10.1) leads to the conclusion, therefore, that if $\sigma \to \infty$ then

$$\mathbf{E} \to -\frac{1}{c_L}[\mathbf{v} \times \mathbf{B}] \tag{10.6}$$

so that the fluid experiences no net electric field in this limit.

10.2. Basic equations

The equations for hydromagnetics are a combination of the equations of fluid dynamics and the equations of electromagnetism (i.e. Maxwell's equations). The link between these two sets of equations is the expression (10.3) for $\rho\mathbf{F}_L$. The theory is entirely classical and does not rely on any quantum concepts.

The equations of fluid dynamics are arranged to account for the fluid-field coupling by including $\mathbf{F}_L$ into the body force. For this purpose write:

$$\rho\mathbf{F} = \rho\mathbf{F}_H + \rho\mathbf{F}_L. \tag{10.7}$$

Here $\rho\mathbf{F}_L$ is given by the expression (10.5), and $\rho\mathbf{F}_H$ represents all the non-magnetic body forces, such as gravity. The insertion of (10.7) into the momentum equation (5.8) then allows for the explicit introduction of the coupling into the theory. The equation of continuity (1.11) remains formally unaffected although the magnetic field does in fact appear implicitly because it affects the fluid velocity. The equation (6.9) for the fluid temperature is, however, affected explicitly. This previous equation including the viscosity is to be augmented by an additional term describing the fluid temperature rise due to Joule heating. The rate of production of heat per unit fluid volume is $(1/\sigma)(\mathbf{j}.\mathbf{j})$; using (10.4) this is alternatively $(c_L^2/16\pi^2\sigma)(\mathrm{curl}\,\mathbf{B})^2$. The corresponding temperature rise is then

$$\Delta T = \frac{c_L^2}{16\pi^2\sigma C_p}(\mathrm{curl}\,\mathbf{B})^2.$$

The fluid equations for hydromagnetics are, therefore,

$$\frac{\partial\rho}{\partial t} + \mathrm{div}\,(\rho\mathbf{v}) = 0, \tag{10.8a}$$

$$\rho\frac{d\mathbf{v}}{dt} = -\mathrm{grad}\,p + \rho\mathbf{F}_H + \frac{1}{4\pi}[\mathrm{curl}\,\mathbf{B}\times\mathbf{B}] +$$
$$+ \mu\nabla^2\mathbf{v} + \left(\zeta+\frac{\mu}{3}\right)\mathrm{grad}\,\mathrm{div}\,\mathbf{v}, \tag{10.8b}$$

$$\frac{dT}{dt} = \alpha\nabla^2 T + \frac{\nu}{C_p}\left(\frac{\partial v_i}{\partial x_k}+\frac{\partial v_k}{\partial x_i}\right)\frac{\partial v_i}{\partial x_k} + \frac{c_L^2}{16\pi^2\sigma\rho C_p}(\mathrm{curl}\,\mathbf{B})^2, \tag{10.8c}$$

referring now to unit fluid mass. In (10.8b) it is assumed that the fluid is not rotating; for steady rotation the term $2[\mathbf{\Omega} \times \mathbf{v}] + [\mathbf{\Omega} \times [\mathbf{\Omega} \times \mathbf{r}]]$ must be added to the right-hand side of this equation.

For a compressible fluid it is assumed in addition that p is a known function of ρ, i.e. the equation of state of the fluid is known.

An equation for the magnetic field vector $\mathbf{B}$ is derived from the equations (10.1), (10.4), and (10.2). Combining (10.1) and (10.4):

$$\operatorname{curl}\mathbf{B} = \frac{4\pi}{c_L}\mathbf{j} = \frac{4\pi}{c_L}\sigma\left\{\mathbf{E} + \frac{1}{c_L}[\mathbf{v} + \mathbf{B}]\right\}. \tag{10.9}$$

Taking the curl operation of this equation and using (10.2):

$$\operatorname{curl}\operatorname{curl}\mathbf{B} = -\frac{4\pi\sigma}{c_L^2}\left\{\frac{\partial\mathbf{B}}{\partial t} + \operatorname{curl}[\mathbf{v} \times \mathbf{B}]\right\}.$$

But we know from vector analysis that:

$$\operatorname{curl}\operatorname{curl}\mathbf{B} = \operatorname{grad}\operatorname{div}\mathbf{B} - \nabla^2\mathbf{B}$$

so that, since there cannot be free magnetic poles (i.e. $\operatorname{div}\mathbf{B} = 0$):

$$\boxed{\frac{\partial\mathbf{B}}{\partial t} = \nu_m\nabla^2\mathbf{B} + \operatorname{curl}[\mathbf{v} \times \mathbf{B}],} \tag{10.10}$$

where

$$\nu_m = \frac{c_L^2}{4\pi\sigma} \tag{10.10a}$$

and σ is measured in e.s.u.

The equations (10.8) and (10.10) are the basic equations of hydromagnetics. For the ideal case of $\sigma = \infty$, $\nu_m = 0$ and (10.10) reduces to

$$\frac{\partial\mathbf{B}}{\partial t} = \operatorname{curl}[\mathbf{v} \times \mathbf{B}]. \tag{10.10b}$$

This equation has exactly the same form as the previous equation (1.42) for the vorticity of an ideal fluid, with the vector $\mathbf{B}$ playing the same rôle in (10.10b) as the vector $\boldsymbol{\omega}$ in (1.39). In the two cases $\boldsymbol{\omega} = \operatorname{curl}\mathbf{v}$ is not zero and $\mathbf{B} = \operatorname{curl}\mathbf{A}$ is not zero. The vector relation

$$\operatorname{curl}[\mathbf{v} \times \mathbf{B}] = -(\mathbf{v}.\operatorname{grad})\mathbf{B} + (\mathbf{B}.\operatorname{grad})\mathbf{v}$$

allows the equation (10.10) including the conductivity to be written in terms of the total derivative:

$$\frac{d\mathbf{B}}{dt} = (\mathbf{B}.\mathrm{grad})\mathbf{v} + \nu_m\,\nabla^2\mathbf{B}. \tag{10.10c}$$

A comparison between (10.10c) and the previous equation (5.10) for the vorticity of a viscous fluid shows that the two equations become identical if we allow the two equivalences $\mathbf{B} \sim \boldsymbol{\omega}$ and $\nu_m \sim \nu$. Thus ν_m plays a rôle for the magnetic case which is quite equivalent to that played by ν in the fluid case; for this reason ν_m is often called the magnetic kinematic viscosity, or sometimes the magnetic diffusivity. This latter terminology arises because the effect described by the term $(\nu_m\nabla^2\mathbf{B})$ is the leakage of magnetic field through the fluid material (see later).

For an incompressible fluid the equations simplify, and the two dominant equations (10.8b) and (10.10) then become, in component form:

$$\frac{\partial v_i}{\partial t} + v_k\frac{\partial v_i}{\partial x_k} = -\frac{\partial}{\partial x_i}\left(\frac{p}{\rho} + \Phi + \frac{B^2}{8\pi\rho}\right) + $$
$$+ \frac{1}{4\pi\rho}B_k\frac{\partial B_i}{\partial x_k} + \nu\frac{\partial^2 v_i}{\partial x_k\,\partial x_k} - 2\epsilon_{ijk}v_j\Omega_k, \tag{10.11a}$$

$$\frac{\partial B_i}{\partial t} + v_k\frac{\partial B_i}{\partial x_k} = B_k\frac{\partial v_i}{\partial x_k} + \nu_m\frac{\partial^2 B_i}{\partial x_k\,\partial x_k}, \tag{10.11b}$$

where the possibility of the fluid being in steady rotation with respect to the co-ordinate axis has been included in the momentum equation (10.11a) and the centrifugal force is assumed to be absorbed in the pressure term.

These equations can be treated either from the point of view of the effect of the magnetic field on the fluid motion, or equivalently the effect of the fluid motion on the magnetic field. Because it is necessary for a magnetic field to be present before the hydromagnetic effects can arise it is convenient to write

$$\mathbf{B} = \mathbf{B_0} + \mathbf{b} \tag{10.12}$$

where B_0 is the externally applied magnetic field (often called the seed field), and b is the magnetic field arising from the hydromagnetic coupling between v and B_0. Usually $b \ll B_0$. The principal unknowns in the equations (10.11) are the vectors b and v.

10.3. Boundary conditions

The hydromagnetic equations are to be solved in any particular case subject to boundary conditions dictated by the specific physical details of the particular case. Two sets of conditions are involved, viz. one set applying to the purely hydrodynamic situation and discussed earlier, and the other set are electromagnetic. Unlike the purely hydrodynamic conditions, the hydromagnetic conditions, therefore, depend upon the nature of the boundary and in particular upon whether the boundary is an insulator or an electrical conductor. The situation is then exactly as that of electromagnetism, the conditions themselves following immediately from the forms of Maxwell's equations applied to the particular system.

10.4. Magnetic field decay

Consideration of the equation (10.10) for the magnetic field allows certain purely electromagnetic features of hydrodynamics to be isolated.

First, suppose the fluid to be at rest. Then equation (10.10) reduces to

$$\frac{\partial \mathbf{B}}{\partial t} = \nu_m \nabla^2 \mathbf{B}. \tag{10.13}$$

This equation has the form of a pure diffusion equation; the magnetic field originally contained in a given fluid volume diffuses into the surrounding fluid at a rate determined by ν_m. The formal solution of (10.13) is $\mathbf{B} = \mathbf{B}_0 \exp\{-t/\tau\}$, where $\mathbf{B}_0$ refers to time $t = 0$. The value of τ can be inferred from (10.13) by dimensional arguments. If L is a length comparable to the fluid volume containing the magnetic field under discussion and τ is the time of field decay, it follows from (10.13) and (10.10a) that, as regards order of magnitude

$$\tau \sim \frac{4\pi\sigma L^2}{c_L^2}. \tag{10.14}$$

Apparently $\tau \propto \sigma L^2$, so that the decay time is large either if σ itself is large or if L is large. This is an important result since it shows that a region of fluid for which the electrical conductivity is not in fact very large behaves when viewed as a whole as if the conductivity were very large if the volume of the fluid region is sufficiently great. Some figures are interesting. For a copper sphere of 1 metre radius the decay time is a few seconds; for a copper sphere with a radius equal to that of the core of the Earth, the decay time would be about 5×10^4 years; for a sphere the size of the Sun the decay time would be of the order 10^{10} years (which is about the age of the Universe). This effect is one of size alone. It follows then, that the exact value of σ is largely irrelevant in cosmic physics; but this is not so in the laboratory (where σ is small) showing the danger of too eagerly using the one type of data to attempt an understanding of the other.

If the fluid is in motion the same general conclusions apply although the details are modified somewhat. The full equation (10.10) is now relevant and the field decay in time at a given point is due to the competition between the two mechanisms of the diffusion of the field according to equation (10.13) and the body movement of the field by the fluid according to the equation (10.10b). If $\mathbf{v}$ is of the order of magnitude of the fluid velocity at the position in question and L is the distance moved by the fluid in some small time interval then, as regards order of magnitude:

$$\nu_m \nabla^2 \mathbf{B} \sim \frac{c_L^2 B}{4\pi\sigma L^2} \quad \text{and} \quad \text{curl} [\mathbf{v} \times \mathbf{B}] \sim \frac{vB}{L}.$$

The diffusion effect is predominant in (10.10) if

$$\frac{c_L^2 B}{4\pi\sigma L^2} \gg \frac{vB}{L}, \quad \text{i.e. if} \frac{4\pi\sigma Lv}{c_L^2} \ll 1,$$

and this is the condition most often found to apply in the laboratory. Alternatively, the fluid transport effect predominates in (10.10) if

$$\frac{c_L^2 B}{4\pi\sigma L^2} \ll \frac{vB}{L}, \quad \text{i.e. if} \frac{4\pi\sigma Lv}{c_L^2} \gg 1,$$

and this is the condition found to apply in cosmic conditions. More particular a moving fluid behaves as if it has an indefinitely large electrical conductivity if

$$\frac{\sigma L v}{c_L^2} \gg \frac{1}{10}. \tag{10.15}$$

This conclusion can be expressed in another way by defining the so-called Magnetic Reynolds number (Re_M). Remembering the definition of Re in (7.14), then (Re_M) will be defined as:

$$(Re_M) = \frac{vL}{\nu_m} = \frac{4\pi\sigma vL}{c_L^2} \qquad (\sigma \text{ in e.s.u.}).$$

The condition (10.15) for the fluid transport of the field to triumph over the diffusive leak is then

$$Re_M \gg 1. \tag{10.16a}$$

10.5. Frozen-in fields

If the fluid electrical conductivity is actually indefinitely large then no relative motion is possible between the fluid and the field. Because then $\nu_m = 0$, equation (10.10c) becomes

$$\frac{\partial \mathbf{B}}{\partial t} + (\mathbf{v}.\mathrm{grad})\,\mathbf{B} = (\mathbf{B}.\mathrm{grad})\,\mathbf{v} \tag{10.17}$$

in this limit. By using the fluid continuity equation (1.11) it is a straightforward matter to transform (10.17) into an equation involving the ratio $\mathbf{B}/\rho \equiv \mathbf{Б}$. The equation for $\mathbf{Б}$ is:

$$\frac{d\mathbf{Б}}{dt} = (\mathbf{Б}.\mathrm{grad})\,\mathbf{v}. \tag{10.18}$$

Any relative motion in a direction other than that of the magnetic field lines must give rise to an infinite coupling force which will destroy the relative motion to which it is due. Consequently fluid motion along the field lines, which does not disturb the field lines, is permitted, but any transverse motion must carry the field with it

15

without slip. Alfvén has termed such conditions as those in which the
magnetic lines of force are 'frozen' into the fluid material.

For the case of the frozen-in field the fluid velocity can proceed
only along the lines of force, and there the flow proceeds unimpeded
by the field. Consequently the right-hand side of (10.18) will be zero
and there follows the result:

$$\frac{|\mathbf{B}|}{\rho} = \text{constant} \qquad \text{i.e. } |\mathbf{B}| = \beta\rho. \qquad (10.19)$$

10.6. Alfvén transverse waves

One of the most important features of hydromagnetics is the ability
of a hydromagnetic fluid to support a transverse wave motion. In this
respect a conducting fluid in a magnetic field is totally unlike an
insulating fluid where only longitudinal motion can be transmitted.
The initial recognition of this new situation is due to Alfvén.

Let us suppose the fluid to be incompressible, inviscid, with indefinitely great electrical conductivity, and not rotating. Further the
seed field $\mathbf{B}_0$ will be assumed to be constant in time and uniform in
space; the disturbances will be assumed small so that we take $\mathbf{b} \ll \mathbf{B}_0$,
and the squares and products of the small quantities $\mathbf{b}$ and $\mathbf{v}$ can be
neglected.

Let $\mathbf{B}_0$ be directed along the z-axis of a Cartesian co-ordinate frame.
Then, under the approximations already listed, the equations (10.11)
reduce to the form:

$$\frac{\partial v_i}{\partial t} = \frac{B_0}{4\pi\rho}\frac{\partial b_i}{\partial z} - \frac{\partial}{\partial x_i}\left(\frac{p}{\rho} + \Phi + \frac{B^2}{8\pi\rho}\right), \qquad (10.20a)$$

$$\frac{\partial b_i}{\partial t} = B_0 \frac{\partial v_i}{\partial z}. \qquad (10.20b)$$

Next take the divergence of the equation (10.20a)

$$\frac{\partial}{\partial t}\left(\frac{\partial v_i}{\partial x_i}\right) = \frac{B_0}{4\pi\rho}\frac{\partial}{\partial z}\left(\frac{\partial b_i}{\partial x_i}\right) - \frac{\partial^2}{\partial x_k\,\partial x_k}\left(\frac{p}{\rho} + \Phi + \frac{B^2}{8\pi\rho}\right). \qquad (10.21a)$$

Because the fluid is incompressible and there cannot exist isolated
magnetic poles:

$$\frac{\partial v_i}{\partial x_i} = 0 \quad \text{and} \quad \frac{\partial b_i}{\partial x_i} = 0.$$

Thus equation (10.21a) reduces to Laplace's equation:

$$\frac{\partial^2}{\partial x_i \, \partial x_i}\left[\frac{p}{\rho} + \Phi + \frac{B^2}{8\pi\rho}\right] = 0.$$

This expression states that the quantity

$$\frac{p}{\rho} + \Phi + \frac{B^2}{8\pi\rho}$$

is a solution of Laplace's equation: because it is constant outside the particular region containing B_0 it is constant everywhere. Thus (10.20a) is:

$$\frac{\partial v_i}{\partial t} = \frac{B_0}{4\pi\rho}\frac{\partial b_i}{\partial z}. \tag{10.21b}$$

The two equations (10.20b) and (10.21b) can be separated into two equations each containing one unknown function only, as follows:

$$\frac{\partial^2 v_i}{\partial t^2} = \frac{B_0}{4\pi\rho}\frac{\partial^2 b_i}{\partial z \, \partial t} = \frac{B_0}{4\pi\rho}\frac{\partial}{\partial z}\left(\frac{\partial b_i}{\partial t}\right) = \frac{B_0^2}{4\pi\rho}\frac{\partial^2 v_i}{\partial^2 z^2},$$

$$\frac{\partial^2 b_i}{\partial t^2} = B_0\frac{\partial^2 v_i}{\partial t \, \partial z} = \frac{B_0}{4\pi\rho}\frac{\partial}{\partial z}\left(\frac{\partial v_i}{\partial t}\right) = \frac{B_0^2}{4\pi\rho}\frac{\partial^2 b_i}{\partial z^2},$$

i.e.

$$\boxed{\frac{\partial^2 v_i}{\partial t^2} = V_a^2\frac{\partial^2 v_i}{\partial z^2}} \tag{10.22a}$$

$$\boxed{\frac{\partial^2 b_i}{\partial t^2} = V_a^2\frac{\partial^2 b_i}{\partial z^2}} \tag{10.22b}$$

$$\boxed{V_a^2 = \frac{B_0^2}{4\pi\rho}.} \tag{10.22c}$$

These equations describe transverse progressive waves travelling with a velocity $\pm V_a$ along the direction of the seed magnetic field. They are called Alfvén waves and V_a is the Alfvén velocity; they are a special case of general magnetohydrodynamic waves.

It is seen that V_a increases with decreasing fluid density, and increases also as the seed field strength increases. Although the formula (10.22c) indicates an indefinitely high velocity in the limit of vanishing density this is not so. The basis of the equations (10.22) is that of small disturbances in continuous matter, and this clearly cannot be valid as $\rho \to 0$. In this limit, in fact, the problem becomes one of electromagnetic wave propagation and it is well-known that the velocity appropriate to such waves is that of light, i.e. c_L. A full investigation of magnetohydrodynamic wave motion including the low density limit must include also the effects of the displacement current which have been neglected here. It turns out that the disturbance (which is, of course, entirely transverse) velocity c_T is given by:

$$c_T^2 = \frac{1}{\dfrac{1}{c_L^2} + \dfrac{4\pi\rho}{B_0^2}}. \tag{10.23}$$

When ρ is *not* nearly zero

$$\frac{4\pi\rho}{B_0^2} \gg \frac{1}{c_L^2} \quad \text{and} \quad c_T^2 \to V_a^2;$$

alternatively when $\rho = 0$, $c_T^2 = c_L^2$.

For liquid densities and for $B_0 \sim 10^3$ gauss, $V_a \sim 10^2$ cm/sec, so that $V_a \ll c_L$ can be expected to hold in the laboratory. For a gas, however, the velocity may be higher; for instance in a gas with a density comparable with that of the solar photospheric layers the Alfvén velocity will be comparable to the local sound velocity.

It appears from the equations (10.22) that the medium is not dispersive, so that Alfvén waves therefore have a group velocity equal to the wave velocity.

10.7. Wave damping

The Alfvén waves are damped by viscosity and finite electrical conductivity. These two effects, if included into the arguments of the last Article, would introduce respectively the term $(\rho \nu \nabla^2 \mathbf{v})$ into the right-hand side of equation (10.21b) and the term $(\nu_m \nabla^2 \mathbf{b})$ into the right-hand side of equation (10.20b). The electrical resistance predominates over the viscosity as a dissipative effect if

$$\nu_m \gg \rho\nu.$$

This is the case almost always; in the laboratory $\nu_m \sim 10^7(\rho\nu)$ and under stellar conditions $\nu_m \sim 10^2(\rho\nu)$. However, in the very tenuous interstellar material the situation is usually reversed. Except in the latter case the damping effect of viscosity can be neglected, the equation (10.20b) is to become now:

$$\frac{\partial b_i}{\partial t} = B_0 \frac{\partial v_i}{\partial z} + \nu_m \frac{\partial^2 b_i}{\partial x_k \partial x_k}. \tag{10.24}$$

Combining the equations (10.24) and (10.21b) in the manner which previously led to the equations (10.22) we obtain, instead of those equations, the pair:

$$\frac{\partial^2 v_i}{\partial t^2} = V_a^2 \frac{\partial^2 v_i}{\partial z^2} + \nu_m V_a^2 \frac{\partial}{\partial z}\left(\frac{\partial^2 b_i}{\partial x_k \partial x_k}\right) \tag{10.25a}$$

$$\frac{\partial^2 b_i}{\partial t^2} = V_a^2 \frac{\partial^2 b_i}{\partial z^2} + \nu_m \frac{\partial^2}{\partial x_k \partial x_k}\left(\frac{\partial b_i}{\partial t}\right). \tag{10.25b}$$

These equations are complicated. They represent the sum of progressive waves travelling along the seed field direction with velocity $\pm V_a$, but with the waves now also diffusing out in the x and y directions as they move. Consequently the wave motion is fully three-dimensional. However, the velocity and magnetic waves are damped differently.

10.8. Effect of Compressibility

So far only incompressible flow has been considered. If the flow is compressible then sound waves also appear which are longitudinal. Such a wave will be unaffected by the seed magnetic field if it propagated along it, but will be affected if it is propagated at right angles to the field.

If c_S is the sound velocity in the absence of the field it would be expected, on such a naïve argument, that the disturbance velocity for a sound wave propagated in a fluid of infinite electrical conductivity and in a direction making an angle ϑ with respect to the seed field direction will have the general form:

$$c_T^2 = c_S^2 + V_a^2 \cos^2 \vartheta.$$

If $\vartheta = 0$, $c_T^2 = c_S^2$: if $\vartheta = \pi/2$, $c_T^2 = c_S^2 + V_a^2$ being the maximum velocity. Detailed calculations (not to be given here) confirm this surmise. If, in addition, dissipative effects arising from finite electrical conductivity and viscosity are also present the diffusive damping characteristics also appear which considerably complicate the picture.

10.9. Hydromagnetic numbers

The dimensionless form of the equations of fluid motion when magnetic effects are irrelevant was discussed in Chapter 7, where a series of numbers were defined which give information about the relative strength of the various forces acting on the fluid. The same arguments can apply equally to the hydromagnetic system and for completeness we isolate now two numbers referring to the magnetic field-fluid coupling. The notation of Chapter 7 will again be used with the addition that B_∞ will represent the magnetic field strength in the absence of fluid motion. The equation of continuity does not involve the magnetic field, and conditions have been assumed iso-thermal† beyond Art. 10.3; under this approximation it is necessary now to focus attention only on the single momentum equation (10.8b). This equation differs from the previous equation (5.8) only through the additional term $1/(4\pi\rho)[\text{curl}\,\mathbf{B} \times \mathbf{B}]$: in terms of datum variables this is written

$$\left(\frac{B_\infty^2}{4\pi\rho_\infty L\rho^*}\right)[\text{curl}^* \mathbf{B}^* \times \mathbf{B}^*].$$

† The inclusion of the temperature equation would not introduce any new hydromagnetic numbers explicitly although a related number is conveniently defined in connection with Joule heating. Compare the last term on the right-hand side of equation (10.8c) with the term $(\mathbf{v}.\text{grad})\,T$. The additional dimensionless grouping $J \equiv (8\pi\rho C_p T/B^2)$ appears which is the ratio of the thermal to magnetic energies. Thus, for the temperature rise ΔT due to Joule heating in a conducting fluid flowing with velocity $\mathbf{v}$, dimensional analysis along the lines of Arts. 7.5 and 7.6 leads easily to the result that, for this case, $[(\rho C_p \,\Delta T/B^2)]$ is a function of the magnetic Reynolds number (Re_M). It follows that (J) $(E)(Ha)^2 = 2(Re)(Re_M)$, giving a relation between J and the Hartman number (Ha).

In carrying through the procedure leading to equation (7.10) the several terms were divided by the datum ratio (v_∞^2/L). When the equation is augmented by the magnetic term we must add the dimensionless contribution (in vector form):

$$\left(\frac{B_\infty^2}{4\pi\rho_\infty v_\infty^2}\right)\frac{1}{\rho^*}[\text{curl}^* \mathbf{B}^* \times \mathbf{B}^*].$$

As in Chapter 7, so here the suffixes will be dropped on the dimensionless coefficient of this term on the strict understanding that only datum variables are involved. This coefficient can be rewritten very easily as follows:

$$\frac{B^2}{4\pi\rho v^2} = \frac{B^2/8\pi}{\frac{1}{2}\rho v^2} = \frac{B^2}{4\pi\rho}\cdot\frac{1}{v^2} = \frac{V_a^2}{v^2}$$

where V_a is the Alfvén wave velocity. Apparently, the ratio of the magnetic energy contained in a unit hydromagnetic volume to the kinetic energy of the volume is equal to the square of the ratio of the Alfvén velocity to the fluid velocity. The ratio of these two velocities themselves is a dimensionless number, called the Alfvén number, Al: thus $(Al) \equiv V_a/v$, so that

$$\frac{B^2}{4\pi\rho v^2} = (Al)^2.$$

This dimensionless ratio of parameters can immediately be arranged to exhibit the normal Reynolds and magnetic Reynolds numbers. For we can introduce the magnetic viscosity, characteristic length, and normal shear viscosity as follows:

$$\frac{B^2}{4\pi\rho v^2} = \frac{B^2}{4\pi\rho v^2}\cdot\frac{v_m}{v_m}\cdot\frac{L^2}{L^2}\cdot\frac{\mu}{\mu} = \left(\frac{\mu}{vL\rho}\right)\left(\frac{v_m}{vL}\right)\left(\frac{B^2L^2}{4\pi v_m\mu}\right),$$

i.e.

$$\frac{B^2}{4\pi\rho v^2} = \left(\frac{1}{Re}\right)\left(\frac{1}{Re_M}\right)\left(\frac{B^2L^2\sigma}{\mu c_L^2}\right).$$

It is immediately clear that the third contribution to the product on the right-hand side of this expression is dimensionless: it defines the Hartman number. Explicitly

$$(Ha) = \left(\frac{B^2L^2\sigma}{\mu c_L^2}\right)^{1/2},$$

the square root being introduced for historical reasons. (*Ha*) represents the ratio of magnetic to viscous stresses in the system. The definition of (*Ha*) means that

$$(Ha)^2 = (Re)(Re_M)(Al)^2.$$

The weakness of the fluid-field coupling for low velocity hydromagnetics. together with the difficulties associated with critically affecting the coupling for incompressible flow, effectively bars the widespread use of model studies to these problems at the present time.

10.10. Hydromagnetic turbulence

Turbulent motion can occur in an electrically conducting fluid under hydromagnetic conditions, although the interaction between the fluid motion and the magnetic field leads to a more complex situation than that treated in Chapter 9. Due to this interaction, the fluid turbulent field must distort the permeating magnetic field and vice versa; one direct consequence can be expected to be the inhibition of the outset of turbulence by the presence of the magnetic field, the greater the field strength the more marked the inhibition.† The theory of hydromagnetic turbulence is in a very elementary state at the present time due very largely to the fact that laboratory experience cannot be widely invoked; only in cosmic circumstances is the fluid-field coupling strong and there we can be nothing other than passive observers.

(i) Preliminary notions

In a general way the arguments of Chapter 9 can still be applied to hydromagnetism with only small modifications. As in the last chapter so also here it will be sufficient to consider only incompressible fluid flow. Because both fluid turbulence and magnetism are involved, interest will centre not only on the kinetic energy spectrum (i.e. the distribution of kinetic energy throughout the various eddy sizes) but also upon the associated magnetic energy spectrum. Formally a cascade of magnetic as well as kinetic energy through the range of

† The situation is greatly complicated if the fluid is also in rotation since then the Coriolis force is active. We neglect now the possibility of overall fluid rotation.

eddy sizes can be defended as being physically plausible and mathematical transition functions can be defined (in a way analogous to the introduction of the function $W(\mathbf{k}\;\mathbf{k}')$ in Chapter 9) to describe the transport of kinetic *and* magnetic energy throughout the turbulent spectrum.

At the small-scale end of the cascade, total turbulent energy is dissipated into heat by the action of viscosity (as in hydrodynamic turbulence) but also by Joule heating due to the non-zero, although finite, electrical conductivity.

(ii) Magnetic field amplification

It is now generally assumed that turbulent motion in an electrically conducting fluid will give rise to spontaneous local magnetic fields from time to time; there is no definite incontravertible proof of this at the present time although there may be claimed to be some indirect evidence for it. Once a spontaneous magnetic field has arisen it is supposed to be amplified by the fluid turbulent motion until ultimately the situation is arrived at where the magnetic energy is essentially equal to the kinetic energy of fluid motion. Such a general mechanism is of great importance in geo- and astro-physics where the magnetic fields of various strengths occurring generally in the universe are ascribed to the amplification of spontaneously arising turbulent magnetic fields; this is the so-called dynamo mechanism which is now thought to be responsible in particular for the magnetic fields of the Earth and the Sun. Although no general theoretical description of such a mechanism is known some useful comments can be made.

To begin with consider again the comparison between the equation (10.10c) for a magnetic field and the equation (5.10) for the vorticity already begun in Art. 10.2. It was seen there that if $\nu = \nu_m$ then $\mathbf{B}$ and $\boldsymbol{\omega}$ satisfy identical equations. Then it follows that the vectors $\mathbf{B}$ and $\boldsymbol{\omega}$ are simply proportional to each other; in particular, if a steady (suitably time averaged) vorticity can exist then so also can a steady magnetic field. Thus when $\nu_m = (c_L^2/4\pi\sigma)$ the magnetic field is in a form of neutral equilibrium where the transport of the magnetic lines of force is exactly balanced by the diffusion of the field through the conducting fluid. Remembering the arguments of Art. 10.4 the field will decay if $\nu < \nu_m$ but will amplify if $\nu > \nu_m$. In terms of the dimensionless numbers (Re) and (Re_M) a small spontaneous magnetic field which might appear in the turbulent conducting fluid will amplify if the condition

$$(Re_M) > (Re) \qquad (10.26)$$

is satisfied. Under laboratory circumstances ν is usually not very much greater than 10^{-3} cm²/sec, while the corresponding ν_m is at least of order 10^4 cm²/sec. Thus in the laboratory any spontaneously appearing magnetic field will be strongly damped; the condition (10.26) is,

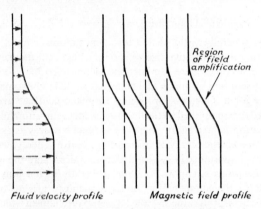

FIG. 25. *Amplification of a magnetic field by the motion of a fluid having indefinitely large electrical conductivity. The fluid velocity profile is on the left and the magnetic field lines are on the right.*

however, often satisfied under astrophysical conditions where σ may be virtually indefinitely great.

Relatively simple conditions will lead to magnetic field amplification as will be seen from the following idealized case. Suppose an initially uniform magnetic field in the z-direction (dotted lines in Fig. 25) permeates a perfectly conducting fluid which is initially at rest. Suppose now the fluid is caused to undergo shear (laminar) flow in the x-direction with the velocity profile shown on the left of the figure. Because the fluid is infinitely conducting, the 'frozen-in' lines of force will move with the fluid and after some time interval the magnetic lines of force will be stretched into the form shown by the continuous lines in Fig. 25. It is seen that the magnetic field has undergone local amplification due to the fluid motion and that an x-component of the field has been created in the region where the fluid velocity gradient is not zero. The increase in magnetic energy has come about at the expense of fluid kinetic energy used up against the inertia of the magnetic field. This simple picture is capable of great generalizations when complex fluid flow patterns are involved.

The equation (10.18) also gives information about the magnetic field amplification. For an incompressible fluid such as is our concern here, (10.18) leads immediately to the physical conclusion that any stretching of the lines of force increases the field strength. The condition $\nu > \nu_m$ then means that the increase in the magnetic energy due to the stretching of the magnetic lines of force by the fluid motion more than compensates for the loss of magnetic energy by diffusion (slipping) of the lines of force through the fluid. The mechanism for the amplification of a magnetic field by an electrically conducting turbulent fluid can now be re-expressed. In turbulent motion any two fluid elements which are initially close together will move apart (diffuse) with time. If the fluid is infinitely conducting the diffusing fluid elements will carry lines of force with them and in this way the permeating magnetic field will be locally amplified by the stretching of the lines of force. It is clear that our arguments so far have been based on considerations of fluid flow, any effect of the magnetic field on the flow being neglected. This is permissible if the magnetic energy is negligible in comparison with the fluid kinetic energy. Amplification of the magnetic field will cease when the magnetic and kinetic energies become of comparable magnitude.

(iii) Dimensional considerations

In the absence of a detailed mathematical theory of hydromagnetic turbulence important information can be derived from purely dimensional considerations. Magnetic field amplification is greater the greater the fluid shear. The small-scale fluid eddies are those associated with the maximum shear and it is highly plausible that for these small-scale components equipartition between the magnetic and kinetic energies is very rapidly set up to produce a steady condition. Such an equipartition is, however, unlikely to apply to the large-scale eddy components. In the nomenclature of Chapter 9 it will be assumed now that equipartition between kinetic and magnetic energy will apply only for those eddies where $\lambda \leqslant \lambda_0$. Then as to orders of magnitude

$$\frac{B^2}{8\pi} \sim \tfrac{1}{2}\rho v_{\lambda 0}^2 \tag{10.27}$$

where B and $v_{\lambda 0}$ are suitable average values of the magnetic field and turbulent velocity. It was seen in Art. 9.10 that according to the Kolmogorov similarity principle at large (Re) the turbulent process is characterized for very large k by only the two functions ϵ and ν. The only combination of these two quantities which has the dimensions of velocity is $(\epsilon\nu)^{1/4}$ so that the spontaneous turbulent magnetic field will, according to (10.27), have the general magnitude after full amplification

$$B \sim \sqrt{(4\pi\rho)}(\epsilon\nu)^{1/4}. \tag{10.28}$$

The equation (10.10c) allows us to obtain an expression describing the amplification of the magnetic field. Remembering that the term $(\mathbf{B}.\mathrm{grad})\mathbf{v}$ refers to the stretching of lines of force while the term $\nu_m \nabla^2 \mathbf{B}$ refers to diffusive loss of field, we may write (10.10c) as to orders of magnitude:

$$\frac{dB}{dt} \sim \frac{Bv}{\lambda_0} - \frac{\nu_m B}{\lambda_0^2} \tag{10.29a}$$

where a positive sign to the first term on the right-hand side refers to an increasing field and the negative sign on the second term refers to a decreasing field. Now $(\epsilon\nu)^{1/4}$ has the dimensions of velocity; remembering the previous equation (9.49) it follows that

$$\frac{Bv}{\lambda_0} = \frac{Bv\lambda_0}{\lambda_0^2} \sim \frac{B(\epsilon\nu)^{1/4}\,\nu^{3/4}}{\lambda_0^2\,\epsilon^{1/4}} = \frac{B\nu}{\lambda_0^2}. \tag{10.29b}$$

Then (10.29a) becomes alternatively

$$\frac{1}{B}\frac{dB}{dt} \sim \frac{\nu - \nu_m}{\lambda_0^2}$$

and this equation has the solution

$$B \sim B_0 \exp\left\{\frac{(\nu-\nu_m)\,t}{\lambda_0^2}\right\} \sim B_0 \exp\left\{\frac{(\nu-\nu_m)}{\nu}(\epsilon/\nu)^{1/2}t\right\}; \quad (10.29c)$$

the magnetic field is amplified (if $\nu > \nu_m$) or damped (if $\nu < \nu_m$) exponentially with the time, the effect being the stronger the smaller the scale of turbulence. If B_0 is a spontaneous magnetic field, then B in (10.29c) will have the equipartition form (10.28) after a time $t = \tau$. The speculative nature of these formulae must be stressed, although they are all that is yet available to us in the absence of any rigorous theory.

Relation between Stress and Strain for a Deformable Body: an Alternative Derivation of the Navier-Stokes Equation

Both continuous solids and continuous fluids are deformable media; any constituent volume element which is subjected to some applied stress for sufficient time will rearrange itself into an equilibrium configuration involving internal strains (deformations) in the volume element, the configuration in the absence of stresses being taken as the standard configuration. The relationship pertaining between the applied stress and the opposing strain is characteristic of the particular system involved, and the case of small strain (small deformation) is especially important. For a simple solid in this case it is known experimentally that the strain is proportional to the applied stress (Hooke's law for a solid continuum): alternatively for a simple fluid the stress is proportional instead to the time rate of change of strain, the constant of proportionality being the shear modulus of viscosity. (Stokes experimental law of friction). A study of the equilibrium between stress and strain forces allows for the construction of the equations of motion for a deformable medium by invoking Newton's laws of motion, and we shall indicate now how the Navier-Stokes equation for a viscous fluid can be derived in this way. The present arguments are alternative to those previously used in Chapter 5.

(a) The stress

For a body in equilibrium the vector sum of all the acting forces must be zero. In the absence of externally applied forces the body is in equilibrium under the action of the forces between the constituent molecules themselves, subject to the condition that the thermodynamical free energy shall have an extreme value, usually a minimum. If, now, the body is deformed due to the action of some externally applied forces this simple equilibrium is disturbed; the total force

224

acting on the body must, of course, still vanish for equilibrium and the externally applied forces are balanced exactly by a system of additional internal body forces (internal stresses) which again arise from the intermolecular forces.

It is a cardinal feature of the kinetic theory arguments for insulating non-polar fluids (simple fluids) that the intermolecular forces are short-ranged, interaction between molecules hardly extending beyond nearest neighbours. It is an immediate consequence that the resultant force exerted on a fluid element by the remaining surrounding fluid must be explicitly a surface force rather than a simple body force. Let $\mathbf{F}^{(1)}$ be that force acting on unit fluid volume which depends entirely upon the state of fluid motion (so that gravitational and other such forces are excluded). The mechanical 'motion' force acting upon the volume element dV is then $F^{(1)} dV$. Newton's third law of motion leads immediately to the conclusion that the resultant force arising from the various interactions within the volume dV is exactly zero: the total force acting on the element due to the remaining fluid is truly a surface force. This leads to an important conclusion. The resultant force acting on some volume ΔV of which dV is an element is $\int_{\Delta V} \mathbf{F}^{(1)} dV$, and this must be explicitly a surface force. Now according to the rules of vector algebra a volume integration can be replaced by an integration over the enclosing surface if the integrand can be replaced by the divergence of some other (and incidentally rather more complicated) function. For the present case, let us write in component notation

$$F_i^{(1)} = \frac{\partial \sigma_{ik}}{\partial x_k}, \tag{A1}$$

where the quantity formed by the several component terms σ_{ik} represents the stress conditions within ΔV. The σ_{ik} are called the components of the stress. If ds_k is a surface element of the full surface enclosing ΔV then we have

$$\int_{\Delta V} F_i^{(1)} dV = \int_{\Delta V} \frac{\partial \sigma_{ik}}{\partial x_k} dV = \oint_{\Delta s} \sigma_{ik} ds_k. \tag{A2}$$

These arguments will not apply if the intermolecular forces are not of only short range. Arguments involving the moment of the total force on the element, taken about any point within the element (and centred about the requirement that the total moment for the entire element must be representable in terms of a surface integral due to the short range of action of the intermolecular forces) lead to the conclusion $\sigma_{ik} = \sigma_{ki}$, i.e. that σ_{ik} is symmetric with respect to the interchange of the suffixes.

The detailed specification of σ_{ik} for any physical system depends upon the nature of the system and particularly on the cumulative properties of the intermolecular forces. For our present purposes it will be found sufficient to specify σ_{ik} in terms of the deformations using data derived from experimental considerations. For a solid this can involve Hooke's law, while for fluids it is Stoke's law of friction that is relevant.

(b) Stress for uniform compression

For conditions of uniform compression, i.e. of hydrostatic compression, there is no difficulty in relating σ_{ik} to physical variables. In this case the surface force acting on any volume element is a simple pressure p, acting normally on each surface. For the elementary surface ds the normal pressure force in the i-th direction is $(-p\,ds_i)$, the negative sign denoting an inward force on the element. By introducing the symbol δ_{ik} we may write the sequence

$$-p\,ds_i = -p\delta_{ik}\,ds_k = \sigma_{ik}\,ds_k$$

where the last step follows from the definition of σ_{ik}. Accordingly we can write

$$\sigma_{ik} = -p\delta_{ik} \tag{A3}$$

so that for a uniform compression

$$\sigma_{ii} = -3p; \quad \sigma_{ik} = 0 \quad (i \neq k) \tag{A3a}$$

where the summation convention for repeated suffixes has been remembered. For a non-uniform compression, $\sigma_{ik} \neq 0$ even when $i = k$.

(c) The strain

Under the action of an applied force any elementary volume of a deformable medium will suffer a change in both shape and volume. If any chosen point in such an element has the co-ordinates x_i in the absence of the applied force, and the co-ordinates x_i' in the presence of the force, then the difference $\xi_i = x_i' - x_i$ represents the body displacement of the point due to the action of the stresses. In the general case, x_i' is a function of x_i so that $\xi_i = \xi_i(x_j)$, in component notation.

Consider two neighbouring points in the medium separated by the elementary distance dl in the absence of deformation, but separated by the elementary distance dl' when deformations are present due to the action of stresses. The respective co-ordinate differences between the two neighbouring points in the absence of stresses and when stresses are present are dx_i and dx_i'. Using the summation rule for component notation we have $dl^2 = dx_i^2$ and $dl'^2 = dx_i'^2$. The distances dl and dl' can be related directly in terms of the displacement components due to the stresses, ξ_i. If $d\xi_i$ is the displacement difference between the two neighbouring points under the action of stresses then clearly

$$dl'^2 = dx_i'^2 = (dx_i + d\xi_i)^2 = dl^2 + 2\frac{\partial \xi_i}{\partial x_k}dx_i dx_k + \frac{\partial \xi_i}{\partial x_k}\frac{\partial \xi_i}{\partial x_l}dx_k dx_l.$$

The last expression can be rewritten by rearranging the suffixes. First notice that we can write

$$\frac{\partial \xi_l}{\partial x_k}dx_i dx_k = \frac{\partial \xi_k}{\partial x_i}dx_k dx_i = \frac{\partial \xi_k}{\partial x_i}dx_i dx_k$$

because summation is over both the suffixes i and k which can, in consequence be interchanged without affecting anything. By the same token the term

$$\frac{\partial \xi_i}{\partial x_k}\frac{\partial \xi_i}{\partial x_l}dx_k dx_l$$

can be rearranged by interchanging the two suffixes i and l:

$$\frac{\partial \xi_i}{\partial x_k}\frac{\partial \xi_i}{\partial x_l}dx_k dx_l \equiv \frac{\partial \xi_l}{\partial x_k}\frac{\partial \xi_l}{\partial x_i}dx_k dx_i = \frac{\partial \xi_l}{\partial x_k}\frac{\partial \xi_l}{\partial x_i}dx_i dx_k.$$

Consequently

$$dl'^2 = dl^2 + \left(\frac{\partial \xi_i}{\partial x_k} + \frac{\partial \xi_k}{\partial x_i} + \frac{\partial \xi_l}{\partial x_k}\frac{\partial \xi_l}{\partial x_i}\right)dx_i dx_k \qquad (A4)$$

is the final form of the relation between dl^2 and dl'^2. For simple fluids the displacements for small deformations must be small: under this very reasonable approximation, (A4) simplifies slightly to become

$$dl'^2 = dl^2 + \left(\frac{\partial \xi_i}{\partial x_k} + \frac{\partial \xi_k}{\partial x_i}\right)dx_i dx_k, \qquad (A4a)$$

and the quantity

$$\left(\frac{\partial \xi_i}{\partial x_k} + \frac{\partial \xi_k}{\partial x_i}\right)$$

describes the state of strain in the medium: we shall denote it now by $2e_{ik}$ so that

$$e_{ik} = \frac{1}{2}\left(\frac{\partial \xi_i}{\partial x_k} + \frac{\partial \xi_k}{\partial x_i}\right). \qquad (A5)$$

The various components of e_{ik} have a direct physical interpretation. First, if $i = k$, the components e_{ii} are the relative extensions of linear elements in the medium which in the unstrained state are parallel to the co-ordinate axes. The remaining components $e_{ik}(i \neq j)$, of which e_{xy} is typical, refer to the cosine of the angle between any two lines in the strained state which, in the unstrained state, are parallel one to the i-axis and the other to the k-axis. Alternatively, e_{ik} can be regarded as the combination of two simple shears, one in which planes perpendicular to the k-axis suffer relative motion parallel to the i-axis and the other in which planes perpendicular to the i-axis suffer relative motion parallel to the k-axis. It is seen from (A5) that e_{ik} is symmetric with respect to the suffixes i and k, i.e. $e_{ik} = e_{ki}$. Also from (A5) it follows that for Cartesian co-ordinates

$$e_{ii} = e_{xx} + e_{yy} + e_{zz} \equiv e = \frac{\partial \xi_x}{\partial x} + \frac{\partial \xi_y}{\partial y} + \frac{\partial \xi_z}{\partial z} = \operatorname{div} \boldsymbol{\xi}. \qquad (A6)$$

$\boldsymbol{\xi}$ is here the displacement vector with Cartesian components (ξ_x, ξ_y, ξ_z) where in the component notation $(\xi_1 \equiv \xi_x, \xi_2 \equiv \xi_y, \xi_3 \equiv \xi_z)$. The quantity div $\boldsymbol{\xi}$, physically the volume increment per unit volume, is the cubical dilatation, or simply the dilatation.

(d) The Navier-Stokes equation

The equation of motion of the deformable medium can now be constructed if a unique relation between stress and strain is valid. It is at this point that the theory of fluids and of elastic solids separate. A simple proportionality between stress and strain (Hooke's law) leads to equations which well describe the behaviour of simple elastic solids. For simple fluids which concern us now it will be seen in a moment that the acceptance of Stokes experimental law of friction, according to which stress is proportional to the time rate of change of strain, leads at once to the Navier-Stokes equation (5.9).

Let us assume that σ_{ik} and e_{ik} are related according to the rule

$$\sigma_{ik} = 2\mu \frac{d}{dt} e_{ik}. \tag{A7}$$

Here μ is the normal coefficient of shear viscosity as can be seen in a very simple way. Suppose there is simple fluid flow parallel to the $(x–y)$ plane and in the x-direction where the velocity is proportional to the distance from the surface in the z-direction, i.e. $v_x = \alpha z$, $v_y = v_z = 0$. α is the rate of shear. According to (A7), (A5) and (A3) it follows in this case that:

$$\sigma_{xy} = \sigma_{yz} = 0; \quad \sigma_{xz} = \mu\alpha.$$

This shows that μ appearing in (A7) is the viscosity coefficient for shear flow.

The body force acting on the fluid due to viscosity is, from (A1) and (A7):

$$F_i^{(1)} = \frac{\partial}{\partial x_k} \left\{ 2\mu \frac{d}{dt} e_{ik} \right\} \tag{A8}$$

where e_{ik} is given by (A5).

Consider the x-component of the force, i.e. $i \equiv x$. Then in Cartesian co-ordinates

$$F_x^{(1)} = \frac{\partial}{\partial x}\left(2\mu \frac{d}{dt} e_{xx}\right) + \frac{\partial}{\partial y}\left(2\mu \frac{d}{dt} e_{xy}\right) + \frac{\partial}{\partial z}\left(2\mu \frac{d}{dt} e_{xz}\right),$$

i.e.

$$F_x^{(1)} = \frac{\partial}{\partial x}\left(2\mu\frac{\partial v_x}{\partial x}\right) + \frac{\partial}{\partial y}\left\{\mu\left(\frac{\partial v_x}{\partial y}+\frac{\partial v_y}{\partial x}\right)\right\} + \frac{\partial}{\partial z}\left\{\mu\left(\frac{\partial v_x}{\partial z}+\frac{\partial v_z}{\partial x}\right)\right\}. \quad (A.9)$$

The force in the absence of shear motion is that due to the pressure, i.e. for the x-component $-\partial p/\partial x$. It is convenient to extract this term from (A9) to give it explicit recognition: while this could be done by a thorough rearrangement of the terms, it is easier to use the more formal approach of introducing the relation between the pressure and the fluid velocity which follows from combining the three expressions (A3a), (A6), and (A7). This relation is easily derived as being

$$\operatorname{grad}\left(p + \frac{2\mu}{3}\operatorname{div}\mathbf{v}\right) = 0. \quad (A10a)$$

The expression (A9) for $F_x^{(1)}$ can now be rewritten as follows. First write

$$F_x^{(1)} = -\frac{\partial p}{\partial x} + \frac{\partial}{\partial x}\left\{2\mu\frac{\partial v_x}{\partial x}\right\} + \frac{\partial}{\partial y}\left\{\mu\left(\frac{\partial v_x}{\partial y}+\frac{\partial v_y}{\partial x}\right)\right\} +$$

$$+ \frac{\partial}{\partial z}\left\{\mu\left(\frac{\partial v_x}{\partial z}+\frac{\partial v_z}{\partial x}\right)\right\} + \frac{\partial p}{\partial x},$$

where the term $(\partial p/\partial x)$ has been added and subtracted to give no net contribution. Now replace $(+\partial p/\partial x)$, the last term, using (A10a):

$$F_x^{(1)} = -\frac{\partial p}{\partial x} + \frac{\partial}{\partial x}\left\{2\mu\frac{\partial v_x}{\partial x}\right\} + \frac{\partial}{\partial y}\left\{\mu\left(\frac{\partial v_x}{\partial y}+\frac{\partial v_y}{\partial x}\right)\right\} +$$

$$+ \frac{\partial}{\partial z}\left\{\mu\left(\frac{\partial v_x}{\partial z}+\frac{\partial v_z}{\partial x}\right)\right\} - \frac{2}{3}\frac{\partial}{\partial x}\{\mu\operatorname{div}\mathbf{v}\}. \quad (A10b)$$

The two further components of the viscous force F_y and F_z can be derived in a similar way.

The expression (A10b) simplifies if the shear viscosity coefficient is independent of the position in the fluid. In this case μ can be extracted from the differentiation operations with the result, after elementary rearrangement,

$$F_x^{(1)} = -\frac{\partial p}{\partial x} + \mu \nabla^2 v_x + \tfrac{1}{3}\mu \frac{\partial}{\partial x}(\operatorname{div} \mathbf{v}) \qquad (A10c)$$

where as usual

$$\nabla^2 \equiv \frac{\partial^2}{\partial x^2} + \frac{\partial^2}{\partial y^2} + \frac{\partial^2}{\partial z^2}.$$

Combining the complementary expressions for $F_y^{(1)}$ and $F_z^{(1)}$, viz.

$$F_y^{(1)} = -\frac{\partial p}{\partial y} + \mu \nabla^2 v_y + \tfrac{1}{3}\mu \frac{\partial}{\partial y}(\operatorname{div} \mathbf{v})$$

$$F_z^{(1)} = -\frac{\partial p}{\partial z} + \mu \nabla^2 v_z + \tfrac{1}{3}\mu \frac{\partial}{\partial z}(\operatorname{div} \mathbf{v}),$$

with that for $F_x^{(1)}$ leads to the vector expression for the force $\mathbf{F}^{(1)}$:

$$\mathbf{F}^{(1)} = -\operatorname{grad} p + \mu \nabla^2 \mathbf{v} + \tfrac{1}{3}\mu \operatorname{grad} \operatorname{div} \mathbf{v}. \qquad (A11)$$

This is the final expression for the force on the fluid including the shear viscosity. The dilatational viscosity effect has not been included in the basic relation (A7) so that the second viscosity coefficient does not appear in (A11).

The fluid equation of motion can now be written down immediately. According to Newton's classical laws of motion

$$\rho \frac{d\mathbf{v}}{dt} = \rho \mathbf{F} + \mathbf{F}^{(1)}$$

where $\rho \mathbf{F}$ is the body force acting on the fluid which is independent of the fluid motion (e.g. that due to gravity). The insertion of $\mathbf{F}^{(1)}$ according to (A11) leads at once to the previous equation (5.8) including the compressibility: for an incompressible fluid ($\operatorname{div} \mathbf{v} = 0$) the Navier-Stokes equation (5.9) is recovered. If the viscosity coefficient is dependent upon position in the fluid then $\mathbf{F}^{(1)}$ must be constructed from the component expressions of which (A10b) is typical.

Bibliography

We list now a number of books which carry the arguments of the previous pages further.

1. LAMB, SIR HORACE, *Hydrodynamics*. (6th Edition.) (Cambridge: University Press, 1932.)
2. MILNE-THOMPSON, L. M., *Theoretical Hydrodynamics*. (2nd Edition.) (London: Macmillan Co., 1950.)
3. LANDAU, L., and LIFSHITZ, E., *Fluid Mechanics*. (London: Pergamon Press, 1959.)
4. RAYLEIGH, LORD, *Theory of Sound*. (2nd Edition.) (Cambridge: University Press, 1896.)
5. SOMMERFELD, A., *Mechanics of Deformable Bodies*. Lectures on Theoretical Physics, Vol. 2. (New York: Academic Press, 1950.)
6. RICHARDSON, E. G., *Dynamics of Real Fluids*. (London: Arnold, 1949.)
7. PRANDTL, L., *Essentials of Fluid Dynamics*. (New York: Hafner Pub. Co., 1952.)
8. SCHLICHTING, H., *Boundary Layer Theory*. (London: Pergamon Press, 1955).
9. BATCHELOR, G. K., *The Theory of Homogeneous Turbulence*. Cambridge Monographs on Mechanics and Applied Mathematics. (Cambridge: University Press, 1948.)
10. MOORE, F. K., *Theory of Laminar Flows*. Vol. IV. High Speed Aerodynamics and Jet Propulsion. (Oxford: University Press, 1957.)
    LIN, C. C., ed., *Turbulent Flows and Heat Transfer*. Vol. V. High Speed Aerodynamics and Jet Propulsion (Oxford: University Press, 1959.)
11. GOLSTEIN, S., ed., *Modern Development in Fluid Dynamics*. (2 vols.) (Oxford: Clarendon Press, 1948.)
12. KNUDSEN, J. G. and KATZ, D. L., *Fluid Dynamics and Heat Transfer*. (London: McGraw-Hill, 1958.)
13. JACOB, M., *Heat Transfer*. Vols. 1 and 2 (London: Chapman & Hall Ltd., 1958.)
14. GIEDT, W. H., *Principles of Engineering Heat Transfer*. (New York: Van Nostrand Co., 1957.)

15. BOSWORTH, R. C. L., *Heat Transfer Phenomena*. (Sydney: Associated General Pubs. Ltd., 1952.)

16. MCADAMS, W. H., *Heat Transmission*. (London: McGraw-Hill Pub. Co. Ltd., 1954.)

17. DURAND, W. F., ed., *Aerodynamic Theory*. (6. vols.) (Guggenheim Fund: reprinted in 1943.)

18. COWLING, T. G., *Magnetohydrodynamics*. (New York: Interscience, 1957.)

19. SPITZER, LYMAN, JR., *Physics of Fully Ionized Gases*. (New York: Interscience, 1956.)

20. FRANCIS, G., *Ionization Phenomena in Gases*. (London: Butterworth Sci. Pub., 1960.)

21. LINHART, J. G., *Plasma Physics*. (Amsterdam: North Holland Pub. Co., 1960.)

22. BRIDGEMAN, P. W., *Dimensional Analysis*, (2nd Edition.) (New Haven, 1931.)

23. PORTER, W., *The Methods of Dimensions*. (London: Methuen Monographs, 1946.)

24. BIRKOFF, G., *Hydrodynamics*: A Study in Logic, Fact, and Similitude. (New York: Dover, 1955.)

25. MARTINOT-LAGARDE, A., *Similitude Physique: Examples d'Applications à la Méchanique des Fluids*. (Paris: Gauthier-Villars, 1960.)

26. COULSON, C. A., *Waves*. (Univ. Math. Texts.) (London: Oliver & Boyd, 1955.)

27. MASSEY, SIR HARRIE, and KESTLEMAN, H. *Ancillary Mathematics*. (London: Pitman & Sons Ltd., 1958.)

28. MARGENAU, H., and MURPHY, G., *The Mathematics of Physics and Chemistry*. (New York: Van Nostrand Co., 1956.)

29. MORSE, P., and FESHBACK, H., *Methods of Theoretical Physics*. (2 vols.) (London: McGraw-Hill Co., 1953.)

30. GANS, R., *Vector Analysis*. (London: Blackie & Son Ltd., 1949.)

31. HAGUE, B., *An Introduction to Vector Analysis*. (London: Methuen Monographs, 1944.)

The bibliography is next related to specific regions of our text:

Chapter 6: references 3, 8, 10, 12, 13, 14, 15.
Chapter 7: references 10, 22, 23, 24, 25.
Chapter 8: references 7, 8, 10, 11, 12, 13, 14.
Chapter 9: references 6, 7, 8, 9, 10, 11, 12, 13.
Chapter 10: references 18, 19, 20, 21.

General mathematical background is contained in references 27, 28, 29, 30, 31.

Index